Fifty Years of Cheshire's Wildlife

Fifty Years of Cheshire's Wildlife

edited by David Norman

THE
wildlife
TRUSTS
Cheshire

First published 2013 by
Cheshire Wildlife Trust
Bickley Hall Farm
Malpas
SY14 8EF

Tel: 01948 820728
www.cheshirewildlifetrust.org.uk

Registered Charity No. 214927. A company limited by guarantee
Registered in England No. 738693

British Library Cataloguing-in-Publication data
A British Library CIP record is available

ISBN 978-0-9572850-1-9

Designed and typeset by BBR (www.bbr.uk.com)
Cover art by Kim Atkinson (www.oriel.org.uk/en/a/kim-atkinson)

Printed and bound by Gutenberg Press, Malta
Gutenberg Press prints for BirdLife Malta

Contents

Foreword   I

Fifty Years of Cheshire's Wildlife   2
David Norman

Agriculture   24
David Norman

Urban Wildlife   38
Jeff Clarke

Marine Life of Cheshire   56
Ian Wallace

The Meres and Mosses   98
Colin Hayes

Rivers   122
Duncan Revell

Ponds – Pearls in the Cheshire Landscape   148
Andrew Hull

Lichens in Cheshire   180
Mike Gosling

Dragonflies and Damselflies   196
David Kitching

Mammals of Cheshire   210
Paul Hill, Penny Rudd and the Cheshire Mammal Group

Birds   222
David Norman

Index   252

Foreword

THE FIFTIETH ANNIVERSARY OF CHESHIRE WILDLIFE TRUST IS A GOOD REASON to review the state of our county's habitats and wildlife. This book's opening chapter provides a summarising overview, including some information on habitats and species not covered in detail elsewhere. The following ten chapters were contributed by species and habitat experts, all acknowledged authorities in their fields with local and national reputations. The emphasis is on changes that have occurred during the last half-century, some of which have been rapid, attributable to a variety of causes including land-use and management, drainage and water abstraction, climate, pesticides, pollution, introduction of alien species, development and other human pressures. A golden anniversary is normally thought of as a positive achievement, but for many species and habitats the last fifty years have not been so golden: we leave it to the reader to judge.

I hope that some will feel stimulated to find out more, so each chapter concludes with some references and suggestions for further reading. We have tried to choose material that is accessible to a general reader, freely available via the internet or public libraries. If more information is required, please contact the author through Cheshire Wildlife Trust.

In compiling this book, my biggest thanks go to the authors who have freely contributed towards this landmark volume. Many photographers have donated their images to enliven the text and illustrate important aspects; they are all credited by their names and/or websites. This book is *by* Cheshire Wildlife Trust but not *about* the Trust; I am grateful for their support in commissioning and publishing it.

Many more people have helped, some of them unwittingly, in development of the ideas that went into this book, including Steve Barber, Adam Cormack, Brian Eversham, Janel Fone, Neil Friswell, Andy Harmer, Simon Mageean, Tom Marshall, Tim Melling, Paul Oldfield, Hugh Pulsford, Judith Turner, Damian Waters and Joan Webber. Others are named in the individual chapters.

I am pleased to acknowledge the skilful and creative design from Chris Reed and Amanda Thompson at BBR.

Finally, I hope that this book will prompt the Trust and other organisations to survey more, to monitor and record what is happening to our wildlife. My biggest wish is that our successors, in another fifty years' time, will follow with a centenary volume.

David Norman

Fifty Years of Cheshire's Wildlife

David Norman

We inhabit an overcrowded island and much of our wildlife has to co-exist with human activities. For too long our natural environment has been seen as a resource to be plundered to benefit man, with no thought for the consequences, but lately there is increasing recognition of the manifold values of the natural world, often encapsulated in the jargon phrase 'ecosystem services'. The recent UK National Ecosystem Assessment (2011) is a massive tome, running to nearly 1500 pages, and covers the subject in depth. Obvious benefits of ecosystem services – perhaps best summarised in the NEA's subtitle 'understanding nature's value to society' – include pollination by bees, butterflies and other insects; flood alleviation by washlands; and carbon sequestration by damp peat-bogs and saltmarshes. Some studies estimate the financial value of ecosystem services as twice the entire global economic output.

Man's adverse impacts on our planet were only slowly recognised. The year 1962 saw the publication in the USA of *Silent Spring*, Rachel Carson's warning of the dangers of uncontrolled pesticide use, to wild creatures and to humans; a book that is often credited with sparking the environmental movement. Cheshire Wildlife Trust was founded in 1962, that seminal year; the half-century of CWT's existence has seen great changes in nature conservation, from a focus on rare species and nature reserves to emphasising landscape-scale habitat schemes and ecosystem services. There have also been some enormous changes in our wildlife, some natural but most of them induced by man in various ways. These have been reviewed nationally in a book called *Silent Summer* (Maclean 2010) and the details for Cheshire follow in the succeeding chapters for a range of habitats and species groups: this overview summarises some of the key points.

Terrestrial habitats

The county's flora has not been comprehensively reviewed since the 1960s (Newton 1971) and a thorough revision would be welcome: it would be interesting to see the effects of changes in habitats and the effects of nutrient enrichment and

Figure 1.1. Oak is by far the commonest Cheshire tree in fields and boundaries. © Peter Clark

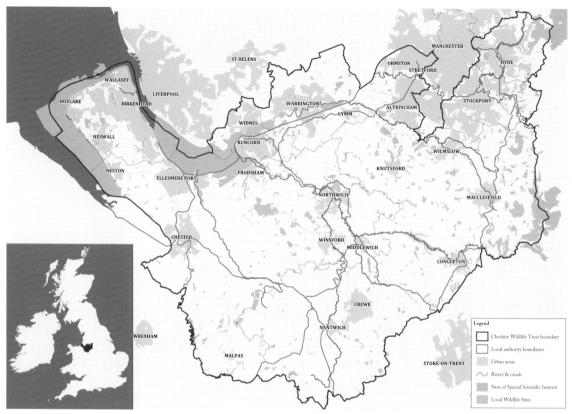

Figure 1.2. Cheshire Wildlife Trust was formed in 1962 to cover what was then the county of Cheshire. Changes to the organisation of local government in 1974, 1998 and 2010 mean that this area is now eight unitary authorities: Cheshire West and Chester, Cheshire East, Wirral, Halton, Warrington, Trafford, Stockport, and Tameside. The land area totals about 2,835 km². The human population has risen from 1,808,323 in 1961 to a total of 2,002,754 at the 2001 census (the latest published figures), this 10.7% rise being much the same as the 11.7% in England as a whole. Despite the impression of a rural county, with the land-use dominated by agriculture, only 21.6% of the population lives in localities classed as 'rural', two-thirds of them in the two Cheshire authorities. Map prepared by Kristina Dunning, Cheshire Wildlife Trust.

climate. Many plants host their own characteristic invertebrate populations and thus determine their distribution and numbers as well. It is doubtful, however, whether any modern-day recorder would agree with the sentiment in the preface to Newton's book, in which the then-Professor of Botany at the University of Manchester writes 'it is encouraging to see that decorative invaders from abroad, such as Himalayan balsam … are now well established'.

Agricultural land

More than two-thirds of the area of Cheshire is devoted to farming (Chapter 2, pp. 24–37), so the state of our agriculture has a major impact on our wildlife. Cheshire has long been a pastoral county, with most agriculture based on grassland; that has not changed much in the last fifty years. But that bald statement masks a revolution, in the application of chemicals, in methods of harvesting the grass, and in animal husbandry. The previous régime of mowing once, sometimes twice, a year for hay allowed much wildlife to co-exist but the present pattern of three, even four, annual cuts of heavily-treated grass for silage permits nothing else to use the fields. The use of fertilisers is also harming the environment. The nitrate content of watercourses roughly doubled from the 1960s to the 1980s – more runs off each hectare of Britain's land than anywhere else in the world – and so much phosphate has been applied to farmland that the world's mines will be exhausted in fifty years or less.

Many Cheshire farmers like to see wildlife on their land and its loss is not a deliberate act. The subsidy system, mostly deriving from the Common

Cheshire's greatest naturalists

The county's natural history in the first half of the 20th century was dominated by two Cheshire men, giants with a national reputation, whose names live on through their books and on the ground. Their work provides the context for the later studies that are summarised in the following chapters.

T.A. (Thomas) Coward (1867–1933) set the scene around the turn of the 20th century with his *The Birds of Cheshire* (1900), jointly with Charles Oldham, followed a decade later by his magnum opus *The Vertebrate Fauna of Cheshire and Liverpool Bay*. He was the first of the *Manchester Guardian's* Country Diarists, starting in 1904 with a daily column, extracting and extending some of them in two books, *Bird Haunts and Nature Memories* and *Bird Life at Home and Abroad*.

A.W. (Arnold) Boyd (1885–1959), an acute observer of all aspects of the natural world, took over writing for the *Manchester Guardian's* Country Diary on Coward's death, with selections published in his *Country Diary of a Cheshire Man*. His best book, on all aspects of country life (not just natural history) in and around Great Budworth, was the *New Naturalist* classic *A Country Parish*.

Coward's memorial fund was used to buy the nature reserves of Cotterill Clough and the Marbury reed bed at Budworth Mere, both now

managed by Cheshire Wildlife Trust, and Boyd is commemorated in the name of the observatory at Rostherne Mere and in a walk around Antrobus parish.

Figure 1.3. T.A. Coward (right) and A.W. Boyd, photographed by Eric Hosking; the site and date are unknown, believed to be probably at Marbury (Budworth) Mere in about 1930. © Eric Hosking Charitable Trust

Agricultural Policy, has distorted the economics and supermarkets have persuaded consumers that food has to be cheap and relentlessly driven the price of staples – notably, for Cheshire, milk – to unsustainably low levels. The closure of many abattoirs and the supermarkets' centralisation of food processing have made an enormous difference to the treatment of livestock, with unforeseen consequences on animal health. Farm animals are vulnerable to disease, whose spread is liable to be blamed on wildlife, from midges to birds to badgers, but not helped, to say the least, by mass transport of farm animals from one end of the country to another.

There are some more hopeful signs as farm support policy for the past two decades has gradually shifted away from subsidising production and towards management of the land to deliver environmental benefits. About two-thirds of Cheshire's farmland is now in Environmental Stewardship, with about one-tenth of that total in the more stringent Higher Level Stewardship. Most of the stewardship options being taken up are those on the field margins, especially leaving uncropped field edges and hedgerow maintenance, benefiting species such as some invertebrates and small mammals, and those like Tree Sparrows and Barn Owls that prey on them; but these measures are of no value to the Lapwings and Yellow Wagtails that shun the edges and use the centres of fields, and are still declining.

Trees and woodland

Cheshire is not now heavily-wooded but this was not always so: in the Domesday Book (1086) over one-quarter of Cheshire was recorded as woodland, a proportion exceeded only by two other counties (Staffordshire and Worcestershire). Most of it went in the following 250 years as the population grew and farming took hold. Ancient woodland – defined as having been continuously wooded since 1600 (and thus likely to have developed naturally, rather than having been planted)

– was catalogued by English Nature at 1687 ha in Cheshire, about 0.7% of the land area, mostly in woods smaller than 5 ha and mainly in inaccessible sites including the Cheshire specialities of clough woodlands. Some of the largest ancient woods, all designated as SSSIs, are Peckforton, Wettenhall and Darnhall, Wimboldsley, and Roe Park Woods (including Cheshire Wildlife Trust's reserve of Limekiln Wood). The Cheshire region Local Biodiversity Action Plan records the extent of all semi-natural broadleaved native woodland (including ancient woodland) as 5594 ha in 2007 (about 2.5% of the county), and aims to maintain and increase this figure.

Woodland of all types now makes up about 5% of the county. The most recent complete survey, the National Inventory of Woodland and Trees, conducted in 1998 (Forestry Commission 2002) found that the total area of woodland in Cheshire (comprising what is now Cheshire East, Cheshire West and Chester, Halton and Warrington) is 10,337 ha (4.4% of the land area), with 961 woods over 2 ha and 4146 woods of 0.1 ha to 2 ha. Of this, broadleaved woodland made up 56%, conifer woodland 20%, mixed woodland 16% and open space within woodlands 8%. The main species are Oak (16% of all trees), pine – mostly Scots and Corsican (15%), Birch (13%) and Sycamore (13%), followed by Larch (7%), Beech (7%) and Ash (6%). The largest continuous areas of woodland are the Forestry Commission plantations of Delamere Forest and Macclesfield Forest, but most of the county's woodland is in private ownership especially the large estates or, increasingly, landholdings by conservation charities especially the National Trust, Woodland Trust and Cheshire Wildlife Trust.

The county's woods have an uneven age structure. In the 1998 inventory, 440 ha was recorded as having been planted before 1900, the disparity between these figures and those for ancient woodland given above being explained by regeneration and re-planting within old woods. Then, in twenty-year periods of the 20th century, 376 ha were planted in 1901–1920; 610 ha in 1921–1940; 1902 ha in 1941–1960; 780 ha in 1961–1980; and 659 ha in the period 1981–1998. Much of the old woodland has fallen or been felled: in 1980 there were 3,646 ha of pre-1900 woodland, so 88% of it was lost between the 1980 and 1998 surveys.

However, the total woodland cover in the county increased by 1100 ha between the two Forestry Commission surveys of 1980 and 1998. The Mersey Forest, designated in 1991 as the largest of twelve English 'community forests', covers much of the northern part of Cheshire and is championing the 'green infrastructure' approach to new woodland and hedgerows. In twenty years, more than 10 million new trees have been planted across the whole Mersey Forest region, and better management schemes promoted for much of the established woodland. Another public-sector initiative, the New Towns of Runcorn (1964) and Warrington (1968) – with the Development Corporations merged in 1981 and wound up in 1989 – included considerable structured tree planting, which has been shown to have had a markedly beneficial effect on the breeding bird populations of that area (James, Norman & Clarke 2010) and presumably on other wildlife.

Hedgerow trees and isolated trees in fields are a notable feature of the Cheshire landscape. The 1998 inventory recorded 195,000 boundary trees, half of which (97,500) are Oak, with 22,000 Ash and 12,000 Beech. 'Middle trees', not on a boundary, totalled 36,000 of which 20,300 are Oak. There has, however, been a massive loss of these during the period between the two surveys (1980 and 1998): 50% of the boundary trees have gone, as have 80% of the middle trees. Much of this demise is attributable to continued agricultural intensification. 'Narrow linear features', often along roads or watercourses, contain 2.4 million trees in Cheshire, of which 307,000 are Poplar, 176,000 are Alder, 167,000 Willow and 125,000 Oak.

Although the Oak (Fig. 1.1) is clearly the dominant tree of the Cheshire countryside, some of the tree species not numerous enough to be listed in the national inventory are locally important, such as the Field Maple, a distinctive feature of south Cheshire hedgerows. Black Poplar – thought to be the most endangered native timber tree in Britain – is the only tree to have a Cheshire region Local Biodiversity Action Plan dedicated to it, aiming to increase the number of established trees in the county from the 1999 figure of 518 individuals to 658 individuals by 2015. In Cheshire the Black Poplar is at the northwestern limit of its range, but most of the trees are too isolated for them to regenerate naturally. The county's population is thought to be almost equally split between male and female trees whereas males predominate elsewhere. Black Poplars are found principally along the floodplains of the Rivers Gowy and Weaver, mostly adjacent to rivers and brooks, with a few next to marl pits, ditches and in hedgerows. Many of the sites are listed in the book on the species (Cooper 2006);

Figure 1.5. Black Poplar is the only tree to have a Cheshire region local biodiversity action plan (LBAP) dedicated to it. © Brian Eversham

Natural Areas, sites with nature conservation designations and Nature Improvement Areas

In the 1990s English Nature examined how each part of England is distinctive, and identified its characteristic wildlife and natural features. From this process 120 'Natural Areas' were defined, covering the whole of England, each with nature conservation goals. Most of Cheshire falls within the 'Meres and Mosses' Natural Area, with the higher land in the eastern part in the South West Peak, and the northern part of the county in the Urban Mersey Basin. The estuarine and coastal habitats are in the Liverpool Bay marine Natural Area.

Natural Areas are not statutory designations but help to guide the natural character and wildlife interest. The main statutory wildlife designation is a Site of Special Scientific Interest (SSSI) of which there are 63 in Cheshire (Cheshire West and Chester, Cheshire East, Halton and Warrington) with 10 in

Wirral and five in the three Greater Manchester boroughs of Trafford, Stockport and Tameside. Of this total of 78 sites, 63 have been designated for their biological interest, eight for their geological or geomorphological features, and seven for both.

SSSIs are considered of national importance while there is a lower tier of non-statutory sites of regional or local importance known as Local Wildlife Sites (LWSs), formerly called SBIs (Sites of Biological Importance) or SINCs (Sites of Interest for Nature Conservation). There are approximately 820 LWSs in the Cheshire Wildlife Trust area.

Recent work, especially 'Making Space for Nature: A review of England's Wildlife Sites and Ecological Network' (chaired by Professor Sir John Lawton), has recognised that designated sites are not enough to maintain biodiversity. This review proposed a new focus on ecological networks, including core areas (primarily existing wildlife sites); corridors and stepping stones, which could be created or restored; and buffer zones that reduce pressures on core areas. The government's Natural Environment White Paper, published on 7 June 2011, accepted the principle and supported creation of Nature Improvement Areas (NIAs), large areas covering hundreds of thousands of hectares of England: one of the first twelve NIAs agreed in 2012, Meres and Mosses of the Marches, includes part of southern Cheshire.

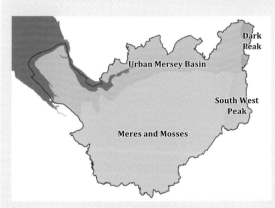

Figure 1.6. The Natural Areas of Cheshire.

one farmland marl pit near Ellesmere Port has been designated an SSSI solely because it has three Black Poplar trees.

Just as trees can be such a prominent part of the landscape, so their loss is equally notable. The last half-century has seen a greater awareness of plant disease as a threat to our countryside, particularly triggered by the outbreak of Dutch Elm Disease, a fungus spread by the Elm Bark Beetle. In 1967, a virulent strain arrived in Britain on a shipment of wood from North America, and within about twenty years more than 25 million trees had died in the UK. Elm was never as important in Cheshire as in more southerly counties but, in the Forestry Commission census of 1979–82, 18,910 Elms were recorded in the county of which 15,220 were already dead. By 1990, very few mature Elms were left in Britain or much of continental Europe. Young Elms can grow from suckers to about 4 m in height but then they are found by the flying beetles and succumb to the disease; some disease-resistant cultivars are being developed and might provide a lifeline for the Elm.

'Sudden Oak death' is the most recent significant tree disease, reaching the UK in 2002: this is caused by the fungus *Phytophthora ramorum* and produces symptoms including leaf blight, twig dieback and stem canker, which can lead to death of the plant. Despite its dramatic and specific name, given in the USA, *P. ramorum* has been identified affecting more than 150 natural hosts including disparate species such as Larch, Rhododendron and Bilberry. It appears that the *Phytophthora* spores are possibly waterborne or windborne, or even spread on the shoes or clothing of ramblers. There have been eight confirmed outbreaks of *P. ramorum* in the natural environment in Cheshire, with the first occurring in 2005 but its impact on the county's trees and other plants is yet unknown (source: The Food and Environment Research Agency, June 2012).

Another newly-discovered type of *Phytophthora* – aptly named from the Greek for 'plant destroyer' – is specific to Alder, and spreads along watercourses. *Phytophthora alni* (named after the scientific name for the alder genus) causes a root disease which weakens, but does not necessarily kill, the infected trees. It was first recognised in Britain in 1993, and within two years had been found in many counties of southern England, including along the river systems of the Weaver, Dane, Goyt and Mersey in Cheshire. As this book was going to press our native Ash population is reported to be under threat from imported trees carrying the fungus *Chalara fraxinea* that has caused widespread damage in continental Europe, including estimated losses of 60 to 90 per cent of Denmark's ash trees.

Urban areas

Urban areas are not well-defined habitats in themselves although the 'Urban Mersey Basin' is the name adopted for the Natural Area covering the north of our county, and developed land makes up 16% of the land area of Cheshire and Wirral. Much of our wildlife has made its home close to man and Jeff Clarke's chapter (Chapter 3, pp. 38–55) demonstrates the value of gardens, ponds, even roadside verges, whilst 'brownfield' – former industrial – sites can be amongst the most productive of all for wildlife. Perhaps most importantly, these are the areas in which most people encounter wildlife, making their value in education and training, plus recording opportunities, especially valuable.

Some species have adapted, famously the Peppered Moth that evolved to cope with polluted industrial areas, and has now reverted to its original form as atmospheric soot particles have all-but disappeared. Some birds have taken to human sites for nesting, such as the Swift, finding suitable spots in the nooks and crannies in house roofs, or the Peregrine, taking tall industrial buildings or other man-made structures as surrogates for their natural cliff sites.

Aquatic habitats

Meres and Mosses

The meres and mosses are the main feature of the Natural Area covering most of the county. The chapter by Colin Hayes (Chapter 5, pp. 98–121) explains their glacial formation thousands of years ago, and their special characteristics including their wonderful flora such as the carnivorous Sundew. These sites have attracted much conservation effort in the last half-century. The only two National Nature Reserves in the county are Wybunbury Moss and Rostherne Mere, and the Cheshire Meres and Mosses are part of a designated site under the Ramsar Convention on Wetlands of International Importance. Twenty-two Sites of Special Scientific Interest (SSSIs) in Cheshire are meres or mosses, as are ten of Cheshire Wildlife Trust's nature reserves. Substantial management work is taking place on some sites including removal of encroaching scrub and re-wetting programmes.

Figure 1.7. The carnivorous Sundew is a feature of some of our meres and mosses. © Colin Hayes

Ponds

Cheshire has been described as the 'pond capital' of Europe, with the highest density of ponds in our landscape, so it is appropriate that they should have a chapter in this book (Chapter 7, pp. 148–179), written by Andrew Hull who led the Pond *Life* Project to catalogue the county's ponds and to foster their conservation. There has been a well-documented decline, with one quarter of the county's farmland ponds lost in just sixteen years (1969–1985) but significant parts of the county contain more than 5 ponds per km², while some parts of the Cheshire Plain attain a density of 15 ponds per km², and 98% of the county is within 1 km of a pond.

Their biodiversity value perhaps used to be taken for granted, but now is recognised, with a Cheshire Local Biodiversity Action Plan for their conservation. The Critical Pond Biodiversity Survey (1995–1998) recorded a total of 265 plant species, with a mean of 21 species per pond. Newts largely depend on ponds, including the globally-threatened Great Crested Newt, present in more than one-third of Cheshire ponds: it is quite likely that the Cheshire population represents the greatest concentration of the species across its range. The locally scarce Mud Snail *Lymnaea glabra* is aptly named, and ponds also host most of the county's Lesser Silver Water Beetle *Hydrochara caraboides*, which used to be widespread but from 1938 was known in the UK only from the Somerset Levels until 1990 when it was found in Cheshire: it now inhabits several sites in the county.

Figure 1.8. *The underside of a Lesser Silver Water Beetle* Hydrochara caraboides, *showing the air bubbles trapped along its body from which it gets the 'silver' part of its name.* © *Andy Harmer*

Figure 1.9. *Natterjack Toads have at best a tenuous hold on Cheshire, in the seasonal pools at Red Rocks on the edge of the Dee.* © *Andy Harmer*

Rivers

Cheshire's rivers, varying from the upland cloughs of the Peak District fringe to the meandering Dee, are described in a chapter by Duncan Revell (Chapter 6, pp. 122–147). From a history of industrial and agricultural pollution, most are now recovering, chemically and biologically, marked by the return of iconic species such as Salmon and Otter.

Rivers now are the subject of intensive monitoring under the European Water Framework Directive, conducted by the Environment Agency, aiming to meet *good ecological status* by the year 2027. This involves chemical and biological sampling, of ammonia, dissolved oxygen and biochemical oxygen demand and of groups of macro-invertebrates such as stonefly and mayfly nymphs. Some of our rivers are blighted by invasive alien species, riverside plants such as Japanese Knotweed, Giant Hogweed and Himalayan Balsam; aquatic plants including Floating Pennywort, Water Fern and Australian Swamp Stonecrop; crustaceans like Chinese Mitten Crab and American Signal Crayfish; and the voracious American Mink.

Marine wildlife

Only about 8 miles of Cheshire faces the open sea, but the tidal estuaries of Mersey and Dee add many more, and almost all of the coastline has one or more nature conservation designation. The Liverpool Bay Special Protection Area covers most of the offshore open sea, and a Marine Conservation Zone is proposed around Hilbre Island following the Marine & Coastal Access Act 2010.

The chapter in this book by Ian Wallace (Chapter 4, pp. 56–97) opens our eyes to the world of the county's sandy beaches, hard shores, estuaries, saltmarsh and the man-made docks and marine lakes.

Species

Lichens

Lichens are fascinating organisms and an important component of our biodiversity, although studied by only a few people. We are fortunate that a lichen atlas of the county was published in 2003 and recent changes are covered by Mike Gosling in this book (Chapter 8, pp. 180–195). Lichens are very useful as indicators – woodlands rich in lichens have a far greater diversity of other wildlife than if the trunks and branches are relatively bare – and help in grading ancient woodland: only one of the thirty species used in the classification is now found in Cheshire, testament to the almost total disappearance of 'ancient woodland' from the county.

Lichens are renowned for their sensitivity to air quality. Clean Air legislation from 1956 to 1974 forced a massive decrease in airborne pollutants, and the recovery from industrial pollution, particularly sulphur dioxide, has allowed

Figure 1.10. A recently-emerged (teneral) male White-faced Darter, a species now extinct in Cheshire. © Andy Harmer

many lichens to re-colonise the county. A more recent effect, however, has been an increase and spread of nitrogen-loving lichens, in urban areas mainly from nitrogen oxides in vehicle exhaust gases, and especially in rural Cheshire where the elevated concentrations of airborne ammonia – amongst the highest in the UK – derive from intensive livestock farming.

Dragonflies and damselflies

The atlas fieldwork, then publication (1992) of *The Dragonflies and Damselflies of Cheshire* revolutionised our knowledge of the county's odonata, including describing the establishment during the 1980s of several colonising species, and fortunately provided the background for the remarkable northward spread of several species that has taken place since then. The chapter in this book (Chapter 9, pp. 196–209) by David Kitching, the county recorder and co-author of the 1992 atlas, describes this range expansion. It is notable that two of the recent colonists – Emperor Dragonfly and Migrant Hawker – are now amongst the commonest and most widespread dragonflies in Cheshire. The main underlying factor is probably climate change, although changes in water chemistry may also have an influence.

One of the county's specialities, White-faced Darter, has been lost in the last decade owing to loss of habitat and neutralisation of the acidic pools where it lived; a reintroduction programme is being considered.

Mammals

Mammal recording is still very much in its infancy in the county, and is now being coordinated and stimulated by the Cheshire Mammal Group, whose members published *The Mammals of Cheshire* (2008) and have contributed a chapter to this volume (Paul Hill, Penny Rudd and the Cheshire Mammal Group, Chapter 10, pp. 210–221). With only sporadic data from the past, it is often impossible to tell whether an apparent spread is due to increased recorder effort or actual range expansion. But Red and Roe Deer have increased, as well as the introduced Grey Squirrel and Mink, and not forgetting our marine mammals, of which the Grey Seal non-breeding population of the Dee has certainly risen.

Declines are perhaps easier to be sure of, including the Cheshire extinction of the Red Squirrel, last seen in the 1980s, and the considerable drop in numbers of Hedgehog and Water Vole, although the latter is responding to recent conservation programmes, also benefiting Otters. Two new mammal species have recently been found in the county, Yellow-necked Mouse (amongst the Hazel Dormouse colony on the Shropshire border) and Lesser Horseshoe Bats, last recorded in Cheshire in 1948.

Birds

Birds have long been the best-studied of the county's, and the country's, fauna and until recently have been the only species whose numbers, as well as distribution, have been recorded. There has been a lot of emphasis on the losses of some species, especially farmland birds, although some woodland species and summer

Figure 1.11. Cheshire has always been important for Great Crested Grebes, now breeding in all suitable waters across the county. © Chris Grady

migrants have declined at least as much and without the same publicity. But in fact there has been a substantial increase in diversity of the county's regularly breeding birds: eight species have been lost as Cheshire breeders since 1960, while 23 new species have started regularly breeding here. It is salutary to recall that one of our commonest birds of towns and gardens, the Collared Dove, first bred in the county only in 1961.

My chapter in this book (Chapter 11, pp. 222–251) gives the details of the changes in bird numbers and distributions, and analyses the causes. Climate change has had a notable effect, perhaps especially in winter in allowing more small birds to survive and migratory waterfowl to winter closer to their breeding grounds, and in the influence of African drought on some of our summer migrants. The improved quality of water and air has benefited some birds, and the reduction in human persecution of raptors and corvids has given us several new breeding species. Habitat changes, especially in farmland, have had mostly negative impacts.

Climate

Our climate is changing. Some dispute the figures, but any observer of the natural world will have seen lots of evidence. In Britain, many plant species are flowering and leaves unfolding earlier; many butterflies are appearing earlier; amphibians are breeding earlier; birds are breeding earlier; most spring migrant birds are arriving earlier; whilst in autumn, deciduous leaves are falling later and mammals are hibernating later (summarised by Walther *et al.* 2002).

The facts are well known: the mean temperature in central England (a roughly triangular area – including Cheshire – enclosed by Bristol, Lancashire

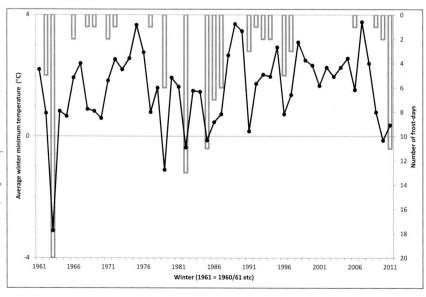

Figure 1.12. The winter (December to February inclusive) seasonal average minimum temperature (line and dots) and the number of 'frost days' (defined as a day on which the temperature did not rise above zero) (bars) for central England (including Cheshire) from 1960/61 to 2010/11 (compiled from data from www.metoffice. gov.uk/hadobs/hadcet/).

and London for which data have been collected from 1772) is now about 1°C warmer than fifty years ago, and we are now in the warmest period since the Industrial Revolution. Globally, nine of the ten hottest years on record have come since the year 2000. A rise of around 1°C in mean temperature, however, does not seem much, and the planet's climate has undergone far greater changes at periods in the past, allowing some to argue for continued waste of energy, while others muddle the discussion by confusing (short-term) weather with (longer-term) climate. Perhaps the key points are the unprecedented rapidity of the change, and that never before has the planet had such a large human population and so much developed land, making it particularly difficult for mankind, and nature, to cope with the effects.

Probably not much in the natural world is particularly sensitive to a rise in mean temperature *per se*, and the effects on our wildlife come about through effects like an earlier rise in spring temperature and an increased number of 'warm' days, giving a longer growing season. Many of our smaller birds, and probably other creatures not as well-studied, have changed their behaviour and increased their numbers from the more benign winters since the 1980s, especially with fewer days of frost (Fig. 1.12). Red Admiral butterflies used to be solely migrant butterflies but increasing numbers now overwinter here. However, although much of the emphasis in climate change is on the rise in temperature, that is not perhaps the most noticeable effect compared to the increased frequency of extreme weather events – such as wind and storms – and for some wildlife probably the biggest impact comes from more episodes of flood or drought.

Local examples of the impacts of climate change occur in several of the following chapters, and are perhaps most noticeable in the changes of distribution in mobile species, especially dragonflies and damselflies, butterflies, and in the breeding and wintering range of birds.

Wildlife recording

Among the most positive aspects of the last half-century has been the rise in wildlife recording. Nationally, the Common Birds Census started in 1962, followed by other networks of quantitative monitoring schemes including aphids and moths since 1968 (Rothamsted Research) and butterflies since 1976, mostly run as 'citizen science' projects with data collection by trained volunteers. Many taxa have their dedicated observers, and often produce annual reports, at national and county level. rECOrd, the Cheshire region's biodiversity records centre, was formed in 2000 to coordinate the archival and usage of local data as part of the National Biodiversity Network (NBN), and most of the county's recording groups now cooperate in depositing their data with rECOrd.

One of the best ways of recording the state of the county's wildlife is by atlases, which seek to cover the whole county, not just the hot-spots, and offer a true reflection of the range of habitats. Atlases of Cheshire's wildlife include

Figure 1.13. A Palmate
Newt, named after the
small webs between its toes.
© Andy Harmer

breeding birds (Guest *et al.* 1992), breeding and wintering birds (Norman 2008), dragonflies and damselflies (Gabb & Kitching 1992), lichens (Fox & Guest 2003) and mammals (Cheshire Mammal Group 2008), all of which are discussed in later chapters of this book.

The amphibian atlas (Guest & Harmer 2006) showed Frog to be the most frequently recorded in the county, with Toad and Smooth Newt also widespread, and all three often using garden ponds. Great Crested Newts also breed commonly in ponds throughout lowland Cheshire, as discussed in the ponds chapter of this book. A century ago, Natterjack Toads used to be widespread in north Wirral, breeding in the dune slacks, but most of their habitat has been lost to development and they may be extinct in the county, last heard calling at their only Wirral site, Red Rocks Marsh, in 2009. This leaves the Palmate Newt as the county's scarcest and most endangered amphibian, found mainly in the eastern foothills and a few heathland sites.

The Cheshire atlas of butterflies (Shaw 1999) showed a depressing tale: five species had gone extinct in the county during the 19th century, with a further six following in the first half of the 20th. Since then, the atlas and status statements from the Cheshire and Wirral annual butterfly reports show varying fortunes, although several species are prone to large fluctuations and conclusions should not be drawn over short periods of time. Even the commonest, the Small Tortoiseshell, underwent a noticeable decline in numbers, losing its status as Cheshire's most widely recorded butterfly in 2003 but regaining that position by 2011. Several of the other common species have increased in abundance and distribution since the 1970s or 1980s, including Peacock, Comma, Speckled

Figure 1.14. Although many butterfly species have declined in numbers or range, these six have increased in Cheshire:
(a) Small Skipper; (b) Speckled Wood; (c) Gatekeeper; (d) Peacock; (e) Comma; and (f) Brimstone. (a) to (e) © Damian Waters
www.drumimages.co.uk; (f) © Roy & Marie Battell www.moorhen.me.uk

Wood and Gatekeeper, all of which are moving north with climate change. The Wall butterfly may even be moving out of Cheshire, however: in 1984 it was the fifth most widely recorded butterfly in the county, but by 2011 had fallen to twenty-fifth position, with mainly a coastal distribution. Nationally, the Wall has been lost across much of central and southern England although it is still abundant farther north and into southern Scotland.

Grizzled Skipper has gone extinct in Cheshire, last breeding here in 1971, but the Small Skipper is now widespread, having been almost unknown in the county prior to 1976. Brimstone is another species increasing since the mid-1970s, assisted in some areas by planting of Alder Buckthorn. Ringlet used to be a county rarity, with no confirmed breeding records from 1937 to 1996, but is now found in the south of Cheshire and its range is spreading northwards.

The heathland specialists are struggling, with Green Hairstreak now scarce in the lowlands and mainly confined to the eastern hills. Silver-studded Blue butterflies were last known in Delamere in the 1920s, and an attempt in 1994 to reintroduce the species on the Wirral appears not to have been successful, with no sightings since 2004. Small Pearl-bordered Fritillary might be going the same way, now known from only one site, Bagmere, where recent conservation measures are aimed at increasing its favoured caterpillar food-plant Marsh Violet.

Most of these changes in Cheshire are part of the national pattern in which many of the habitat specialist butterflies are in decline while generalist species are stable or increasing (Fox *et al.* 2011). The terms 'generalist' or 'specialist' usually apply more to the caterpillars than to the adult butterflies themselves: the larvae often have specific food-plants, while flying butterflies may well be more catholic in their requirements. Although some of their life-cycles – especially the complicated symbiosis with ants shown by most 'blues' – have been unravelled only in recent decades, butterflies as a group have been recorded better, and longer, than probably any other British insects (except possibly dragonflies and bumblebees). Their changes in range and abundance are also likely to apply to many of the lesser-studied invertebrates such as hoverflies, weevils and spiders, and we should take the, mostly negative, effects on butterflies as indicative of a wider environmental malaise (Thomas 2010).

Harlequin Ladybird

I give here, as just one example of the speed at which some changes can happen, the spread of the Harlequin Ladybird *Harmonia axyridis*, described as the most invasive ladybird on Earth. This alien species was first found in south-east England in 2004 and they bred prolifically and moved rapidly northwest at a rate of around 100 miles per year! They were first recorded in Cheshire in 2006; on 31 October 2009 I found the ultimate insult when they were breeding in the gatepost of Cheshire Wildlife Trust's headquarters at Bickley Hall Farm. Harlequin Ladybirds can seriously affect native ladybird species. Their voracious appetite

Figure 1.15. Harlequin ladybird adults and immatures at Bickley Hall Farm. © David Norman

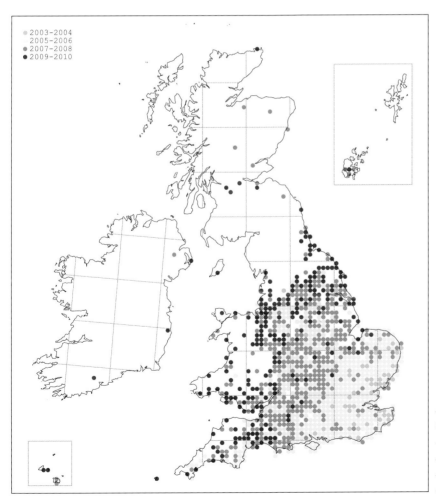

Figure 1.16. The recent rapid northwestward spread of the invading Harlequin Ladybird. Map from Natural Environment Research Council and www.ladybird-survey.org.

means they can east vast numbers of aphids, out-competing other species, and, when aphids are scarce, the Harlequins consume other prey including ladybird eggs, larvae and pupae, butterfly and moth eggs and caterpillars. There is, however, probably little that can be done to stem their spread.

Summary

It is noticeable that most of the changes in our wildlife are attributable to large-scale factors, especially climate and habitat, and their conservation needs widespread advocacy and policy; local measures, including direct conservation activity, are important for some localised and immobile species, but tend to have relatively limited impact. A positive sign is the increase in recording and systematic monitoring, especially in citizen science projects, as is the rise in interest in natural history, such that some presenters of wildlife television programmes are at least as well-known as many so-called celebrities.

References and Further Reading

Boyd, A.W. (1946) The Country Diary of a Cheshire Man. Collins, London.

Boyd, A.W. (1951) A Country Parish. Collins, London.

Carson, R. (1962) Silent Spring. Houghton Mifflin, Boston.

Cheshire Mammal Group (2008) The Mammals of Cheshire. Liverpool University Press.

Cooper, F. (2006) The Black Poplar: Ecology, History and Conservation. Windgather Press, Bollington, Cheshire.

Coward, T.A. & Oldham, C. (1900) The Birds of Cheshire. Sherratt & Hughes, Manchester.

Coward, T.A. (1910) The Vertebrate Fauna of Cheshire and Liverpool Bay. Witherby, London.

Coward, T.A. (1922) Bird Haunts and Nature Memories. Warne, London.

Coward, T.A. (1927) Bird Life at Home and Abroad (with other nature observations). Warne, London.

Forestry Commission (2002) National Inventory of Woodland and Trees: county report for Cheshire. www.forestry.gov.uk/pdf/cheshire.pdf/$FILE/cheshire.pdf

Fox, B. & Guest, J. (2003). The Lichen Flora of Cheshire and Wirral. Nepa Books, Frodsham.

Fox, R., Brereton, T.M., Asher, J., Botham, M.S., Middlebrook, I., Roy, D.B. and Warren, M.S. (2011) The State of the UK's Butterflies 2011. Butterfly Conservation and the Centre for Ecology & Hydrology, Wareham, Dorset.

Gabb, R. & Kitching, D. (1992) The Dragonflies and Damselflies of Cheshire. National Museums & Galleries on Merseyside.

Guest, J.P. & Harmer, A. (2006) Atlas of the Amphibians of Cheshire and Wirral. Nepa Books, Frodsham.

Guest, J.P., Elphick, D., Hunter, J.S.A. & Norman, D. (1992) The Breeding Bird Atlas of Cheshire and Wirral. Cheshire and Wirral Ornithological Society.

James, P., Norman, D. & Clarke, J.J. (2010) Avian population dynamics and human induced change in an urban environment. *Urban Ecosystems* 13: 499–515.

Maclean, N. (ed.) (2010) Silent Summer: The State of Wildlife in Britain and Ireland. Cambridge University Press.

Newton, A. (1971) Flora of Cheshire. Cheshire Community Council, Chester.

Norman, D. (2008) Birds in Cheshire and Wirral: a breeding and wintering atlas. Liverpool University Press.

Rackham, O. (2003) Ancient woodland – its history, vegetation and uses in England. Castlepoint Press, Kirkcudbrightshire.

Shaw, B.T. (1999) The Butterflies of Cheshire. National Museums and Galleries on Merseyside, Liverpool.

Smart, R. (1992) Trees and Woodland in Cheshire. Cheshire Landscape Trust, Chester.

Thomas, J.A. (2010) Butterflies, pp. 430–447 in Maclean, N. (ed.) (2010).

UK National Ecosystem Assessment (2011). The UK National Ecosystem Assessment Technical Report. UNEP-WCMC, Cambridge.

Wainwright, M. (ed.) (2006) A Gleaming Landscape; a hundred years of the Guardian's Country Diary. Aurum Press, London.

Wainwright, M. (ed.) (2007) The Guardian Book of Wartime Country Diaries. Guardian Books, London.

Walther, G-R., Post, E., Convey, P., Menzel, A., Parmesan, C., Beebee, T.J.C., Fromentin, J-M., Hoegh-Guldberg, O. & Bairlein, F. (2002) Ecological responses to recent climate change. *Nature* 416: 389–395.

About the author

David Norman moved to Cheshire in 1978 and pursued his interest in wildlife and nature conservation alongside his professional life as a physicist at Daresbury Laboratory.

As well as being active in fieldwork, mostly ringing, nest-recording and surveying birds, and analysing and publishing the results, David has been a strong advocate in committee rooms and organisations. He likes to summarise the range of skills and interests from advocacy to fieldwork in the phrase 'from pin-stripe suits to welly boots'.

He was founder chairman of several local charities: the Mersey Estuary Conservation Group, rECOrd (the local biodiversity records centre for Cheshire) and Groundwork Mersey Valley, as well as being one of the founding trustees of the Mersey Gateway Environmental Trust and a trustee of Cheshire and Wirral Ornithological Society. He was Chairman of Cheshire Wildlife Trust 2004–12, having chaired their Conservation Committee 2002–04, and nationally, David was appointed a Council member of English Nature (1996–2002), acting as Chairman for six months, and elected to the Council of RSPB (Royal Society for Protection of Birds) (2004–09).

Agriculture

David Norman

FARMING USES BY FAR THE BIGGEST PROPORTION OF LAND IN ENGLAND, SO THE state of our agriculture largely defines the appearance of our landscape and has a big influence on the state of our wildlife. It is just the same in our county, with the benign climate, moderate rainfall and accommodating soils – mostly underlain by sand or clay – allowing farming to account for nearly 70% of the area of Cheshire and Wirral. In the official agricultural land classification, 15% of the farmland is of the highest quality (Grades 1 and 2): the small areas of Grade 1 are mostly in the north of the county, around Warrington, on underlying peat, and the Grade 2 land is spread widely across the Cheshire Plain. The vast majority of the county's farmland (72%) is of moderate or good quality (Grade 3), with just 13% of it Grade 4 or 5, mostly at the highest or lowest elevations, on thin soil in the eastern hills or land frequently flooded in the river valleys.

Fifty years of change

The national and international scene has changed enormously since half a century ago. The wartime emphasis on food security – although that modern phrase was not used at the time – carried over into peacetime, and the introduction of powerful agrichemicals (inorganic fertilisers, herbicides and insecticides) triggered massive increases in productivity: UK arable farm yields (output per ha) almost doubled from 1945 to 1965, and doubled again from then to the year 2000 (Robinson & Sutherland 2002). 1962 was the year that the Common Agricultural Policy (CAP) came into force, initially for the six member countries of the European Economic Community, then applying to Britain after EEC membership in 1973.

Changes in food retailing have had a major impact on farming practice. The mass retailers of food have chosen to compete almost entirely on price with the result that spending on food and non-alcoholic drinks has dropped sharply from 33% of a weekly household budget in 1957 to just 15% in 2010 (Office for National Statistics Family Expenditure Survey). This has left a niche for selling based on quality, local provenance and seasonality, underpinning the recent rise of 'farmers' markets', but transport is so cheap – despite campaigns against the cost of fuel – that supermarkets are content to shift produce around the country, and indeed around the world.

Figure 2.1. A typical Cheshire landscape, looking north from Beeston Castle. © David Kitching

There has been a revolution in animal husbandry, vividly and grimly illustrated by the differences between the progress of the two major outbreaks of foot-and-mouth disease (FMD) in the last half-century. Cheshire was the centre of the 1967–68 epidemic, and bore the heaviest burden: 1,016 of the 2,346 recorded occurrences, and 90,431 cattle slaughtered of the 208,811 total (Hughes & Jones 1969). In the 2001 outbreak, Cheshire escaped relatively unscathed – although it did not feel like it at the time – with just 11 of the 2,030 recorded incidents, and 2,584 cattle slaughtered of the 700,000 national cull. The progress of the disease was vastly different: in 1967, FMD took about six months to cover about 100 miles, mostly dispersed by wind or by vehicles; in 2001, within a few days the disease had leapt hundreds of miles across the country, largely by transport and trading of animals from infected farms and markets. The closure of many abattoirs and the supermarkets' centralisation of food processing have made an enormous difference to the treatment of livestock, with unforeseen consequences on animal health.

The adverse impacts on our planet of the changing agriculture took some time to be appreciated. The crucial year of 1962 also saw the publication in the USA of *Silent Spring*, Rachel Carson's warning that uncontrolled pesticide use was harming and even killing not only wild creatures, but also humans; a book that is often credited with sparking the environmental movement. In Britain, millions of birds had already died, largely unnoticed, in the late-1950s and early-1960s from what was later found to be poisonous agricultural seed-dressings. Better testing and tighter regulation ought to mean that direct poisoning is unlikely these days, but the newest insecticides, neonicotinoids – designed to disturb the central nervous system of aphids and beetles – are now known to disorient bumblebees and honeybees, so that they fail to return to provide food for the growing colony. The consequent decline in bee populations has potentially disastrous consequences for the pollination on which much of our food depends. Other impacts on the environment come from inorganic fertilisers and the concentration of livestock. The nitrate content of watercourses roughly doubled from the 1960s to the 1980s – more runs off each hectare of Britain's land than anywhere else in the world – and so much phosphate has been applied to farmland that the world's mines will be exhausted in fifty years or less.

In the last half-century farming has been very successful in its primary aim of producing food, too successful in some ways, and the CAP has been adjusted to minimise surpluses. Some farmers have diversified the use of their land, perhaps planting energy crops or woodland, but almost all of Cheshire's farmland is used for growing food. Milk quotas affected the county most, introduced in 1984 and due to finish in 2015, to limit production and penalise countries (and individual farmers) who exceeded the prescribed figures. 'Set-aside' operated from 1992 to 2008, with farmers being paid not to farm some land, largely to reduce grain production, but also for some environmental benefit. Being aimed mainly at arable land, set-aside had little impact in Cheshire, temporarily taking around 3000 ha out of production, around 2% of the county's farmed area compared to more than 8% in the eastern England region. Some of the unintended adverse consequences of intensive agriculture are also being addressed, including the pollution of watercourses and aquifers. Nitrate Vulnerable Zones impose stringent rules and now cover almost two-thirds of England including virtually all of Cheshire; the underground water tables are so enriched with nitrogen, however, that it might take another half-century to return them to potable levels.

Farming in Cheshire

The review by Mercer (1963) – the founder Principal of the Cheshire School of Agriculture at Reaseheath – is based on data from 1956/57 and conveniently records the state of Cheshire agriculture around the start of our fifty-year review period. Although there have been many changes since then, the broad pattern has remained the same over the past half-century, and more; it is a pastoral county, dominated by grassland and livestock (Fig. 2.2). The colour of Cheshire has not been as blatantly affected as many other counties, turning yellow as rape flowered, or blue with linseed; the Cheshire countryside has always been mostly green, although its shade has changed subtly with the types of grass grown. Fifty years ago there was as much clover, *agrostis* (bents) and fescues as ryegrass (Davies 1960) but now the fields are predominantly of the higher-yielding perennial ryegrass, sustained by chemical fertilisers and slurry: more than 80% of grass seed sold is now of this single species (Hopkins 2008).

    Probably one of the biggest changes has been in the way in which grass has been cut and stored. Traditionally it was mown dry, as hay, although suffering

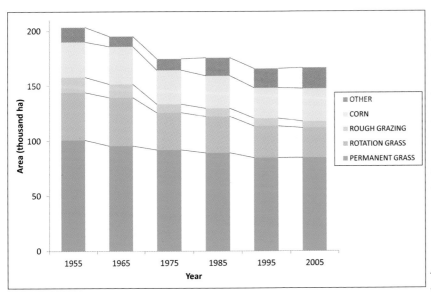

Figure 2.2. The area used by each of the main categories of agriculture in Cheshire 1955–2005. Definitions are 'permanent grass' > 5 years; 'rotation grass' (includes clover) < 5 years; 'corn' is wheat, barley, oats, rye and maize; 'other' includes potatoes, horticulture, orchards, etc. From 1955 to 1985 the area is Cheshire county; in 1995 and 2005 it is Cheshire, Halton and Warrington. Data from www.defra.gov.uk/statistics/ foodfarm/landuselivestock/ junesurvey/junesurveyresults/.

Figure 2.3. Silage collection, Cheshire, 1955. This field is now under the M6 near Allostock. © Roger Hollingsworth

from susceptibility to rain around haymaking time, and hay was of relatively low nutritional value, needing supplements especially for feeding to milking cows. A wartime campaign encouraged farmers to switch to silage as an alternative to imported concentrated animal foods – with a 1944 Ministry of Agriculture leaflet describing silage-making as a 'duty'! – but its production was not popular and did not really take off until techniques improved in the mid-1960s. Fifty years ago, about two-thirds of the mown acreage in Cheshire was taken as hay, with the remaining one-third as silage. This proportion of the fermented silage was already perhaps the highest in the country, as the response to the national silage campaign was said to be 'more marked in Cheshire than in any other part of the country because here the cows are thickest on the ground, the need for semi-concentrated fodder the greatest' (Mercer 1963). Since then there has been a tenfold increase nationally from the mid-1960s to the mid-1980s (Brassley 1996), and many Cheshire farms now take three cuts for silage, with some having even four a year. There is not much chance for any wild flora or fauna to live in these fields.

The grass, and silage, is especially for cattle, and Cheshire is known as the biggest milk field in Europe. For about two centuries, to 1920, the red or roan Shorthorn was almost the only breed of cattle to be seen in the county. Some

Milk

The retail price of milk has dropped phenomenally: in 1938 it took an average worker more than 20 minutes to earn the price of a litre of milk; by 1970 this was down to 8½ minutes and the 1994 deregulation of the milk market saw another large drop. Now (2012), supermarkets sell a litre of milk for less than 4½ minutes of a worker's time at today's *minimum* wage, and bottled water at twice that price! It is perhaps not surprising that from 1985 to 2005 the number of Cheshire dairy farms halved, from 1748 to 887, dropping further to 566 in 2010. The number of dairy cows has fallen less steeply, however (Fig. 2.4), as farms became larger to meet the economies of scale, with the average number of cows per dairy farm doubling (from 83 to 167) in the quarter-century 1985 to 2010.

Ayrshires started to be reared from about 1924 as they were more resistant to tuberculin, and had a higher milk yield, but the biggest change was the introduction of Friesians, which were in the majority by the mid-1950s. These black-and-white cattle came to dominate the Cheshire landscape; from the 1980s some Friesian herds were replaced by the similar-looking, but somewhat bigger, Holstein, giving even higher milk yields but perhaps being higher maintenance.

Most of the dairy output goes as liquid milk. Production of Cheshire cheese – said to be Britain's oldest variety – has declined from a peak of around 40,000 tonnes in 1960 to about one-sixth of that level today. Very few farms now make their own, and the long-established crumbly cheeses are another victim of supermarket domination as they do not pack, or travel, well. Yoghurt manufacture used to provide another dairy outlet but the county's main processing plant was closed in 2007. Pigs were often kept on the cheese-making farms, being fed on the whey and other locally-sourced waste products, but this habit has declined and most of

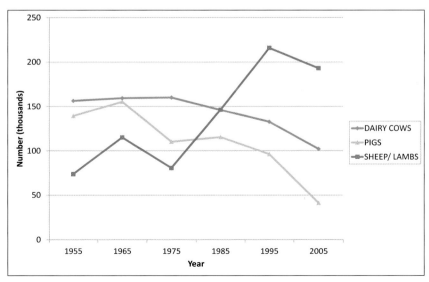

Figure 2.4. Some measures of change in Cheshire livestock, 1955–2005. Data from www.defra.gov.uk/statistics/foodfarm/landuselivestock/junesurvey/junesurveyresults/.

the county's pigs are now kept in specialised units. Cheshire has not traditionally been a county for sheep, although a few used to be kept on most farms with some more substantial flocks in the eastern hills. There has been a substantial rise in sheep and lambs over the last half-century although, with the normal conversion factors of one dairy cow being approximately equivalent to ten sheep, the total of 'livestock units' grazing in the county has declined considerably in recent years.

Cheshire's climate means that it has never been a great arable county, and most of the crops grown are used as fodder for the livestock. The last half-century has seen major changes (Fig. 2.5). Oats used to be the dominant grain crop, but rapidly fell out of favour in the 1960s, being largely replaced by barley. In just a couple of decades, oats went from being the staple for the county's livestock to a speciality food for our breakfast. In the late 1980s, some Cheshire farmers started growing maize, and by 2010 the area planted was second only to that of wheat. At first maize was only suitable for south-facing light soils but the warming climate and, especially, introduction of new varieties, has allowed it to be grown almost anywhere. It is mostly for cattle food – with some interesting diversification into public attractions as 'maize mazes' – and is often incorporated into silage. This is the only crop nowadays that is regularly left as winter stubble but is of little value for wildlife, perhaps being visited by Pheasants and corvids, with occasional flocks of geese when a field floods. Much more wheat is now being grown, but the drop in potato production has gone largely un-noticed. Mostly planted in the north of the county, Cheshire's early potatoes used to be famous but, with crops elsewhere under glass or poly-tunnels, world-wide imports and the transformation of seasonal foods into year-round staples, the area devoted to potatoes in the county has halved.

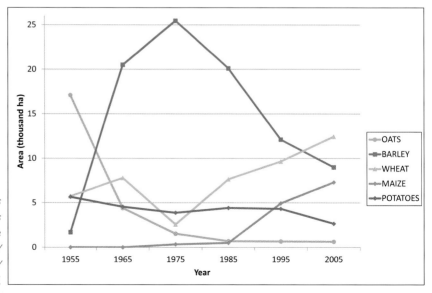

Figure 2.5. Some measures of change in Cheshire crops grown, 1955–2005. Data from www.defra.gov.uk/statistics/ foodfarm/landuselivestock/ junesurvey/junesurveyresults/.

Figure 2.6. The eastern part of Cheshire differs from the rest of the county in landscape and agriculture, depicted here on the slopes of Shutlingsloe, rising to 506 m in the Peak District National Park. Sheep predominate, with some hardy beef cattle. © Nigel Danson www.imageandlight.net

Although the official statistics provide a comprehensive record of cropping and livestock, they do not tell the whole story. Farms have, on average, become bigger and the number of small or medium family-run farms has declined. There used to be more variety within a farm, and across the county; but nowadays the traditional mixed farms have tended to become more specialised, either dairy, arable or other livestock as a reduced labour force concentrates on particular business strengths. Among the arable crops, there has been a major shift from spring to autumn planting, with consequent loss of winter stubbles, and 'weeds' are now scarce in the 'cleaner' agricultural environment. Within England, agriculture in this review period has become almost wholly polarised, with an arable east and pastoral west. Perhaps the most telling comment from Mercer's book about Cheshire agriculture (1963) was that 'more than half the land of the county would be unfarmable were it not drained', and drainage has continued and intensified. Many hedgerows have been removed, with the length in England and Wales being halved between 1960 and 1990 (Robinson & Sutherland 2002), although Cheshire is said still to have a greater length of hedgerow than any other county (CGS 2006).

Farming and wildlife

Agricultural statistics have been collected for more than a century but – despite its being by far the largest land-use – the wildlife of our farmland has not been well studied until relatively recently, and few data, in Cheshire or elsewhere, go back fifty years. Nevertheless, there is a widespread assumption that – with the notable exception of the Corncrake – the extensive agriculture practices that existed until the mid-twentieth century enabled the co-existence of farming and wildlife and that the effect of farming practices on wildlife was relatively benign before the advent of agrichemicals (Norris 2010). The longest-running quantitative monitoring data are for birds, particularly the volunteer-based surveys of breeding birds organised nationally by the British Trust for Ornithology. The Common Birds Census (CBC) started in 1962 and a national index of farmland bird populations has been produced from 1966 (Fig. 2.8) for a suite of 19 species. From 1966 to 2009 the national farmland index has more than halved, falling by 53%, although there are big differences between species within the index. Woodpigeons have thrived, their population more than trebling, while Lapwings initially rose, perhaps as winter climate ameliorated, then fell to below the 1966 level. Other species characteristic of farmland have shown dramatic declines, including Skylark (-61%), Yellow Wagtail (75%), Grey Partridge (-91%) and Tree Sparrow (-97%).

The Breeding Bird Survey, replacing the CBC from 1994, sampled about ten times the number of plots and with a much wider geographical coverage, allowing robust calculation of population indexes on a regional scale. This shows a further decline of 11% in the farmland bird index for England from 1994 to 2008 (included within Fig. 2.8), but considerable regional variations with the indexes for the NorthEast, Yorkshire and the NorthWest (including Cheshire) stable, reflecting the different types of agriculture across the country.

These data for birds serve as a proxy for much of the rest of the natural world, especially their food items (invertebrates, seeds, berries, small mammals), as the declines in farmland bird populations have been caused by three main factors: loss of nesting areas; lack of breeding season food (almost always invertebrates); and reduction in winter food (mostly seeds and hedgerow fruits). More national schemes have been introduced for annual monitoring of farmland populations of other wildlife including butterflies (from 1990), Brown Hares (from 1995) and Common Pipistrelle bats (from 1998).

Concern over the impact of intensive agriculture on landscape and wildlife has been gradually reflected in changes to farm support policy, in Britain and in the EU CAP, away from subsidising production and towards management of the land to deliver environmental benefits. Various schemes pay farmers in return for this change of emphasis, in recognition that this might cost them, in time or money or potential losses through reduced production. The Environmentally Sensitive Areas (ESA) Scheme was introduced in 1987, offering incentives for maintaining or improving habitat or landscape features in selected areas, which included part of the Cheshire moorland in the South West Peak District ESA from 1993. Countryside Stewardship (CS) was introduced in 1991 as the main agri-environmental policy instrument outside ESAs, applying to the whole country with objectives to improve and protect wildlife habitat, landscape beauty and to improve access. Both ESA and CS were closed to new entrants in 2004 and replaced by Environmental Stewardship (ES), which has two elements: Entry Level Stewardship (ELS) and Higher Level Stewardship (HLS), with organic

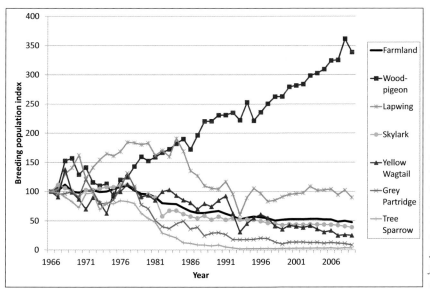

Figure 2.8. The national index of farmland breeding bird populations (bold line), with some selected species, redrawn from CBC (Common Birds Census) and BBS (Breeding Bird Survey) data in http://archive.defra. gov.uk/evidence/statistics/ foodfarm/enviro/observatory/ indicators/d/de5_data.htm.

farming options as well. The primary objectives of Environmental Stewardship are to conserve wildlife (biodiversity); maintain and enhance landscape quality and character; protect the historic environment; protect natural resources (water and soil); and to promote public access and understanding of the countryside. There are also secondary objectives for genetic conservation (rare breeds), flood risk management, and an overarching objective to contribute to climate change adaptation and mitigation. Payments to farmers depend on their taking up a variety of options including hedgerow maintenance, trees in fields and hedges, uncultivated field margins, crops for pollen, nectar and seed production, mixed livestock, reducing or eliminating fertiliser and pesticide inputs, maintenance and creation of ponds, and access footpaths and educational tours around farms. ELS is intended to be attainable by every farm, while HLS is a competitive grant scheme for those pursuing a greater range and number of options.

About two-thirds of Cheshire's farmland is now in Environmental Stewardship, with about one-tenth of that total in HLS. Most of the stewardship options being taken up are those on the field margins, especially leaving uncropped field edges and hedgerow maintenance, benefiting species such as some invertebrates and small mammals, and those like Whitethroats, Tree Sparrows, Reed Buntings and Kestrels that prey on them, all of whose populations have increased

Figure 2.9. Wildbird seed plots are amongst the options in the Environmental Stewardship scheme. © Jake Freestone (Farm Manager – Overbury Farms)

Figure 2.10. A 6-metre field margin, one of the agri-environment options in Environmental Stewardship. © Nigel Jones

Figure 2.11. A pollen and nectar crop, another Environmental Stewardship option. © Brian Barker

in the last decade; but these measures are of no value to the Lapwings, Yellow Wagtails and Skylarks that shun the edges and use the centres of fields, and are still in decline. Although not included in the national farmland birds index, the Barn Owl has become an icon for successful nature conservation in Cheshire. The county population was 240 pairs in 1932 but only 35 pairs in 1982–85 and just seven pairs in 1998 before local groups started working with landowners on creation of suitable feeding habitat in field margins and alongside watercourses, largely funded by CS or ES. The birds bounced back – the county now holds probably 150–200 breeding pairs – and it brings joy to a conservationist's heart to hear farmers boasting about how many Barn Owls they have on their land. It is also good to see some of the county's most enlightened farmers enter the Farming and Wildlife section of the annual Cheshire Farms competition.

Acknowledgments

I am very grateful to Bill Pearson (Reaseheath College), and to several local farmers, especially Keith Siddorn (Meadow Bank Farm, Broxton) and Richard Owen (Bickley Hall Farm), for information and helpful comments on farming in Cheshire. Data have been extracted from official sources, mostly the Office of National Statistics and DEFRA.

References and Further Reading

Brassley, P. (1996) Silage in Britain, 1880–1990: the Delayed Adoption of an Innovation. *Agricultural History Review* 44: 63–87.

Cheshire Grassland Society (2006) Changing Cheshire and the Future. Reaseheath College.

Davies, W. (1960) The grass crop: its development, use and maintenance. Spon Agricultural Books.

Fuller, R.J., Gregory, R.D., Gibbons, D.W., Marchant, J.H., Wilson, J.D., Baillie, S.R. & Carter, N. (1995) Population declines and range contractions among lowland farmland birds in Britain. *Conservation Biology* 9: 1425–1441.

Hopkins, A. (2008) *United Kingdom, Country Pasture/Forage Resources Profile.* Rome: United Nations Food and Agricultural Organisation. www.fao.org/ag/AGP/AGPC/doc/Counprof/britain/unitedkingdom.htm

Hughes, Herbert and J. O. Jones, eds. (1969) Plague on the Cheshire Plain: An Account of the Great Foot-and-Mouth Epidemic, 1967–68. Dennis Dobson, London.

Mercer, W. B. (1963) A Survey of the Agriculture of Cheshire. Royal Agricultural Society of England, London.

Norris, K. (2010) Agriculture, woodland and semi-natural habitats. In *Silent Summer: the state of wildlife in Britain and Ireland*, ed. Norman Maclean. Cambridge University Press.

Robinson, R.A. & Sutherland, W.J. (2002) Post-war changes in arable farming and biodiversity in Great Britain. *J. Appl. Ecol.* **39**: 157–176.

UK National Ecosystem Assessment (2011) The UK National Ecosystem Assessment: Synthesis of the Key Findings. UNEP-WCMC, Cambridge.

As well as consulting official statistics and the scientific literature, I have enjoyed learning from a number of personal accounts from Cheshire farmers:

Clifford, M. (1959) Hill-Farm Hazard. The Country Book Club.

Lea, J. (1998) Down the Cobbled Stones. Memories of a Cheshire Farmer. Churnet Books, Leek, Staffordshire.

Lea, J. (1999) Reach For My Countryside. Churnet Books, Leek, Staffordshire.

Salt Museum (2008) A Celebration of Farming in Cheshire Past and Present. DVD. Cheshire County Council.

Wright, G.W. (2008) From Corncrake to Combine; Memoirs of a Cheshire Farmer. The History Press, Stroud, Gloucestershire.

About the author

David Norman was Chairman of Cheshire Wildlife Trust 2004–12. Although his uncle was a farmer, he has no practical experience of local agriculture and this chapter owes much to official statistics, published literature, discussions with Cheshire farmers and his own observations especially for bird ringing and recording. He judged the Cheshire Farms Competition 'Farming and Wildlife' section in 2004 and 2010.

Urban Wildlife

Jeff Clarke

OVER 90% OF THE UK POPULATION LIVES IN THE URBAN ENVIRONMENT. IT'S THE habitat within which most of us enjoy our encounters with the natural world. A connectedness with our urban fauna and flora is critical in establishing our awareness of the vital role that it plays in enhancing and improving our lives, which includes our health and mental well-being. If this sounds a little far-fetched, or romanticised, imagine an urban world without bird song, or trees, or bumblebees; a colourless world save that which we have artificially created. So be glad that nature does not begin where the urban environment ends. This is a celebration of arguably the most important wildlife habit in Britain, but before we begin to tell the stories of Cheshire's urban nature, we must first decide the boundaries of the urban environment.

It is reasonably straightforward to understand what constitutes the core habitat for urban wildlife; it is the built environment in which we find pockets of green space. What is less certain is defining where urban wildlife habitat ends. The Office for National Statistics defines urban as '…an extent of at least 20 ha and at least 1,500 census residents. Separate areas are linked if less than 200 m apart. Included are transportation features'. Should a review such as this include the often vast areas of 'brownfield' sites that are so often found within, or bordering, the urban landscape? To ignore such locations would be to undervalue the immense biodiversity that can become established on these former industrialised and waste disposal sites, so in this article they are included as a significant element of the urban environment.

This chapter depicts a number of 'case studies' to show the critical importance, value and interest of Cheshire's urban wildlife.

Peppered Moth

In 1809 Charles Darwin began his near five-year journey of discovery aboard HMS Beagle from which he was to draw so much of his inspiration as he constructed his thoughts and observations which would eventually lead to his world changing publication in 1859 of *On the Origin of Species* in which he describes his 'theory of evolution'. Eleven years before its publication the first 'black' *carbonaria* form of the Peppered Moth was noted in Manchester, a footnote at the time, but the start of one of the most extraordinary examples of an observable evolutionary process

Figure 3.1. The unusually brown female Peregrine Falcon at a Cheshire industrial complex. © Jeff Clarke

*Figure 3.2. The normal and melanic (*carbonaria*) forms of the Peppered Moth at Wigg Island, Runcorn in 2005. © Jeff Clarke*

in a wild animal. The industrial areas of the NorthWest, including Cheshire, were to become the nucleus of a textbook example of what Darwin described as the 'survival of the fittest'.

The Peppered Moth is a common species throughout most of the UK, including the urban landscape. As the industrial revolution took its toll on the urban environment with its pall of soot and ash, this species' peppered appearance became ever more obvious to potential predators, principally birds, as it rested during the day on pollutant coated tree bark, that first masked and then killed off the encrusting lichens against which the moth was previously so well camouflaged. The chance mutation of the genetically distinct *carbonaria* form coincided with this human-altered treescape. Its survival against the blackened trees allowed it to prosper, while the converse was true for the usual form. As early as 1895 this dark (melanic) form of the moth came to represent some 98% of the population of the Peppered Moth in the industrialised areas of the NorthWest. Cheshire has been part of the history of this moth's evolutionary story. The Leahurst Field Centre, near Neston, was a contributor to the research of Bernard Kettlewell, the geneticist, who in 1956 began a series of experiments into natural selection and the influence of Industrial Melanism on the Peppered Moth. To this day local scientists carry on the research into this celebrated lepidopteran.

Cheshire's active community of moth trappers can themselves point to a more recent twist in the storyline. The Clean Air Acts of the 1950s and '60s and the Control of Pollution Act of 1974 resulted in a dramatic decline in airborne pollutants. The return of lichens to the trees of our urbanised areas has seen an equally dramatic reversal of fortune for the two colour forms. Few, if any, moth trappers within Cheshire have reported capturing a Peppered Moth of the *carbonaria* form since 2005 (Clarke *pers. comm.*).

Lichens and Long-tailed Tits

The return of lichens to our urban landscape has also contributed to an upsurge in the fortunes of another, increasingly familiar, urban species, the engaging Long-tailed Tit. As recently as the 1970s this species was little more than a winter visitor to the more urban areas of Cheshire. Its requirement for lichens in the construction of its exquisite nest acted as a natural barrier to the occupation of the urban landscape during the breeding season. Today in the second decade of the 21st century this bird has become an integral element of the breeding bird community, over the greater part of most urban and industrialised areas in Cheshire.

Evidence for this was gathered in 2004–06 by volunteers who put in tens of thousands of recorder hours culminating in the milestone publication of *Birds in Cheshire and Wirral: A breeding and wintering atlas* (2008) by David Norman

Figure 3.3. A typical Long-tailed Tit nest, decorated with lichens. © Emilio Dicerbo

on behalf of CAWOS. The data expressed on the maps of this important book convincingly illustrate the significant gains made by the Long-tailed Tit in the intervening years from the previous county bird atlas, where mapped data had spanned the years 1978 to 1984. The gains almost perfectly mirror the urban and industrialised areas of Cheshire, stretching from Crewe in the south to Macclesfield in the east and perhaps most pertinently of all to the infamously polluted landscape of Halton (Runcorn and Widnes) and Warrington. The upswing in the fortunes of the Long-tailed Tit in this latter trio of towns was analysed in detail (alongside the Chaffinch, another now common urban breeding bird in Cheshire, with a requirement for lichens in its nest building materials), in a paper published in Urban Ecosystems (2010): the authors (James, Norman and Clarke) concluded that 'it seems highly likely that the dominant factor is lichens and that…the improved air quality accordingly explains the increase in distribution of these two bird species in Halton and Warrington between 1978–84 and 2004–06'.

Swifts

Picture a blue sky, its perfect azure punctuated with towering cumulus clouds and there, high up, almost at the limits of your vision, scimitar-winged shapes cut across your retinas, tumbling, twisting, stuttering flicked wing beats, accelerating in a blink, mouth agape, to ensnare a flying ant, a ladybird, or a spider floating on a gossamer thread. A bird plummets from the heights, it nears you and you see that its crop is bulging. It flies headlong into the junction between the soffits and the brickwork of the nearest house, but there is no sickening thud, no cartoon pall

Figure 3.4. A flock of Swifts.
© Keta (Wikimedia Commons)

of feathers drifting to the ground. It almost seems as if the house has swallowed the bird. A short while later the bird momentarily drops from its barely visible nest entrance hole, flickers its wings and climbs relentlessly back into the blue. Enjoy the moment; you are watching one of the avian wonders of the world.

The Common Swift is a species whose success and abundance in the UK is ultimately and intimately reliant on the urban habitats of the UK. Urban Cheshire is where you find this bird in some of its highest population densities. The locations that seem most critical to its future and where the largest colonies occur are former council housing stock, most of which are now owned and maintained by Housing Trusts. Walk down Princes Road in Ellesmere Port, or Dykin Road in Widnes in the hour or two before sunset on a late May evening and you will be assailed by the sounds of screaming Swifts, as parties of the birds careen over the terraced rooftops. So long the bastion of the Swift, these important places could soon just be a ghostly echo of their former glory if we do not take steps to protect these populations from the inconsiderate and inappropriate refurbishment of these properties. Cheshire has its own Swift Champion in the form of Brian Martin of Grappenhall. Here we have an example of a local naturalist who has worked tirelessly to encourage local authorities of Cheshire to take seriously their responsibilities for protecting Swift nest sites. Although some of our populations have been impacted recently – 'there have been large scale losses around Chester, with smaller losses around Northwich, Crewe and Macclesfield' – (Norman 2008) many more have been protected and continue to thrive. With the continued vigilance and help from those who care about the value of urban wildlife the Common Swift will be gracing Cheshire's towns and cities and villages for generations to come.

Peregrines

The clanking of the machinery is nearly deafening as a small group of figures ascends the stairs in one of Cheshire's major industrial complexes. All around, a film of powdery limestone residue coats the surfaces and hangs like fine veil in the disturbed air. A tiny gap in the shuttering allows a preview of the target. The chicks are well feathered but masses of down still sprout from various parts of their bodies. It's the annual visit of the Merseyside Ringing Group to one of Cheshire's most productive Peregrine Falcon eyries. The female sits, keen-eyed and alert, watching over her chicks while the smaller male rests on a nearby pylon having recently provisioned his brood. The ringers move quickly and expertly. The chicks are bagged, brought to a safe spot, quickly assessed for their vital statistics and each has a unique ring placed on its legs. The male flies agitated at a distance but the female is less bashful, protesting the imposition loudly and making repeated close passes. Even though she has seen this performance for several past years her indignation is unabated. She is an unusual bird: adult Peregrines are normally steely grey with a pale grey rump, but this bird has retained a strong brown cast to her plumage. She's unique in the Peregrine world and she's a good mother. The chicks are returned safely and within moments she is back on the ledge guarding her brood.

Whilst the Peregrines of Beeston Castle and Helsby Hill are well known, the supply of natural nest sites in Cheshire is severely limited and so this most emblematic of our predatory birds has taken to nesting on substitute man-made structures. Power stations, bridges and industrial complexes have been adopted by Cheshire's urban Peregrine Falcons, following a model seen in other parts of the world. Free from major molestation these urban Peregrines are doing well and provide a thrilling sight as they pursue a Feral Pigeon across a metropolitan backdrop. From a low point in the 1960s following the devastating environmental poisoning caused by organochlorine pesticides like DDT, this majestic predator has returned to reclaim its domain, adding a new title and extending its realm to become the Queen of the urban skies.

With a bit of wit and imagination we could further encourage Cheshire's Peregrine population by incorporating nesting structures within our high rise buildings and industrial mega-structures. The Cheshire Wildlife Trust is well placed to encourage businesses and local authorities with regard to biodiversity-enhancing opportunities. It is easy to envisage a scenario where one of the UK's leading road haulage distributors has sponsored the construction of a successful Peregrine nesting platform on the new Mersey Gateway, stretching between the industrial towns of Runcorn and Widnes. As one of their familiar pantechnicons traverses the bridge the falcon gazes down, sees the passing lorry and is acutely aware of the figures approaching her from the Merseyside Ringing Group!

Roadside botany

A leaden sky looms ominously from the north, riding on the vanguard of a blast of arctic air. The thermometer is plummeting and the icy rain turns to snow. Flashing orange lights herald the imminent passing of a 'gritter'. Its dispersing load chatters into the paintwork of your vehicle. It is gone and the 'shushing' of your tyres and the squeak of your window wipers is the only sound you can hear above the noise of your engine. Four months later you are driving along the same stretch of highway and you notice the scorched earth at the side of the road where your tyres, along with thousands of others, had thrown the rock-salt-laden slush. The ground looks dead but then you notice a line of white marking the boundary between the dead zone and the green of fresh vegetation. From the car it's not easy to make out exactly what it is. Step from your car and take a closer look for here marking the boundary between where plant life is possible and where conditions are too hostile is a pioneer, a survivor. A plant exploiting the maritime-mimicking conditions of a spray washed coastline. Here like a ribbon of defiance lining Cheshire's urban road system we find Danish Scurvy Grass. Our urban networks are heavily reliant on the spreading of salt to keep them flowing

Figure 3.5. Danish Scurvy Grass along a Runcorn dual carriageway. © Jeff Clarke

during the winter months and this plant has made the successful jump to exploit a new human-induced niche. As its name suggests this plant is an antiscorbutic, a plant used previously to treat, or cure, scurvy, an affliction often associated with mariners on long sea voyages in the days of sailing ships. The disease is caused by a deficiency of vitamin C. Danish Scurvy Grass is rich in vitamin C and was consumed as an antidote to the condition; though few modern palates would enjoy the bitter taste of the leaves.

Many other plants have made the urban environment their home but are seldom found in the wider countryside. Some of these plants are non-natives to the UK having arrived by a variety of human agencies. Pineapple Weed, a species of wild chamomile, arrived from North America shortly before 1900. It thrives on compacted soils and quickly spread through the urban environment from its initial appearance in ports. Most of the seed dispersal appears to be from car tyres and like the scurvy grass is rapidly spread along road networks, to become a coloniser of pathways and roadsides. The compacted earths of many brownfield sites are particularly to its liking. Crush the leaves of Pineapple Weed and you soon discover the origins of its name. The aroma of pineapple is very distinctive. The plant itself has a number of medicinal uses: it is known to be an effective wormer, the crushed juices act as an insect repellent and it is also edible, though rather bitter to the taste if eaten raw.

Gardens

If you are lucky enough to have a garden – and, according to Natural England, there are fifteen million of them in the UK – you are responsible for a small part of the UK's largest nature reserve; and, despite the fact that gardens are stocked with mostly non-native species of plant, they still represent a very important natural resource. Compare the availability of nectar sources with your nearest area of farmland and you will soon be aware that gardens contain a vastly greater variety of flowering plants and that these nectar sources are available for a significantly greater part of the year. According to Cheshire Wildlife Trust's own advice sheet 'Building an Invertebrate Habitat', 'an average garden could hold over 2,000 different species of invertebrate'. Some of the invertebrate species found in gardens are rarely found elsewhere as they are non-native to the UK and are reliant upon the alien plants which we select to grow in our blessed plots. For instance, the startlingly scarlet but largely unloved Lily Beetle *Lilioceris lilii*

Brownfield sites

Brownfield sites themselves are, on the whole, remarkably biologically diverse. They are often no-go areas for the public, sealed off on health and safety grounds. The outcome is an explosion of plants and animals, many of which have become exceedingly rare in the wider countryside. Most brownfield sites in urban Cheshire are post-industrial sites and as often as not they are contaminated in some form. They frequently contain a diverse range of soil conditions, low nutrient and compacted ground, rubble mounds, broken concrete etc. Here, plants that have been lost elsewhere find a place to flourish, free from the threat of herbicides and pesticides that wash much of our countryside. Governments and politicians are still largely unaware of the importance of brownfield sites as reservoirs of biological diversity and still by default opt for their redevelopment ahead of biologically impoverished 'greenfield' sites. Today nature conservation organisations are pushing hard to have their value recognised: 'Brownfield land is as important to wildlife as many protected habitats in the UK and can act as great places for people to interact with nature in urban areas' (Buglife 2009).

Figure 3.6. An example of biological diversity at a brownfield site: Goatsbeard at Hale Road Woodlands LNR, a former landfill site. © Jeff Clarke

is found almost exclusively in garden settings, whilst the exquisitely-marked Rosemary Beetle *Chrysolina americana* has recently been discovered in Cheshire gardens and looks set to spread widely in line with the growing of its aromatic food plant.

If you were to pick out one element of a garden that would encourage wildlife more than any other, it would be a garden pond (see Chapter 7) and more specifically one that did not contain fish. According to the charity Pond Conservation the UK has two million garden ponds (www.pondconservation. org.uk). A plethora of invertebrates will rapidly colonise a garden pond, some more obviously than others. For most of Cheshire's garden pond owners a visit from a Common Darter, or Broad-bodied Chaser dragonfly would be eye-catching, though most freshwater invertebrates associated with garden ponds are far less obvious. One of the most delightful is the Dance Fly *Poecilobothrus nobilitatus* that forms leks on floating duckweed. Here the white-tipped-winged males signal to each other and to prospective mates by flashing their wings like an animated ground controller's paddles on an airport apron.

The ponds of urban Cheshire are also home to a very large amphibian population. Common Frogs and Common Toads can be found in many ponds, as can Smooth Newts, whilst many garden ponds in Cheshire are also home to one of Europe's protected amphibian species, the Great Crested Newt. Cheshire is the pond capital of the UK but as the farm ponds are lost through drainage, infilling, or development, the importance of our urban garden ponds becomes ever more critical. Many people are resistant to the idea of putting a pond in their garden, fearful of the danger to young children, but properly managed a garden pond is a place of endless adventure and a window into the natural world that will be cherished from childhood, long into adulthood.

Bats

The land around you is growing quieter, the evening bird song has finished with the exception of your local Robin, who as usual shows a reluctance to retire for the night and still sings from a nearby Sycamore. As the light fades, the bulb on your bat detector stands out like a yellow beacon. You check the dial, it's set to 45 kHz. A slight persistent hiss emanates from the instrument. Suddenly it bursts into life as a series of rapid clicks and slapping noises heralds the arrival the first bat of the night. You rotate the dial until the sounds are at their loudest and deepest. It settles at 55 kHz. A zip-like sound announces the demise of the first of perhaps a thousand, or more, mosquitoes to be consumed that night by this one tiny denizen of the dark. It is a Soprano Pipistrelle and it has just emerged from the eaves of your modern house in the middle of a leafily landscaped, but distinctly built up, part of your housing estate. The bat you are now watching darting against the vestiges of light from the set sun is extraordinary in many ways. Leave aside its sensory abilities to echo-locate, the fact that it is a mammal that can fly, even

Figure 3.7.
Brown Long-eared Bat.
© Andy Harmer

the fact that it weighs less than half as much as a Wood Mouse, but can live four, perhaps even five times longer. Remarkable as that may be, even more surprising is that as a species it did not even officially exist until 1999 when it was finally recognised as a separate species from the familiar Common Pipistrelle.

Both Common and Soprano Pipistrelles 'form maternity colonies in trees, buildings (old and new) and bat boxes' (Cheshire Mammal Group 2008). It is clear from the distribution maps shown in the same publication that both Pipistrelle spp. are widely distributed throughout Cheshire and this includes all of the major conurbations. Cheshire has an impoverished bat fauna; to date, from a UK total of eighteen species, just eight species have been identified as breeding in Cheshire and two others are known to occur. Though many species are strongly associated with woodland, many of them occur in some of the most urbanised Cheshire settings. It is clear that sensitive house construction and the provision of bat boxes on street trees or buildings could further enhance the environment of urban Cheshire for these and other species of bat.

Ladybirds

How many species of ladybird do you think there are in Cheshire? This was a question put to Primary School Children at 25 schools across the county in 2011. It was part of the Dot2Dot Ladybird Project operated by rECOrd (the local biological record centre for the area); the money to run the project came from the Awards for All lottery funding. Eager hands would spring into the air and a flurry of guesses would pour forth. In truth, the real answer is unknown. Some of the schools visited as part of the project were in moderately rural locations but most were in distinctly urban settings. Tree branches would be tapped, leaves sieved, tree trunks and other structures visually searched and grass would be swept or even sucked with a converted leaf-blower. Excitedly the children would gather up all the ladybirds that could be found and begin the process of putting names to their warningly coloured beetles. The children then added their findings to the rECOrd database and dots started to appear on maps. In most cases the ladybirds they found were new for that 2-km square and very often even for the surrounding 10-km square. Nine- and ten-year-old children were successfully identifying ladybird species that their teachers and parents did not even know existed and had never previously seen. They were adding to our knowledge about the wildlife of Cheshire, whilst being enthused about the wildlife of their urban environment and having enormous fun all at the same time.

It turns out that the children found an amazing variety of species, twenty-three in total, in seemingly mundane school grounds. This included 18-Spot Ladybirds in Congleton, 22-Spot Ladybirds in Ellesmere Port and Larch Ladybirds in Wilmslow, all in very urbanised settings. This was just the tip of the iceberg. Each school, on average, would find eight or more Ladybird species

Figure 3.8. Orange Ladybirds (left) were found in 13 out of 25 schools during the Dot2Dot Ladybird Project. Cream-streaked Ladybirds (right) are scarce in Cheshire but can be the commonest ladybird on urban planted Black Pines. © Jeff Clarke

present in their grounds. There was nothing remarkable about the school grounds in general, the range of trees and bushes was typical of those found throughout urban Cheshire – Sycamore, Oak, Ash, Lime and some conifers such as Scots Pine. The project was a demonstration of just how valuable and biologically diverse the urban environment of Cheshire actually is and how important it is that we educate our children to enable them to connect with the nature on their doorstep. It is far more likely that they will spend the majority of their lives in a local urban environment than the Masai Mara or the Amazon Rainforest. For most of Cheshire's children there is more to be gained from gazing into the compound eyes of a Seven-Spot Ladybird, than they will ever receive from words and pictures about a remote far-off land.

Do you know how many species of ladybird occur in Cheshire? Thanks to this local 'citizen science' project some 5,000 ten-year-old Cheshire children probably have a better idea than you do!

Figure 3.9. Cheshire children recording Ladybirds during the Dot2Dot Project. © Jeff Clarke

Figure 3.10.
Tree Bumblebee.
© Tim Melling

Wildlife recording

Plotting the distribution of species is something that we can all get involved with. We can record what we find in our gardens, our local park or that bit of roadside verge on the way to the local paper shop. It's an enjoyable experience to feel part of something and better still if what you are recording is new for you, or even your county. Species populations naturally ebb and flow, some species that were previously common become scarce, or even disappear and others appear for the first time and quickly become ubiquitous in the urban environment. In recent years, most gardens have witnessed the decline of the House Sparrow and the rise of the Goldfinch, the virtual disappearance of the once common Wall Brown butterfly, but the gain of the Speckled Wood that now dances around in the dappled light of even the most sparsely wooded areas of urban Cheshire. The Red Squirrel, which once graced the rural woodlands of Cheshire has been usurped by the muscular Grey Squirrel, which finds much of our built environment very much to its liking, penetrating right to the heart of our towns and cities.

As the effects of global warming take hold, the UK is becoming home to an increasing range of species, mainly invertebrates, which, due to their rapid reproductive processes, are able to respond quickly to the changes and colonise new lands. Urban areas are heat islands and they are often the first places where these changes take full effect and are most obvious. In recent years the Harlequin Ladybird has made a spectacular arrival in the UK (see p. 20). The species first appeared in southeastern England in 2003 and in 2006 the first ones were identified in Cheshire. 'By 2010 it had spread throughout the county, with the largest populations concentrated in more urban settings' (Clarke 2012).

In the same vein, against a backdrop of noticeable decline for most of our native bumblebees, a new species of bumblebee has reached our shores and is beginning to colonise. The Tree Bumblebee *Bombus hypnorum* made its first entrance in the county by flying through the window of the rECOrd office at Chester Zoo on the 17th June 2010. Three days later several specimens were watched and photographed collecting nectar in a garden in Penketh, Warrington (Clarke *pers. comm.*) At the time of writing this species has amassed a total of forty nine records, the majority from urban locations. The Tree Bumblebee is a distinctive tri-coloured species (Fig. 3.10); easily recognised, it provides the perfect example where the non-specialist urban wildlife enthusiast can get involved in mapping the spread of a pioneering species.

Autumn bird migration

You stick your nose outside your door as the first glimmer of dawn leaches across the sky from the east. The fresh-cleansed smell of a mid-October morning fills your nostrils. The overnight rainclouds have cleared to leave a crispness in the air and you can hear a gentle rustle as a steady, but light, south-easterly breeze plays with the diminishing number of leaves still clinging to the nearby Sycamore. It's just after 7.00 a.m. and the first commuters of the day are already rumbling along the dual carriageway and around the roundabout, which sits less than 100 m from the house. Above the noise of the traffic your ear catches a sound, a penetrating, drawn-out, slightly hoarse 'tzseee'. You smile; the scene is set, the players are ready to take the stage and you are about to witness one of the most enduring and epic dramas in the natural world. You make your final preparations and as the curtain of night is finally thrown aside you take your seat and wait in high anticipation for the show to begin.

You have chosen your seat carefully; it's facing north, with a maximum sky view, but you are using your own house to shield you from the noise of the nearby A-road. With the temperature in single digits you are wrapped up warmly, vapour rises steamily from your large mug of coffee. Binoculars are around your neck, on your knee you have a clipboard, a pencil and some recording forms. For a short while nothing happens, you begin to wonder if you have misread the script. Then suddenly the music begins. The initial pace is slow, a 'sip' and a 'chup' here and there as a few bit-part players get a chance to voice their lines.

The sun finally breaks the horizon and high in a blue sky, twinkling in silent progress, wings beating a powerful rhythm, the first of the major players rush the stage. It's a powerful performance, full of intensity and purpose; in the space of just a couple of hours over two thousand of them have been counted heading due south. The Woodpigeon probably wouldn't make it onto any birdwatchers top-ten list and yet here in the heart of urban Cheshire they undertake one of the most spectacular, visible and yet largely un-noticed migrations of any familiar British bird. Perhaps even more surprisingly, we are not sure exactly where they come from, or where they are going to. Perhaps the revolution in electronic tagging will finally provide a more definitive answer.

There are lots of cameo roles in this particular production. A few small groups of late-moving Swallows jink past with their House Martin cousins for company. A Yellowhammer calls and stops briefly on a neighbour's roof, pausing for a moment in the spotlight before quickly moving on. The main storyline of the morning, however, is a Scandinavian saga. It began in earnest some half an hour after sunrise, the pre-dawn calls giving notice of their imminent arrival. Sometimes in small parties, occasionally in impressive force, Redwings and Fieldfares surge past. Driven by a relentless, innate desire to migrate, the majority are heading southwest. The Redwings, nippy, with their clipped wing beats and deep-russet stained underwings, the Fieldfares more languid, often less direct, in dispersed flocks like oil on water, their passage is betrayed by loud 'tshak' calls. These birds may be heading for Iberia, or Ireland. They may not even winter in the same place in consecutive years. They live an almost nomadic existence during the winter months, always ready to move on if the winter weather dictates it a necessity.

Figure 3.11. Pink-footed Geese migrating over Cheshire towards their Norfolk wintering grounds. © Jeff Clarke

You move your head this way and that. Did you hear something? There it is again, an almost mechanical yet strangely musical note, it quickly becomes a sound like distant conversations in an echoing room. They are coming! It's time for the stand-out number in the show. Everyone stops to take in and enjoy the moment. It's no longer a distant conversation, it builds to a crescendo, a rabble-rousing chorus, there above you, in gloriously ragged 'V' formations, are the Icelanders. The Pinkfeet are back, more than three hundred voices in a thrilling cacophony, yodelling their triumphant return. These birds have crossed an ocean to get here. They rested briefly to refuel on the Lancashire mosses and have set course for the end-point of their journey, the Norfolk coastline. To get there they fly over Cheshire's peopled heartlands, Widnes, Runcorn, Warrington, Knutsford, Macclesfield, Congleton and Crewe. For brief moments each year these 'wonders' from a volcanic wilderness connect with the observant denizens of our urban world and help to remind us that nature isn't something remote, inaccessible, or irrelevant to our cosmopolitan lives.

We are as much a part of the natural world as the Pink-footed Goose, or a pipistrelle bat. We cannot live our lives separately from the natural world for we are inextricably an integral part of it. Despite man's best efforts, nature pervades our lives. For most urban dwellers their only awareness of it comes from the unsettling spider scuttling across the carpet, or the pesky wasp disrupting summertime beer drinking – nature is often something to be avoided. On the converse side, for the unconditioned child and those lucky enough to have grown up being mentored by enlightened teachers and parents, the urban landscape of Cheshire provides just as much scope and possibility to indulge our instinctive inquisitiveness in nature as could be gained from any official nature reserve.

Postscript

The final account of bird migration over of our Cheshire townships may appear almost utopian and unlikely, but it is firmly based on real events that happen every year on a number of autumn days. The numbers of birds and species involved can be staggering and it is possible to witness these events in almost any Cheshire town or village. This particular account is taken from the author's own notes of bird migration occurring above his urban garden on the west side of Warrington.

References

Buglife (2009) Planning for Brownfield Biodiversity: A best practice guide. Buglife – The Invertebrate Conservation Trust, Peterborough.
Cheshire Mammal Group (2008) The Mammals of Cheshire. Liverpool University Press.
Clarke, J.J. (2012 in preparation) The Provisional Atlas of Cheshire Ladybirds.
James, P., Norman, D. & Clarke, J.J. (2010) Avian population dynamics and human induced change in an urban environment. *Urban Ecosystems* 13: 499–515.
Norman, D. (2008) Birds in Cheshire and Wirral: a breeding and wintering atlas. Liverpool University Press.

About the author

Jeff Clarke is a freelance Environmental Educator and Ecologist and has worked professionally in connection with the natural environment since 1988; a large proportion of that time has been spent enthusing and educating urban communities about the biodiversity potential of the industrial and urban environment, for example he is a regular broadcaster on BBC Radio Merseyside as part of the Nature Watch team. Jeff can't remember a time when he wasn't fascinated by the natural world; today he specialises in birds, mammals and invertebrates, dividing his time between running wildlife holidays and courses, carrying out ecological surveys and delivering schools lessons on a wide range of environmentally linked topics. In his capacity as County Recorder for the *Coccinellidae* he is authoring the new 'Provisional Atlas of Ladybirds in Cheshire'. You can find out more about Jeff via his website at jeffclarkeecology.co.uk.

Marine Life of Cheshire

Ian Wallace

WITH ONLY ABOUT 8 MILES OF SEAWARD-FACING COAST, CHESHIRE WOULD NOT seem to be one of the UK's significant maritime counties. However the tidal estuaries of Mersey and Dee add many more. The dominant coastal habitats are the sandy beaches of the north Wirral, the sand and mud flats of the two estuaries and the saltmarshes. There is little rock, the Hilbre Islands being the only significant natural piece of rocky shore between the Ormes at Llandudno and Barrow in Furness, a coastline of nearly 200 miles, with a short length at Eastham. Eroding cliffs on the Mersey at Hale Head and the Dee at Thurstaston give a boulder and pebble shore while man-made sea defences at New Brighton and at Leasowe have added a little rather indifferent hard shore, and lagoons, in the form of docks and marine lakes also increase diversity.

Our shores are at the edge of Liverpool Bay, a very shallow part of the Irish Sea filled with sediment mainly derived from past glaciations. Coupled with a very large tidal range, the result is our magnificent vast gently shelving beaches. These used to lead into extensive dunes, but apart from a tiny remnant at Leasowe and between Hoylake and West Kirby our beaches now are all backed by concrete sea defence. The tidal range has another significant consequence for wildlife in the large difference between neap tides, with an average between high and low water of about 13 feet and a spring tidal range of twice that. At neap tides, significant parts of the upper shore can for days on end be baked in summer, frozen in winter and drowned with freshwater rain at any time. Another conspicuous feature of our shores is instability. It is not only the sands that are regularly shifting, but channels move in estuaries and saltmarshes, and even the rocky shores have not been immune to some quite dramatic changes over the last few decades.

From a conservation point of view, the most important element of the marine life is the birds. However they are here due to the abundance of food, which is the subject of this chapter. I will not describe every species – and many of the commoner ones can be identified by naturalists equipped with a general seashore book – but I will single out some for particular attention and hope to provide some insights into special features of our marine habitats that can be observed by a reasonably observant general naturalist, and others which I hope will interest marine naturalists visiting from other parts of the country. Equipment to study this environment can be pretty basic. I suggest a trowel, kitchen sieve, cat-litter

Figure 4.1. The Hilbre Islands are part of the Dee Estuary SSSI, European Special Protection Area and Special Area of Conservation, and the surrounding area is proposed as one of Britain's first Marine Conservation Zones, especially to protect the Blue Mussel beds and the important peat and clay exposures frequented by the burrowing clams called piddocks. © National Oceanography Centre

Figure 4.2. The massive flocks of wading birds on the Dee, Mersey and north Wirral coast (including these Knot) eat hundreds of tonnes of invertebrates every winter from the fertile mud. © Richard Steel

tray, and a small fine-mesh net as used for aquarium work – and of course, the obligatory x10 hand lens and wellies. This chapter takes the inquisitive naturalist on an exploration of our Cheshire marine life.

Sandy Beaches

The hostile environment of our upper beaches means that a trowelful of sand may reveal no buried animals. The best place to search is where the surface is covered in a thin layer of water, although be aware that occasionally wet sand also indicates quicksand. The very familiar Lugworm casts may be the only obvious sign of buried life but a closer look at the surface of the sand may reveal star-shaped patterns, rather like irregular bird footprints, which of course are also likely to be seen. Each pattern is produced by the feeding tube of a Tellin (a small clam) as it sucks sediment from the surface. It is after single-celled plants and bacteria-covered finely divided organic debris that have settled onto the surface. It has gills with a sophisticated sorting system to discard the large amount of fine sand particles it inevitably ingests with its food. The organic material that feeds these organisms, when analysed is mainly decaying plankton, faecal pellets of other creatures and 'other'. For most animals eating this material it is the bacteria that are decomposing it and attached to it passively that are the actual food.

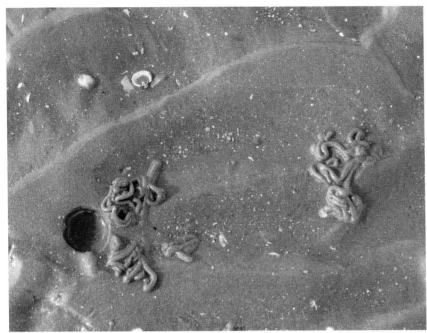

Figure 4.3. A very familiar feature of sandy beaches is Lugworm casts. This lives in a U-shaped burrow and swallows sand at one end, causing a cone-shaped pit, and at the other end are the spiral casts of defecated sand. The worm spends its time between eating at one end of the burrow and defecating at the other end. © Ian Wallace

Nature Conservation Designations

Marine areas have long been the Cinderella of nature conservation. Terrestrial sites, including intertidal areas, have been designated as Sites of Special Scientific Interest (SSSI) since the 1949 National Parks and Access to the Countryside Act, and Ratcliffe's landmark *A Nature Conservation Review* (1977) provided the basis for a representative series of SSSIs. But the *Review* did not include marine habitats on rocky shores or below low-water mark and designation of UK marine areas for their nature conservation interest was led by the European Directives, with Special Protection Areas (SPAs) under the 1979 Birds Directive and Special Areas of Conservation (SACs) under the 1992 Habitats Directive.

Almost all of the Cheshire coastline has one or more nature conservation designations extending as far as the low water mark: the Dee Estuary as SSSI, SPA and SAC; the Mersey Narrows and North Wirral Foreshore SSSI, proposed as SPA in 2001 but not then designated, and a further consultation conducted in 2011, its outcome yet unknown; New Ferry foreshore as an SSSI; and the Mersey Estuary as SSSI and SPA. The Liverpool Bay SPA, designated in 2010 as one of the first Marine Protected Areas, was selected for its wintering populations of Common Scoter and Red-throated Diver and goes from the mean low water mark outwards. A network of Marine Conservation Zones is promised following the Marine & Coastal Access Act 2010. A suite of 127 MCZs around England and Wales has been proposed although these are currently in abeyance. One of them is in Cheshire, an area of 5 km² around Hilbre, proposed for designation to protect the Blue Mussel beds and the peat and clay exposures that are home to the burrowing clams called piddocks: the holes they create provide an important micro-habitat for species such as crabs and anemones.

Cockling

Cockles reach breeding age when two years old, and usually die by their fourth year. Their fertilised eggs and larvae (spat) can be carried by the tide and deposited (spatfall) in suitable but unpredictable places. Done carefully, the larger Cockles can be harvested for human consumption without causing damage to Cockle stocks, or other wildlife – as Cockle beds support lots of other species and the birds that feed on them all.

But events such as the 2010 pillage of the beds at Leasowe, by large gangs of itinerant gatherers from across the country, seemed to do little for the local environment, economy or the reputation of the apparently ineffectual regulations. Prolonged freezing weather is another hazard for Cockle populations and the 1962/63 winter, for example, effectively finished commercial fishing in the North West for a while.

Dig up a trowel of sand from under the star pattern and rinse it in the sieve and you are likely to reveal the creator. It will have closed its two shells but if you place it quietly in a flooded runnel it will hopefully open up and rock its way back into the sand. A muscular foot digs it in, but it is not just brute force. If you pat your hand on wet sand it will liquefy, and the Tellin's movements as it digs in help liquefy the sand. This is the quicksand effect and you can actually bring buried Tellins to the surface by repeatedly patting the sand. Few birds feed on the sandy beaches but among those that do are the adaptable gulls which can sometimes be seen undertaking the same paddling work to bring buried life to the surface to eat. The other common shellfish to appear by this method is the Cockle. In fact tapping the surface with a board is the usual way of getting them out of the sand for rake harvesting. Partly buried Cockles are easy to spot but if you watch carefully as you walk you may see little spurts of water that reveal completely buried individuals. If there is sufficient depth of water you may see adjacent pairs of tubes surrounded by a raggy off-white fringe. These are the feeding tubes of the Cockle, which unlike the Tellin feeds mainly on the single-celled plankton as they float in the water. Winter is a time of low temperatures and no food for Cockles, meaning a check to their growth that can be seen as a line around the shell. Unfortunately, though, counting the number of such lines is not always a sure way of ageing Cockles as some, especially if the population is particularly dense, may end up in parts of the shore where feeding time is severely curtailed and if problems are prolonged a growth check may result.

Your rinsed trowel full of sand is also likely to have collected a variety of worms, and Amphipod Shrimps, marine relatives of the freshwater shrimp. Many of these are also adept at re-burying themselves if placed on the water-covered sand. The reburial of the White Cat Worm is particularly graceful and the huge back legs of the Amphipod *Haustorius* are equally impressive. Other worms, such as Lugworms, are slower at re-burial. The red colour of many worms is due to possession of haemoglobin to assist oxygen capture when buried. One of these

Figure 4.4. A mixed group of Thin Tellins and Baltic Tellins. These are attractive pink shells; the Baltic Tellin, the fatter rounder species, is commoner. © Ian Wallace

Figure 4.5. A group of Common Cockles showing the lines around their shells when feeding has been difficult, usually, but not always, in winter. © Ian Wallace

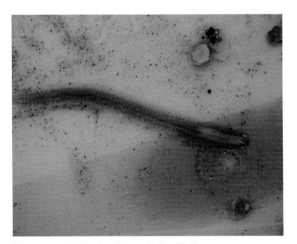

Figure 4.6. White Cat Worm. © Ian Wallace

Figure 4.7. The ends of Sand Mason Worm tubes protruding from the sand. © Ian Wallace

worms is called *Scolelepis* and although it itself is only occasionally encountered its presence is made clear by the egg cocoons which appear as grape-sized spheres of jelly a centimetre or so across attached to the sand by a short stalk. An alternative strategy to being able to rebury is to try to fix the sand together. The best known is the Sand Mason whose tubes protrude above the sand, often in quite dense aggregations. The crown at the summit of the tube is a support for the sticky particle-catching tentacles that lie along them when the rising tide covers the

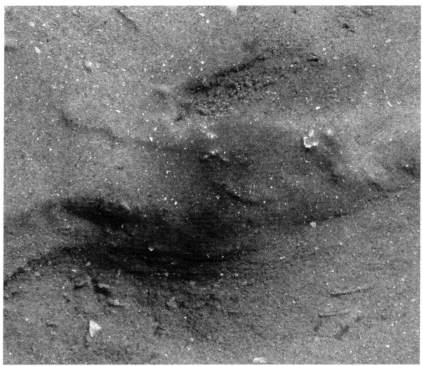

tube. Other much smaller worms of a group called the Spionids produce tubes and are responsible for the very thin fine tubes that will probably be part of your sand sievings. These worms feed in a similar way to the Sand Mason but have two actively waving feeding tentacles.

To the naked eye the wet sand may look barren, but under a microscope a variety of life can be seen in the water film around the sand grains, ranging in size from bacteria up to miniscule worms and crustacea. This is usually invisible, but when the sea has been calm for a few days in summer then a curious, and rather off-putting yellow brown scum starts to develop on wet sand and at the bottom of runnels and pools. These are masses of a single-celled plant called a diatom. Like all plants they need sunlight and move through the sand to expose themselves at the surface, and if conditions are quiet they will multiply rapidly; Liverpool Museum's Curator of Botany, Dr Geraldine Reid, noted twenty species in a sample I brought her from Meols. As plants on land are at the bottom of the food chain, so these tiny plants are for the beach. Three other 'single-celled' organisms are worthy of mention as they may proliferate in warm weather and are conspicuous *en masse*. A sort of thin porridge in the runnels may be the alga *Phaeocystis* and very occasionally you might have the astonishing spectacle of your footsteps at night striking fire with every step on the wet sand – the aptly named *Noctiluca scintillans*, a protozoan, is responsible. We also get occasional 'red tides' caused by the dinoflagellate *Gyrodinium*.

The lower down the shore, the more species you are likely to encounter but be careful on our shallow Wirral shores about following the usual encouragement in the seashore books to follow a good spring tide down as the edge of the sea is often a long way out and it comes in with alarming speed when the tide turns. The best shore is, or certainly was, at Leasowe where a community dominated by both species of Heart Urchin and Pod Razor developed. This was also one of the most productive shores for birds. It was the site for the Cockle grab of 2010 and it is hoped that it will again recover, as it has had to in the past.

Often the most striking things seen on the sand, apart from jellyfish, are empty shells. Most species represented do not live on the beach but come from offshore. They provide a glimpse into the abundance of life in the otherwise inaccessible environment, and further afield in the Irish Sea. Some of the species such as Trough Shells, Wedge Shells, Razor Shells, as well as Heart Urchins, Masked Crabs and Swimming Crabs are characteristic of the mobile sand that occupies the sub-littoral to a depth of about 3 metres which may stretch a few miles to sea, but others come from a little further out where the bed becomes muddier. In 1973, studies concerning the laying of a new long-sea outfall sewer at Meols revealed more about this unstable world and why we so often get 'wrecks' where the drift lines are suddenly strewn with scores to thousands of dead and dying individuals of one or a few species; it is worth noting that our gently shelving shore and wide tidal range means drift lines appear at different parts of the beach according to the varying height of the tide. Planktonic larvae settle where they can, and often establish single age populations. These often die at one time and wash in *en masse*. However, the usual cause of these wrecks is a storm that will move around particular parts of the offshore sediment. Stormy weather combined with heavy frost and low spring tides are particularly deadly as animals dislodged by the waves are too torpid to re-bury and die when moved onshore and exposed to the frost. However, shore creatures do not just wait around to be

Black sand

The abundance of life around sand grains is also evidenced by the black sand phenomenon. Unless there is a good water flow through the sand then the bacteria present use up all the oxygen in their decay of the settled organic material. A separate group of bacteria then take over but their respiration produces not carbon dioxide but hydrogen sulphide that reacts with the rust that coats any sand grains turning it into black iron sulphide which also stains buried dead shells; some of these bacteria are related to the very first life on earth, before oxygen filled the atmosphere. Should wave action expose the sand and shells the unstable iron sulphide reverts over time to rust. Often considered some form of pollution, this natural cycle of iron changing between oxide and sulphide, depending on where it is in the sand, is taking place all the time. This black sand has a characteristic metallic smell but within a few days in air, much of the black colour will usually be fading.

Figure 4.9. Some of the variety of shells that may be found on our shores. (a) the white bivalve Synodesma alba; *(b) The mollusc* Arctica islandica *has various names such as the Icelandic Cyprine but sometimes the Ocean Quahog. Careful analysis of the growth rings has revealed the astonishing fact that some individuals had lived well over a hundred years, but it stops growing after the age of about 50; (c) Common Whelk, the largest of the common species of snail; (d) Necklace Shells: this group shows how bashed and worn empty shells can become; (e) whole shells and fragments of the Common Oyster; (f) the Prickly Cockle: the prickles along the ridges soon get worn away as the empty shells are rolled around by waves; (g) a mollusc known as* Spisula subtruncata; *(h) the Common Cockle (left) and Prickly Cockle (right); (i) Otter Shells; (j) Sand Gapers (top row) and Otter Shells (bottom row); (k) the Common Wentletrap is one of the most attractive snail shells to be found on local beaches but is, alas, quite rare; (l) a species known as* Spisula solida; *(m) a group of Pod Razor Shells; (n) Bean Razors; (o) Peppery Furrow Shells.* © *Ian Wallace*

frozen. Shrimps and Gobies move offshore, and worms can emigrate too, but even slow-moving life such as Baltic Tellins move down the shore, as the higher up the beach the lower temperatures you are likely to experience! In the muddier sand a little further offshore the dominant two species are the cone worm *Pectinaria* and a little white bivalve *Synodesma alba*, both species that undermine the surface and move around whilst feeding. As the populations mature the individuals get larger and the disturbance increases and the loosened bed is ripe for being swept away in a storm, often leaving coarser deposits behind that may be colonised by another community dominated by worms that bind together the sand and protrude their tubes above the surface. This roughened surface slows the bed current and encourages mud to settle that either eventually smothers the worms or they reach the end of their life and the mud is perfect for settlement by the planktonic larvae of *Pectinaria* and *Synodesma*. Of course in this unstable place alternation cannot be guaranteed. The longer the habitat remains undisturbed the more diverse it becomes but then the more is lost when it is eventually upset. 'Wrecks' have been recorded in the literature for a long time: for example in 1892 it was the Spiny Cockle, not a species usually affected, and in 1929 was *Synodesma*, Wedge Shell, and Sand Mason Worm while in 1939 it was a common victim, the Rayed Trough Shell. In the 2010 winter there was a pretty minor wreck, surprising considering the very cold weather, of Rayed Trough Shell, Bean Razor and Pod Razor; a major wreck can be defined as necessitating mechanical beach cleaning of the corpses and land fill to prevent a public health issue and the Rayed Trough Shell is often the culprit. Another occasional cause of mass mortality is when a planktonic bloom of something like *Phaeocystis* settles on the sand and its decay removes the oxygen and produces a toxic blanket that can smother the buried fauna or force it to leave in desperation.

Figure 4.10. The drift line after a wreck of shells following very cold weather in 2010, dominated by Rayed Trough Shells with some Bean and Pod Razors. © Ian Wallace

Figure 4.11. A pocket of drifted material showing particularly the brittle starfish Ophiura, *and shells of Blue Mussel, Rayed Trough Shell, Bean Razor and Pod Razor. © Ian Wallace*

Among the variety of species of shell, it is at first surprising to see that the burrowing clam Piddock is not uncommon. The books suggest these bore into rock, but they also use peat laid down when sea levels were lower, as well as the stiff glacial clay that underlies the peat beds. Both peat and clay are quite common offshore and the existence of these beds was an important factor in the proposal that the Hilbre Island group is made into a Marine Conservation Zone.

One criticism of noting the species of shell as a way of recording what is on and offshore is that we do not know how long the shells last. In 1987 Frank Tyson collected a shell of the American clam *Mercenaria* at Hilbre. This may well have come from an unsuccessful attempt to establish this edible species made in 1882, having emerged from a long period of burial. The orange colour of many of the Oysters suggests they too have been buried for some time. At Caldy and

Figure 4.12. White Piddock: piddocks are usually regarded as rock borers but this species lives in burrows it creates in stiff glacial mud and peat offshore. The shells are released by erosion of the surrounding matrix.
© www.aphotomarine.com

Figure 4.13. Dead shells may become broken by wave action and turned into smaller and smaller fragments. Waves may sort these out by size and weight. An attractive shell gravel beach is found at the west end of Hilbre. Common Cockles make up the majority of the gravel with intact shells of Common Blue Mussel and the occasional Common Winkle on the top. © Ian Wallace

Hilbre, I have noticed that the sea will sometimes move sediment to expose beds of dead shells of Peppery Furrow Shells and Sand Gapers that may have died a long time ago. As tree ring data can now be linked to produce a dendrochronology, the evolving field of sclerochronology is doing the same with sea shells and eventually it may be possible to date some of these shells. Long-lasting shells may also have drifted along the shore from their origin.

The general sediment movement in our area is from North Wales along the Wirral and out at the Mersey which separates our sediment 'cell' from that of the Sefton Coast. Wirral beaches have always had fewer species than those of North Merseyside and shells such as Rayed Trough Shells and Pod Razor Shells were very scarce. So uncommon were fresh Pod Razors that in 1987 Liverpool Museum was pleased to accept one as a donation, yet now it is one of our commonest and frequently 'wrecked' shells – but if you are reading this a few years after the book was published it might well have changed again. Certainly it is among razors that there has been another dramatic change. There is, or was, a common large curved Razor shell *Ensis arcuatus* and for years I have just recorded it as such without too much examination. In 2011, self-confessed Razor shell enthusiast Paul Dansey realised that the alien American Razor was widespread in our area. It arrived in Europe, probably in ballast water about 1989 and in the south east of England, e.g. the Wash, it is now the commonest Razor. It has obviously arrived in our area and may become equally common. There are several lessons here – that change can be rapid and un-noticed, and that it is dangerous to become complacent in

Figure 4.14. A wreck of shells of the Pod Razor, sorted by the waves and left in a lined up group. © Ian Wallace

Figure 4.15. The American Razor (top) and the American Piddock (bottom). These may be in the process of replacing their native counterparts the Sword Razor and the White Piddock in our area. © Ian Wallace

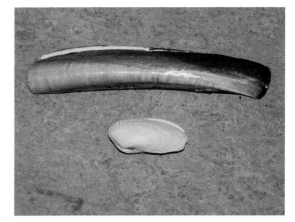

Figure 4.16. Cast shell of a Shore Crab. © Ian Wallace

Figure 4.17. The characteristic paddle on the hind leg that distinguishes the Smooth Swimming Crab. © Ian Wallace

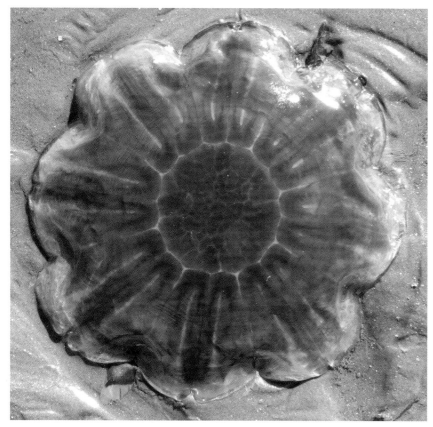

Figure 4.18. A cast-up Brown Lion's Mane Jellyfish, one of the only two stinging jellyfish likely to be encountered – the Blue Lion's Mane is very rare. © Ian Wallace

identifying common easy species! Another alien shell, the American Piddock has now reached Wirral from the west and may replace the native White Piddock; unlike our native species, the American Piddock has a strong ligament between its shells so finding paired empty valves is common.

There are often apparently a lot of dead crabs on the beach. Most dead crabs are actually not that, but shells cast as the crab grows. If you can insert a finger between the back of the shell and the legs and flip the back up to reveal just brown feathery gills AND it does not smell awful – then it is a crab cast not a corpse. Shore Crabs are the commonest species, but look at the back legs as if they are paddle shaped and the crab is pinkish tinged it is the Smooth Swimming Crab from offshore, another common species.

Shells are quite heavy and presumably unable to travel very long distances when dead, unlike jellyfish which may be all too common. Whilst only the brown-jellied Lion's Mane is reported as stinging, delve inside the huge Barrel Jellyfish and you will find it too has stings inside its stomach, presumably to immobilise its planktonic prey. On some occasions, the edge of the sea will be strewn with little ovoid jellyfish the Comb Jellies. Their popular name of Sea Gooseberry belies their extraordinary beauty. If they are common, try to get an undamaged one

Figure 4.19. A beached Barrel Jellyfish. © Ian Wallace

Figure 4.20. The exquisite beauty of a Sea Gooseberry. © Bernard Picton

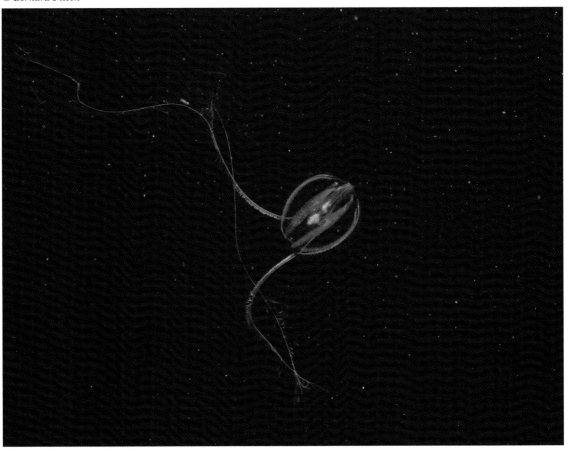

from a runnel into a glass of seawater. Its transparency and rainbow shimmering swimming combs make this one of our most exquisite wild creatures. The Mersey ferry crew are less enamoured of it as they may have to clean the cooling water filters more frequently when it is super abundant.

True seaweeds are common but may have come from quite far afield, floating using their air bladders. George Russell and Chris Felton, two Liverpool Museum colleagues, have studied these seaweeds for years and regard the Isle of Man and Anglesey as being likely sources for several. These seaweeds can also carry quite large stones, the largest my friends have noticed so far weighing 550 g. Given a fair wind, it is not far from Ireland to here as was seen by only a few weeks taken for plastic ducks, escaping from the River Liffey after a duck race, to make it to Merseyside. Many of the drifted seaweeds do not grow on our small amount of hard shore, and one example is the Wire Weed, *Sargassum muticum*, an alien originally from the Far East, not yet found in Wirral. It may not find suitable shores to colonise but could find the marine lakes and docks very much to its liking and join another alien Wakame, or Japanese Kelp *Undaria pinnatifida* first recorded from the dock system in May 2012.

Other notable components of beached life are seaweed-looking things, which may not be seaweeds but colonial animals that either filter feed (seamats and bryozoa) or are carnivores of plankton (hydroids). The shallow sea and abundant fine sediment make the water usually turbid so that light does not penetrate meaning offshore seaweeds would have a problem even if they found

Figure 4.21. Sargassum Weed. This alien seaweed originates from Asia and is steadily spreading around the UK. It now grows in North Wales and occasionally lands as drifted pieces on Merseyside shores, but has not yet been found in Wirral. © Ian Wallace

Figure 4.22. Many things can grow on shells whilst they are occupied and when they are dead. Barnacles are one of the commonest of these encrusters but (a) has a bryozoan growing on it while (b) shows a hydroid with a bristly skeleton that colonises shells inhabited by hermit crabs. There is always a bald patch in the hydroid covering where the shell has rubbed along the ground as the crab moves about. Shells of Common Oyster may be found that are riddled with holes (c). These holes were made after the oyster had died and the shell was colonised by a boring sponge called Cliona. *Eventually it too dies and the shell may land on the strandline.* © Ian Wallace

somewhere to attach, but these colonial animals do not need light. They require some firm object for attachment offshore, usually in the form of pebbles and beds of dead shells. The full extent of offshore gravel is not known: there are no shingle spits on the Cheshire side, but they are a conspicuous feature just across the Dee at Talacre and Gronant, indicating a plentiful resource. Stopford in 1949 used the shrimping boats working the Dee as a way of recording the fauna and took a lot of hydroids and sea mats such as Horn Wrack proving that at least some of the material that washes up on our beaches has a local origin.

When these become detached, they tangle together and often arrive on our beaches in rolls. Tangles can also form around pieces of man-made debris like

Figure 4.23. A small 'roll' of a hydroid and a bryozoan known as 'mud fingers' that will have been growing offshore with a little Enteromorpha *from the shore. © Ian Wallace*

pieces of rope. These hydroid rolls have always been a feature of our shores and in 1860 Liverpool Museum was given a collection of 34 species of hydroid and bryozoans that had been found at Bootle. The most seaweed-looking animal is the Horn Wrack, which has a pleasant lemon smell when fresh.

As proper seaweeds carry stones ashore, these animal seaweeds can carry things like small shells and for the beach recorder, examination of these rolls is often fruitful. The other great carrier of animals and plants is man-made plastic. The largest animal that attaches to this debris is the Goose Barnacle but Wirral is tucked away in a corner of the Irish Sea so rarely gets these and other oceanic drifters like the By-the-Wind Sailors, that can be inches deep on southwestern

Figure 4.24. A piece of the bryozoan Horn Wrack amongst other bryozoan and hydroids cast ashore; all lived offshore and arrive in quantity on the strand line. © Ian Wallace

Figure 4.25. Egg masses of the Common Whelk are also frequent constituents of drift line debris. © Ian Wallace

coasts in some years. A report in 2006 concluded that marine litter was one of the most persistent marine pollution problems and was showing no signs of decreasing. It might be exciting to find strange things on ageing plastic but the litter and possible undesirable aliens it carries has a more un-attractive side to it. Speed of ships and the ballast water they carry makes alien transportation a major problem today but the potential for ships to bring in aliens is not a new phenomenon. In 1867 Garner Roberts noted the abundance of alien and still live barnacles on wooden ships in the Mersey.

It is worth celebrating the disappearance of some drift-line objects. The oxygen load of the sewage that entered the Mersey had little effect on outer estuary shores, but the untreated sewage had many unpleasant objects. As well as the usual contraceptives and sanitary products, we also had the infamous Mersey Fat Ball. A product particularly of edible oil processing effluent, these sickly smelling unpleasant grey lumps ranging in size from peas to potatoes made drift line searches exceedingly unpleasant. Wash your hands before eating is always a wise precaution but these disgusting objects required washing hands, boots, and feet in strong detergent. The simple pleasure of studying the drift-line of our local beaches was denied us until the discharge of untreated sewage ceased. Now we can celebrate the diversity of this life and the 30 species of shell, 5 of crab, 3 of urchin, 3 of starfish and 15 of hydroid that are quite common.

A final thought about offshore must include the growing number of wind farm supports. They may have aesthetically ruined the magnificent empty sunset

Figure 4.26. The Dead Men's Fingers are a common constituent of the drift line and a type of soft coral. Their polyps are soft and feathery in life but only the skeleton with its gruesome appearance ends up on our beaches. © Ian Wallace

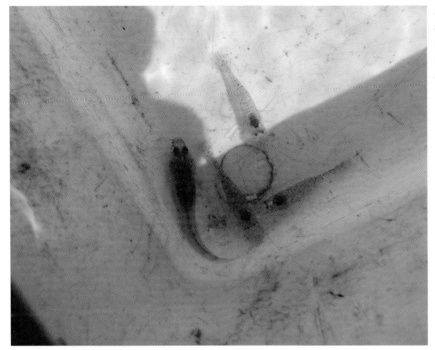

Figure 4.27. A Common Goby and three Shrimps captured using a small aquarium net and placed in a tray of sea water. © Ian Wallace

views we used to experience, and there may be concerns about the effect on birds and cetaceans and sharks and rays but for species requiring a firm place to live they will be a great boon. No doubt they are regularly inspected for safety but I hope someone takes time to note what is growing on them. I predict they will already support gardens of pastel-shaded Plumose Anemones, feathery hydroids and Dead Men's Fingers (a soft skeleton coral), and many of the delicate sea slugs that feed on them.

There are many runnels, channels, temporary pools and the edge of the sea itself. Armies of shrimp-net carrying children are a common feature working these places. In the absence of a net, the kitchen sieve used as such produces acceptable results. Shrimps and Common Gobies are indeed common; there are two very similar Goby species separable with difficulty even by experts with the Common Goby being a shore animal found in pools and the Sand Goby at the edge of the sea. One of the most intriguing animals at the edge of the sea is a little round crustacean about 5 mm long which the naturalist with a hand-lens will see has star-shaped chromatophores. This is called *Eurydice pulchra* and they are fierce carnivores and scavengers which will nibble, harmlessly, at legs and toes. When these are common, dropping a small piece of sandwich into a runnel will provide a miniaturised version of a flock of seagulls around a bag of chips as individual *Eurydice* take and try and run off with fragments.

Finally, in your exploration of life in runnels and pools, you will also collect a large number of small flatfish. Our shallow sandy shore and shallow sea is a

Figure 4.28. Several of the little crustacean Eurydice *feeding on a drowned bumblebee. © Ian Wallace*

major nursery for juvenile flatfish. The enormous mortality of them caused by shrimping vessels was studied in the 19th century and is still a slight cause for concern today, but is generally thought insignificant compared with the massive natural mortality of such fish.

Estuaries

The estuaries are possibly Cheshire's most important wildlife habitat but much of them are dangerous and inaccessible – past surveys of the inner banks of the Mersey have actually required hovercraft! They are accessible in their outer parts, and at the edges of their more inland sections at places like Thurstaston for the Dee and New Ferry and Hale for the Mersey. This inaccessibility means extensive surveys are costly to undertake and have usually been done in response to proposed developments. Binoculars often reveal large numbers of birds feeding out there, but on what?

Surveys of the fauna of the Dee Estuary proper are more limited than for the Mersey. The Hilbre Swash, the channel alongside the island is mentioned quite often in 19th century lists but the only extensive survey of the Dee's invertebrates was by Salford University in the late 1970s, in connection with the impact of proposed bridge crossings and barrages. There had been earlier surveys of the accessible sections by Liverpool University staff in the 1940s and 1960s and a comparison between them and the 1970s suggests that the Dee has changed little, in stark contrast to the dramatic improvements on the Mersey. The gradual change over time is the migration of habitats towards the mouth as the saltmarsh encroaches, and the estuary generally fills with sediment.

There is no clear division between the sandy beaches and the estuaries but as you move up them, more stable muddy sand and mud become significant habitats. On either side of the Wirral, the Narrows make the outer Mersey shores rather uninteresting, while the wide shores of the Dee at West Kirby and Caldy, by contrast, offer a wide range of habitats.

A number of different burrowing communities exist, each dominated by a different set of species. The fine sand of the outer estuary is the province of species able to cope with this mobile environment and is much the same as found on the sandy beaches. Among worms there are the Cat Worms, Lugworms and *Scolelepis*. For molluscs there are Cockles, Baltic and Thin Tellins and *Hydrobia* and for crustacea the dominants are *Bathyporeia* and *Haustorius*. The sands in the main channel are mainly used by the Baltic Tellin, the Cat Worms and *Scolelepis*. These habitats are not particularly productive due to their instability but as you move up the estuary then more stable and sheltered conditions prevail and the shore becomes in general more muddy. On the outer, open shore, beaches, a trowelful of sand run through a sieve will often produce a reasonable number of individuals but by contrast a trowelful of muddy sand or firm mud from an estuary will often be found stuffed with animals. It is not so easy to get to the estuarine shores but, armed with a pair of wellies, you can reach the edge of the muddy sand at places like Thurstaston and New Ferry. There, a trowelful will often show that the black anaerobic sand layer is often quite close to the surface.

Figure 4.29. Shells of the tiny greyish conical snail Hydrobia *can become aggregated by wave action.* © *Ian Wallace*

The most conspicuous feature, if you are careful not to crumble the trowelful will probably be many burrows. The 'U' shaped examples of the crustacean *Corophium* are abundant in patches or you may find a lot of free-living worms or a mass of small burrows that resolve themselves into fine tubes when you wash the trowelful through the sieve. Astonishing numbers of some individuals can be found. The dominant worms are the Ragworm and the little predatory paddle worm *Eteone longa*. The dominant molluscs are the Baltic Tellin and Peppery Furrow Shell. The Sand Gaper also lives in this habitat and while not usually numerous, grows to be a large and impressive mollusc. In stable muddy places, another little worm *Pygospio elegans* becomes very important. It makes a tube out of sand-grains and feeds by trailing a pair of sticky tentacles over the surface to pick up organic particles. There are several related Spionid worm species in our area, all important stabilisers of the sand and mud, at least on a temporary basis. There is interesting interaction between species. For example, the worms and molluscs disturb the sand and may force *Corophium*, which needs stable conditions to build a burrow, to leave. But *Corophium* when dense eats the settling larvae of the molluscs and worms and prevents them establishing. And of course there are the shore crabs, the only numerous surface dwelling predator that must hide in the sediment or elsewhere when the tide goes out, not to mention birds and fish. The Ragworm is actually a very flexible feeder as it can make a plankton catching net and draw water through it, or feed on detritus on the surface, or become a predator if those food sources fail. This general community is reckoned to take five years to reach maturity and stability but stormy weather probably never allows this to happen.

Exactly what the estuarine birds are eating is not always easy to determine as they are a long way out pecking at something. They cannot be taken in large numbers for stomach analysis and their droppings are laid a long way out so

Figure 4.30. *The Common Ragworm in its burrow. The worm's movements bring oxygenated water into contact with the black anaerobic muddy sand and the black colour changes to brown.* © *Ian Wallace*

Figure 4.31. *The abundant crustacean* Corophium *lives in shallow U-shaped burrows in muddy sand.* © *Ian Wallace*

Figure 4.32. Regurgitated pellet of a bird that had fed on Baltic Tellins, showing broken shell fragments. © Ian Wallace

faecal analysis is also not possible; but from careful observations elsewhere of the sorts of food they eat, we can make a correlation between what is there and what it is likely they are eating. The Salford team reckoned the main prey items on the Dee were, with the maximum densities per square metre recorded: Baltic Tellins (20,400), Ragworm (1,540) *Hydrobia* (11,680), *Corophium* (29,920), Peppery Furrow Shell (1,860), Eteone Paddle Worm (6,360), Cockle (1,480) and *Pygospio* (80,000). Although the maximum numbers are at times of spat fall and include many small individuals, they do indicate an awful lot of potential food out there: the RSPB quotes figures for estuarine mud of more than 4,000 calories per cubic metre, the equivalent in energy of 15 Mars bars!

The invertebrates are most active when covered by the tide, and are then inaccessible to birds. They are most vulnerable to bird predation at the edge of the falling tide as they try to get the last second of feeding time when the water cover gets shallow or intermittent; wave action can also disturb settled sediment and provide a pulse of food. Once the water has fully receded, the animals will ensure they are buried or hunkered down. There will be a lag between the water covering them again on the rising tide and activity resuming. This is probably the reason for the interesting observation that birds feed most avidly on a falling tide.

The recovery of the Mersey estuary

Although the story of how the Mersey died and recovered is generally well known, it is a story that stands re-telling. It is not possible to know when the Mersey Estuary was at its most hostile for life as there were (astonishingly?) no samples taken between 1938 and 1971. From fishing records we know it was still going downhill in 1938 and from oxygen data we know that it was on the way back by 1971. The late Peter Jones, of the Environment Agency, thought the estuary's nadir was probably the mid 1960s. Certainly by the late 1950s there were no fish to be taken upstream of the mouth. In 1970 most of the 1938 invertebrate species had not re-colonised the inner estuary, though were found in the outer estuary; only 2 out of the original 15 being found in the inner estuary.

The first detailed post-war survey was by Salford University between 1976 and 1978. The inter-tidal banks in the Runcorn area were devoid of life in 1976, yet by 1978 had very dense colonisation by Common Ragworm and Baltic Tellin. Those species remained the dominants in surveys in 1980, 1990 and 2005. Factors other than pollution might have caused the banks to be initially barren as studies between 2002 and 2007 show the great variation between seasons, sites and years. However, even a comparatively short period of anoxic conditions can kill many species, not only from lack of oxygen but from other consequential chemicals such as ammonia which is highly toxic. Once the water quality had improved to a point that anoxia was not an annual or even more frequent event then there were abundant planktonic larvae swept in from further up the estuary to take advantage and set up sustainable populations.

What has particularly changed between 1970 and now is an apparent upstream migration of species, from two species in the inner estuary in 1970 to six in 1978 to around 20 between 1980 and 2005. It seems to be a particularly good place for marine worms as of the total estuary list for 1980 of 135 species, 50 were worms. In 1990 there were the first records of *Corophium* from the inner estuary but the Lugworm was still, and I think remains, an outer estuary animal, but Sand Gapers were back for the first time since 1938. (Of added interest was that the sampling period also coincided with a major storm in February 1990 which disturbed and re-deposited a lot of mud around the inner estuary but it was re-colonised very rapidly.)

Fish as well as birds showed an increase in number of species and that has been matched by an increase in the number of fish-eating birds such as Cormorant, Grey Heron and Great Crested Grebes. Between 1976 and 1978, 25 species of marine fish were taken on industrial plant in-take screens. 1980s trawl-surveying increased the list to 40, though only 10 were generally common.

Anglers also provided useful data. In 1979 Geoff Swift of Liverpool Museum, a keen angler, gave me his knowledge of current Mersey angling. There was boat angling off Weston Point where they took Dab, Flounders and Plaice, and Silver Eels in the summer. By 1989 the fish caught by anglers in the inner estuary added Bass, Eel, 5-Bearded Rockling, Lesser Weever, Sole and Whiting. By 2007 fish such as Bass were common above Runcorn, along with resident flatfish and gobies. The main edible fish taken in the Narrows, twelve species, varied little between in 1979 and 1989, suggesting that the Outer estuary was much less affected by pollution as far as fish were concerned. There has been little change in that area to date except that the Thornback Ray seems to have moved in and become one of the residents, as opposed to many species that use the estuary as a feeding or breeding ground. The promenades and dock walls of the Mersey Estuary provide nationally recognised good sea angling. The information regarding the Dee is less extensive but suggests a similar species list, but with Salmon and Sea Trout being significant; hopefully the Mersey will become the same. They had long disappeared from the Mersey, which used to be a major Salmon river, but – as detailed in the Rivers chapter of this book (pp. 128–9) – Atlantic Salmon have been regularly recorded in the Mersey since at least 2001.

In both estuaries the most numerous fish is 'Whitebait', which is mainly Sprats but with a few juvenile Herring. Vast shoals move in from the sea and used to be the main food of very large flocks of terns in the Narrows in the autumn that attracted birdwatchers from across the country. These large flocks no longer form. The whitebait may be less numerous, for example one shoal in 1965 was 10 miles long and stretched from Crosby to Bromborough. There has also been speculation that the fish encountered the polluted water and, forced to the surface in a dazed state, were easy prey.

Listen to barnacles!

If you visit a barnacle-rich place on a falling tide during a quiet day when there is virtually no noise, such as the end of Hilbre or the tidal-defence groynes you may hear a hear a sort of crackling hiss which you will eventually track down to the noise of thousands of barnacles shuffling their closing plates as the water recedes. Once fully closed, larger barnacles in particular need a bit of effort to smash open but when in this shuffling stage they can be caught napping and picked out by fast-acting birds such as Turnstones.

Figure 4.33. A group of the alien Australasian Barnacles with their grey shells and only four wall plates. © Ian Wallace

The improvement in Mersey water quality was also probably reflected in the dramatic increase in numbers of birds between 1961 and 1971. Lifeless sandbanks would not have supported the numbers recorded but other factors could have been the birds being forced to find new habitat as the Dutch Polders were drained, or changes in sedimentation and channel movements forming sediment banks amenable to colonisation. In normal estuaries the main channel as it meanders migrates over a period of many years between the two banks; for reasons not fully understood, this did not happen in the Mersey between 1900 and 1958. The most important invertebrates for birds in the Mersey in the late 1980s were regarded as Ragworm, *Hydrobia*, Baltic Tellin and Spionid Worms, all of which were very numerous in the sandbanks of the inner part. Tubificid worms are eaten by species such as Dunlin but unless very numerous do not provide so much energy per unit of effort to collect them.

Was the Mersey Estuary ever truly lifeless? Shores such as at Egremont probably maintained life throughout, with a few fish to be angled. Tubificid worms are pretty tough critters being full of haemoglobin to capture oxygen, even when it is at low concentration, and release it for use when there is none in the water. Their common name of sludge worm reflects their association with sewage work outfalls and they are indicators of organic enrichment. The banks of the middle and upper estuaries probably had reasonable populations at all times, unless the additional problem of the cocktail of industrial chemicals proved too much. By 1978 there were up to 40,000 worms per square metre of mud at Hale Head and in 1986 one species, another enrichment indicator worm *Capitella* still dominated those banks. They are present in smaller numbers today and have other marine invertebrates as neighbours but in the very weak salinities of the extreme upper estuary these hardy worms are still (2007) about all that will be found and that situation is not likely to change.

So is the Mersey's wildlife no-longer affected by pollution? The re-working of the sediment as the channel migrates maintains the dynamism of the system but is also responsible for recycling buried and polluted sediments in the Mersey so maintaining slightly raised levels of some persistent materials, but this is a decreasing problem as these deposits are diluted by fresh material entering the estuary. It is likely they have little effect anyway on the short-lived invertebrates and most fish. However, the estuary is also affected by so-called feminisation of male fish, particularly flounders that are resident in the estuary. Professor Chris Frid of Liverpool University is an expert on this phenomenon and tells me that it is a decreasing problem but the exact chemical, or chemicals, involved may never be determined. A large number of chemicals, natural and man-made, can trigger the hormone receptors in the fish. Some work at miniscule concentrations and they may work synergistically.

Hard Shores

Naturalists familiar with the clean shores of say, Anglesey or Pembroke will probably decide that Cheshire's rocky shores are impoverished, mud-infested and that there is almost no sub-littoral rock to supply the usual range of exciting goodies. Turn over most stones on the shore and the underside will be covered in black mud and only a few worms and the inevitable shore crab. Overturn a rock in a pool and after the mud has settled you will see only very common species such as crabs, winkles, beadlet anemones and the occasional prawn and small fish. The shores used to be much richer as shown in the accounts of visits during the second half of the 19th century by the likes of Cuthbert Collingwood, an expert on sea slugs, for which the shores were particularly good, John Price of Chester, Isaac Byerley of Wallasey, and Liverpool Museum staff. While for the Mersey, pollution was a major factor, it is the general increase in sediment, filling up the spaces under rocks that has been most significant in loss of habitat. Both estuaries are sediment sinks and are filling up extremely quickly in geological time. Due to

Figure 4.34. Common Blue Mussels, themselves covered in barnacles, have filled up many of the spaces between boulders on the groynes. © Ian Wallace

Figure 4.35. A Turnstone feeding. © Tom Marshall

its shipping importance the Mersey area has had its bathymetry carefully scrutinised for a long time. For reasons unknown there seems to have been a threefold increase in sedimentation along the North Wirral between 1912 and 1936 and the Mersey lost 10% of its volume over that period. It is estimated that between 1911 and 1961 the Mersey, despite dredging, lost 75 million cubic metres of water volume due to sedimentation. The ineffectual efforts to stop the Dee silting up and to maintain the Port of Chester are well documented! In-filling of estuaries naturally accelerates as reduced water volume means there is less water to send incoming sediments back out to sea.

While it is always possible there will be channel shifts to scour the end of Hilbre, the general trend is for a further rise in general sedimentation and loss of even more crevices and the last sub-littoral rock. In places, there has been a loss of sediment and sea defences threatened. This has been halted at some points by groynes which themselves provide a little hard shore. The most dramatic impact of these is at New Brighton. The Egremont Promenade was made in the 1850s and the Kings Parade in the 1930s but by the 1990s loss of sediment was threatening to undermine both. An idea in the 1950s had been to attract sediment by dumping the rubble from the demolition of war-damaged buildings on to the shore, but this failed to produce the result they wanted, but did lead to the formation of an intriguing rocky shore and superb mussel beds and encrusting barnacles, the latter being the main food of an internationally important flock of Turnstones. The series of sand-accreting groynes installed by 1998 means the rocky shore at New Brighton has now all but vanished and the glacial clay and war-time dumped rubble lower shore are now under many metres of sand; it persists to some extent at New Ferry where it was used to try and protect the boulder clay cliffs. The first casualty of this habitat change was the Turnstone feeding ground. The bird, though in smaller numbers, now uses the barnacles growing on the new groynes.

The dominating influence of sediment on the rocky shore is well seen in the seaweeds. In the 1890s there was the normal zonation of green to brown to red as you progressed down the tidal range i.e. a typical three zone shore. Today if you look at the vertical 'Wall' on Hilbre the zonation is in summer green to brown to green or in winter green to brown to grey; barnacles occur from below the first green layer to the sub-littoral but the perennial fucoids fade out towards the bottom of the tidal range. The lowest levels are colonised in summer, when there is plenty of light and warmth for their growth, by annual green algae such as Sea Lettuce and *Enteromorpha*. The typical lower shore red and sub-littoral oarweeds are missing, yet all three *Laminaria* species used to grow here.

Sediment has two impacts on plants. Below a certain depth of water, not enough light can penetrate and Dr Russell estimates this as 25 cm in the Mersey Estuary. He has coined the term 'tidal night' to describe how when the tide comes in it is effectively night for the seaweeds. I was always intrigued that one seaweed

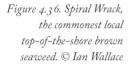

Figure 4.36. Spiral Wrack,
the commonest local
top-of-the-shore brown
seaweed. © Ian Wallace

Cladostephus lived under rock ledges at the bottom of the shore, often encrusted with mud yet somehow managed to get enough light to maintain itself.

Dr Russell recorded 80 species at Hilbre in the 1970s. The flora of our other rocky shores is similar but less extensive. Nature Conservancy Staff, when using national criteria to assess the shores in 1990, struggled to find much of interest due to the absence of any nationally scarce species or habitats but did select this two-zone shore as of interest. Incidentally, it can sometimes seem a struggle to decide between Bladder and Spiral Wrack and its hybrids. In the Mersey this is no longer a problem as studies have shown that the original parents have apparently disappeared and the weed we now see is all hybrid ranging in appearance from typical Bladder to Spiral.

The sediment also has another effect. It smothers sporelings or covers the rocks with sediment through which they cannot attach. The latter point was demonstrated very well by a student of Dr Russell who brought small *Laminaria* plants from Anglesey and planted them on Hilbre – they grew well. It may be that the absence of many of animals we would expect such as top shells, sponges and sea squirts may owe as much to their vulnerability when young as their inability to survive when adult. Mrs Nora McMillan recorded her last Grey Top Shell in 1938 but found Chitons still occasionally in the 1960s. A tiny bit of Breadcrumb Sponge was present in 1980 but an insignificant sponge *Sycon* was found by the experienced Nature Conservancy team in 1990; it may have been overlooked

Figure 4.37. A particularly interesting feature of local shores is Plumose Anemones, shore-dwelling animals whose fine tentacles catch larger zooplankton. White (a) and salmon (b) are the two commonest colour forms, with olive being the rarest. They look very different when out of water (c). (a) and (b) © Ian Wallace; (c) © www.aphotomarine.com

by me in 1980. No sea squirts were found, yet from their presence in the docks, planktonic larvae must be around.

Another feature that is particularly unusual is being able to see Plumose Anemones as littoral animals. Although the best displays are seen hanging from rock ledges or on boulders at spring tides, they can, in pools, extend higher up the shore, in fact at Red Rocks, opposite Hilbre I even found one in a pool that was above high water neap level. Some of these shore-dwelling Plumose Anemones were unusual enough to be recognised as a separate variety in the past. The main colour forms have always been salmon-pink and white, with olive brown as a rarer colour. I have never seen the grey form that is supposed also to occur.

Figure 4.38. An attractive form of the Cave Anemone has orange tentacles rather than the usual mottled green and grey. © Ian Wallace

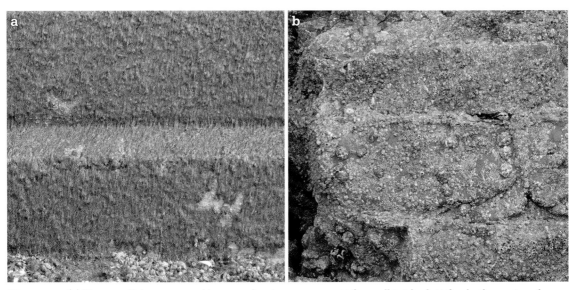

Figure 4.39. (a) The sea walls become covered by green algae in summer, except for small patches kept free by the grazing of Common Limpets. At other seasons the limpets are much more difficult to spot as they are covered in barnacles, as in (b) where the limpets are preventing the colonisation by seaweeds of this piece of rock at Hilbre. © Ian Wallace

Staying with anemones, the absence of the Beadlet Anemones was noted in 1860, but is no longer the case. Dahlia Anemones are now rare but in 1860 it was impossible not to stand on them as they were so common. However, the commonest species has probably always been the Cave Anemone. This lives in cracks in the sandstone rocks and has a long column that can stretch to put the tentacles above any mud. Often the presence of a crack can be seen in an otherwise uniform mud layer by a line of round holes made by the crevice dwelling anemone below. Mottled green tentacles are the usual colour form but in Cheshire we are blessed with a variety called var *nobilis* by Philip Gosse when he wrote his 1860 monograph on the British Sea Anemones, using notes sent him by the famous 19th century naturalist Lady Cust of Leasowe Castle based on specimens from Cheshire. The true *nobilis* with its blue-black disc and orange tentacles I have never seen, but ones with chocolate brown disc and orange tentacles are not uncommon. Lady Cust's main claim to fame these days is as the probable source of the long established alien the Buttonweed *Cotula* that still grows near the lighthouse on Moreton Common.

The other interest of our hard shore is its isolation from other rocky shores. Should a species become extinct, it may be a long time before the planktonic larvae find it again for re-colonisation. Limpets are seriously affected by cold weather and on Hilbre may have been virtually eliminated by the 1962/63 hard winter. Certainly it was noted there were lots of empty shells around Little Eye after that event. In 1979 only one Limpet was known to myself and the then warden, on a ledge on the 'Wall' at the south side of Hilbre. In the late 1980s they started to be seen more commonly on the islands and the breakwaters at Leasowe and along the King's Parade sea wall. They are found on the sandstone but it is rather soft for scraping off sea-weed sporelings, a favourite food. Harder surfaces are preferred. Again the 'Wall' at Hilbre shows this very well as the concrete reinforcement has a large population and is incidentally free of green algae, whereas the population elsewhere is sparse and the wall green. In summer, on the King's Parade the presence of limpets can be seen at a distance by the alga-free circles, the limpets themselves being hard to see being usually heavily covered with barnacles.

Another often very well camouflaged species is the Common Oyster. In January 1999 Tony Bell saw his first one at Hilbre and now knows of a handful more. None had been seen in previous decades by other workers, but the very long-lived empty shells are not uncommon on the beaches. Presumably this is a recent coloniser. It is an example of where collection of specimens should be strongly discouraged as it might be some time before we were visited again by larvae.

One mollusc that seems in no danger of extinction is the Common Mussel. It is abundant on all our rocky shores and at Hilbre and on the Wallasey break-waters it has grown into such piles that it fills up crevices. Coping with silt is not

Figure 4.40. Slots in the surface of a limestone rock made by the worm Polydora. *© Ian Wallace*

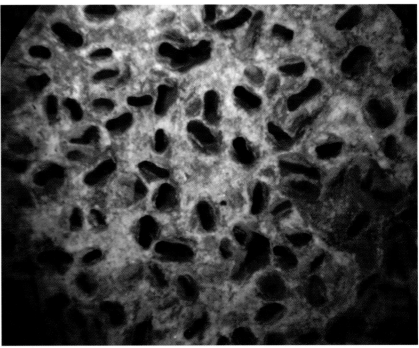

a problem for the Mussel. The silt, rolled up into pseudo-faeces and ejected, can make pools look as if tiny grey spaghetti has been sprinkled on the bottom; the water may be unusually clear too.

During the 1979 and 1980 survey of Hilbre, the hard shores everywhere were dominated by a crust of tubes made by the worm *Polydora ciliata* which the popular books suggest lives mainly as a 'U' shaped burrow in shells and limestone. It seemed able to grow and smother everything, except the hydroid *Hydractinia*, known mainly as an animal on hermit-crab inhabited shells and the bryozoan *Alcyonidium mytili* both of which seemed able to fight it off – and the cave anemone was able to extend through it. It seemed to disappear during the 1980s and has not returned but in 1990 was noted as common on the North Wales coast. In 1948 *Polydora* was well known from the Mersey but not the Dee. Peter Bailey, warden at Hilbre for eight years in the 1960s-70s, noted a cycle between worms and mussels and this has been recorded elsewhere. The mussels colonise the bare rock and are then overgrown and smothered by *Polydora*. Supported only by dead mussels and increasingly unstable the whole mass may be swept away in a storm. The same phenomenon occurs with barnacles which grow tall as they crowd together and try and extend above the mud crust or each other. When this community is swept away the lower shore barnacles, mainly *Balanus crenatus*, leave behind their shelly bases rendering the whole rock surface white; the upper shore species have a membranous base. *Polydora* may return in quantity.

Another worm makes even more spectacular rock cover. *Sabellaria alveolata*

Figure 4.41. (a) A small piece of Sabellaria *reef, with (b) detail of the tube ends made by the* Sabellaria *worms. © Ian Wallace*

binds the sand very firmly into a hard reef and in the late 19th century Hilbre was possibly *the* place in the UK to see the best reefs. A fine section of reef on display in the Invertebrate Gallery of the British Museum (Natural History) came from Hilbre. William Herdman estimated, in 1919, that there were 28,080 worms per square yard and with many square yards there were millions of worms making structures that rose in places to form massive hummocks and reefs each many yards in extent and up to a yard high. He also noted that *Sabellaria* reefs extended offshore and could be dredged up from 10 fathoms and these sub-littoral reefs were known to local fishermen as knarrs, but this might also have been its offshore relative *Sabellaria spinulosa*, which we see on the shore in cast-up shells.

Reef seems to have been there in 1919 but by 1935, when Mrs McMillan started her surveys, there was none, and quizzing other naturalists suggested that remained the case for a very long time. A very small group of worms was found in the extreme bottom of the littoral in 1980 and freak weather about 1990 swept away a lot of sediment from the south side for a short while and the base of old *Sabellaria* reef was seen. This together with the previous sub-littoral find suggested that perhaps rising sediment levels meant we no longer had any shore at the right tidal level. Then, as mysteriously as it had gone, it returned with small reefs being first seen in the late 1990s. The reefs continued to grow and it was found also at New Brighton in and at places on the North Wales coast between 2008 and 2010. It is known to be sensitive to frosts and at some of its sites was decimated during the 1962/63 hard winter. It was therefore with great interest that I surveyed the worm after the record low temperatures of the 2010 winter. Perhaps the worms, and the limpets that can also be badly affected, were lucky and that wind did not also blast them at that time. All the reef along the north side at Hilbre and the top section of reef on the south side of Hilbre and Middle Eye were indeed dead, as were the reefs along the Wallasey promenade but the lower section on the south side of Hilbre, and lower down the shore at New Brighton

Figure 4.42. Newly established Sabellaria *worm tubes, the basis of a new reef.* © Ian Wallace

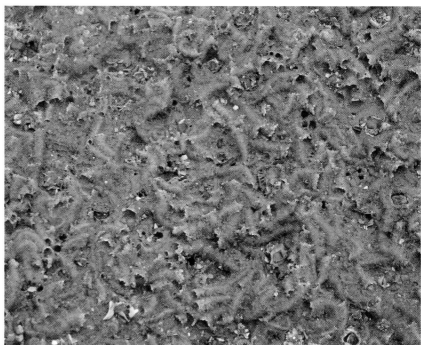

had survived and new reef was forming. Of interest is that another worm, the Red Threads Worm *Cirratulus* – named from its possession of many writhing particle-grabbing tentacles – had colonised empty tubes of the dead reef.

The alien Australasian Barnacle *Elminius* reached us, in its UK spread, in the mid 1950s. It is pale grey in colour as opposed to the white of the native Acorn Barnacle *Semibalanus*. When I first visited the Mersey shores twenty years later it was dominating the upper shore, for example the base of the Perch Rock Light at New Brighton was grey from a distance, now the same lighthouse base is whiter as *Semibalanus* returns. I would expect *Elminius* always to be a feature of our shores. It grows faster but is mechanically weaker so does best in sheltered places. However, on most of our estuary shores you will find both species on any rock you examine.

Good rock pools are not common. The best is the large one between Hilbre and Middle Eye. The depth of this has varied quite a bit over the years, and one reason is that it can become naturally dammed, as currently, by growth of *Sabellaria* reef and mussels. It was there recently that I found, apparently for the first time for 150 years in our area, the Little Brittle Starfish. The old paddling pool at New Brighton was another excellent rock pool but has succumbed to the general sand accrual of that shore.

It is natural to focus on Hilbre but there are other shores. The groynes are the best of the man-made hard shores but are at quite a high tidal level. It is interesting to see how Limpets, Dog Whelks and Beadlet Anemones have colonised,

Figure 4.43. The legs of a navigation marker completely covered by barnacles. The grey individuals are the alien Australasian Barnacle Elminius, *and the occasional white barnacle is the native Acorn Barnacle* Semibalanus. © *Ian Wallace*

Figure 4.44. There are several features of interest in this photograph of a part of the shore at Hilbre exposed by a low spring tide. The first is the general muddiness of the water and the film left on the rocks. Two large Common Starfish have been stranded. Dead shells of the Common Blue Mussel litter the shore. The small circular white scars left when the lower-shore barnacles have died and been washed away can be seen easily. © *Ian Wallace*

Figure 4.45. A seaweed 'forest' of Knotted Wrack covers the rocks at Eastham, and is well known nationally amongst seaweed enthusiasts. © *Ian Wallace*

possibly from the Hilbre base. I am not sure if another Hilbre specialist, the Flat Periwinkle, has colonised. Up to 1985 it was known from New Brighton, probably as a survivor from an original population. A visit to Job's Ferry at Eastham Country Park may provide attractive views of cliff and estuary panoramas but the shore is very muddy and has few species on the boulders that protrude from the mud. One of them is the Knotted Wrack, forming almost a seaweed forest that Dr Russell tells me is very unusual and was actually commented on in 1890 so has presumably survived the polluted years.

Marine Lakes and Docks

The mud in the water, and when it has settled on the rocks, mentioned as making life so difficult on Hilbre for some species, settles out in the docks and to a lesser extent the marine lakes. The vertical walls remain generally free of silt and the water is clear. Larvae of sensitive species carried in the currents from cleaner shores can colonise and normally sub-littoral algae can receive enough light to grow. Filamentous Red Algae (but not any oarweeds) are abundant as are sea squirts and sponges, so conspicuously absent from the shore, are common, as are encrusting sea mats. The Leathery Sea Squirt – yet another ship-borne alien, native to the Pacific around Korea and Japan – was first recorded on Merseyside in 1989 and is in many docks and the marine lake at West Kirby, and was in the lake at New Brighton before it was re-modelled. It is the UK's largest sea squirt. Liverpool's Albert Dock has been the best-studied local site but a survey

Figure 4.46. A dried-up Common (Moon) Jellyfish. Anyone who doubts that a jellyfish is 95% water will be convinced when they see a dried individual. © Ian Wallace

undertaken by Liverpool University indicated that the fauna of docks and floats on the Wirral side are similar.

These sites are generally inaccessible to the public, which is a pity as a clear-bottomed viewing tube will reveal an attractive and diverse flora and fauna. Mussels dominate that fauna, and by feeding on the algae that develop in still waters in the same way they may develop in over-fed garden ponds, prevent the water going green. Mussel poo sinks to the bottom and gets locked in the sediment, stripping nutrients from the system and further reducing the chance of algal blooms.

Other very common inhabitants of the walls are the shore crabs, always on the lookout for dead mussels to scavenge, silver-sided marine relatives of the stickleback, prawns and shoals of sea-horse look-alike Mysid Shrimps, although it is usually impossible to get close to these animals. The most visible of the dock animals from the sides are often the summer shoals of Common (Moon) Jellyfish pulsing in the water. Rainwater may make the already estuarine-weakened water even less salty and it is the Brackish Water Prawn and the Brackish Water Barnacle that are more likely to be seen than the usual shore kinds.

Whilst not free of floating sediment, floating structures have less settled sediment and are usually well-clothed with barnacles and things like Plumose Anemones, but alas are not visible to the shore-based viewer.

Saltmarsh

There is insufficient space to devote to the principally terrestrial fauna and flora of the saltmarshes, but one extraordinary plant deserves a mention. Common Cord Grass *Spartina anglica* arose around 1890 from the accidental hybridisation of an uncommon southern England saltmarsh grass with a deliberately introduced north American relative. The potential of the hybrid to grow with great vigour and colonise tidal mud was seized upon by those interested in land reclamation. It was planted in both Mersey and Dee and perversely was controlled in the 1980s in the Mersey using herbicides, by conservation agencies concerned about loss of bird-feeding habitat. Other plants colonise the accumulated sediment but Common Cord Grass has been responsible for starting most of the saltmarsh now filling the Dee. In their early stages saltmarshes are just muddy shore with a few saltwort plants and *Vaucheria* alga; as the plants take over the marine fauna is restricted to the channels but these erode into pools where it is easier for the general naturalist, or child with net to investigate. Shore crabs are abundant but there are also specialists such as the delightful *Sphaeroma* that looks like a swimming woodlouse with bulging eyes, that rolls up if threatened. (The prawn found here is the Brackish Prawn.) As the saltmarsh advances pools get more infrequent fillings of seawater, and the freshwater fauna starts moving in. The least desirable is the (Parkgate) Mosquito *Aedes detritus*. Recent work at Parkgate has involved draining the pools and creating more gullies for sea flow, in an

Figure 4.47. A group of the little snail Assiminaea *(with a strange English name of the Dun Sentinel) grazing algae from the surface of the mud. © Ian Wallace*

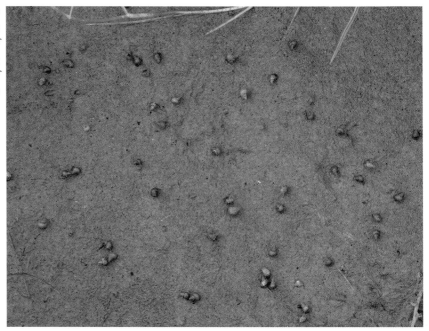

attempt to enhance bird habitat and reduce mosquito numbers. Like many pest insects the mosquito has at least one redeeming feature in looking beautiful at all its stages under a low-power stereo microscope.

Look out for the little black snail *Assiminaea* at the edge of creeks and under debris. It arrived here about 2005. Native to the Thames Estuary the reason for this spread is not known but it is now abundant. The alien Chinese Mitten Crab lived in the same Thames area for decades but recently expanded its range and has now reached our estuaries (p. 131). It lives in burrows in the freshwater parts of estuaries, but the females, carrying eggs, have to migrate downstream to the sea as the hatching larvae cannot survive in freshwater. Only one or two specimens have been taken on the shores, but shrimp fishermen report the migrated females have been common in spring at the mouth of the estuaries for six years. It is therefore presumably now a common animal of inaccessible gullies.

Conclusion

Cheshire's marine habitat is more than a lot of nice views, a place to walk the dog, and lots of birds. It deserves to be understood and appreciated as a diverse natural asset.

References and Further Reading

Much of the chapter was based on a series of not formally published reports that are 'grey' literature, from the pre-electronic era and not readily available from libraries. A comprehensive list of citations is available from the author on request. By contrast, the latest Mersey survey is available online at www.merseygateway.co.uk/wp-content/uploads/2011/ Documents/Environmental_Statement/chapter_11/eschapter11.pdf

Barne, J.H., Robson, C.F., Kaznowska, S.S., Doody, J.P. & Davidson, N.C. (eds.) (1996) Coasts and seas of the United Kingdom. Region 13 Northern Irish Sea: Colwyn Bay to Stranraer, including the Isle of Man. Joint Nature Conservation Committee, Peterborough. jncc.defra.gov.uk/PDF/pubs_csuk_region13.pdf

Buck, A.L. (ed.) (1993) An inventory of UK Estuaries: Volume 3 North-west Britain. Joint Nature Conservation Committee, Peterborough.

Craggs, J.D. (ed.) (1982) Hilbre, the Cheshire Island: its history and natural history. Liverpool University Press.

Curtis, M.S. & Baker-Schommer, M. (2003) The Mersey Estuary – Naturally Ours. National Museums Liverpool.

Greenwood, E.F. (1999) Ecology and Landscape Development: a History of the Mersey Basin. Liverpool University Press. Several articles in this book relate to the present chapter, including Doody, P. Saltmarshes and sand dunes – natural or not? (pp. 167–174); Hawkins, S.J., Allen, J.R, Fielding, N.J, Wilkinson, S.B & Wallace, I.D. Liverpool Bay and the estuaries: human impact, recent recovery and restoration (pp. 155–166); and Russell, G., Jemmett, A.W.L. & Wilkinson, S.B. Marine algae: diversity and habitat exploitation (pp. 177–184).

Jones, P.D. (2000) The Mersey Estuary – back from the dead? Solving a 150-year-old problem. *Journal of the Chartered Institution of Water and Environmental Management* 14: 124–130.

Marine Biological Association of the UK www.mba.ac.uk/

Marine Conservation Society www.mcsuk.org/

Shaw, D.F. (ed.) (1990) The Irish Sea – an environmental review: Part one Nature Conservation. Irish Sea Study Group, published by Liverpool University Press

About the author

Ian Wallace joined Liverpool Museum, then called Merseyside County Museums, as an invertebrate zoologist in 1974 and remains in that role, the museum now being called World Museum Liverpool. Fascinated by plants and invertebrates from an early age, Ian's research was on caddis larvae, but the museum job enabled him to maintain a wide range of interests. A particular influence was a colleague, the late Nora McMillan, the museum's 'shell lady' who introduced Ian to the wonders of the local shores. Encouraging species recording has always been a significant role for the museum and Ian is currently involved in providing recording material for beach work via the Cheshire Local Record Centre rECOrd.

The Meres and Mosses

Colin Hayes

'THE JEWELS IN OUR CROWN' MIGHT BE AN APT EXPRESSION TO DESCRIBE Cheshire's meres and mosses and afford them the respect they truly deserve. Not only does a dedicated group of humans find them beautiful and a suitable focus for hours of fascinating study, but a diversity of wildlife is also attracted to them. This is hardly surprising because these wetlands have been with us for a very long time – longer than our most ancient woodland – so there have been thousands of years for their biodiversity to increase and adapt. Indeed, the flora and fauna of these ancient wetlands have had to adapt – their prevailing environment has been severe and demanding since day one. Our mossland communities survive under particularly harsh conditions: wet, exposed and acidic enough to pickle 10,000 years of bog vegetation, even on days when we might describe the weather as 'fantastic'! Although challenging conditions prevail, the essential ingredients of life – water, air and energy from the sun – have been available in abundance, so where humans have feared to tread, wildlife has thrived and become both highly specialised and extraordinarily diverse.

How were the Meres and Mosses formed?

Meres and mosses come in all shapes and sizes ranging from small, circular or oval basins filled with water or peat, through twin basins and clusters, to enormous expanses of peat such as Risley Moss or the complex deposits of Danes Moss, where its lobes of peat spread out in several directions from the core. This diversity of shapes and sizes, as well as the apparent clustering of deposits in parts of the three-county plain, has all been dictated by the action of several phases of

Figure 5.1. The extensive fringing reeds of Hatch Mere SSSI. © Colin Hayes

What are the Meres and Mosses?

The Meres and Mosses are a series of water- or peat-filled hollows in the glacial drift that covers the Shropshire–Cheshire–Staffordshire Plain. Open waters take the name 'meres' and the peat bogs are known locally as 'mosses'. Over millennia, meres can develop into mosses, so the site names are not always definitive: Bagmere is now a moss, while the names Blakemere Moss, Flaxmere Moss and Mere Moss Wood hint at the common ancestry, but do rather confuse the issue!

Figure 5.2. Sphagnum magellanicum *and* S. papillosum *at Whixall Moss.* © *Colin Hayes*

Figure 5.3. Cranberry in flower at Black Lake. © *Colin Hayes*

glaciation between 5,000 and 10,000 years ago. I appreciate this is going back rather more than the 50 years this book celebrates, but understanding how our meres and mosses were originally formed has been fundamental to our belated efforts to conserve them. During a cold phase, glaciers would spread down from the north, bringing debris from Scotland and the Lake District and levelling all before them. A blanket of slow-moving ice as much as a kilometre thick has covered Cheshire on at least three occasions, with outflows from the receding glacier remaking its landscape each time the climate warned. At its limit, the largest ice-sheet extended south as far as Wolverhampton and the Shropshire Hills, as evidenced by the kettle-hole named Cranmere Bog, near Bridgnorth and the more extensive peatland around Patshull Park in South Staffordshire. Perhaps the hundreds of glacial hollows scattered between Whitchurch and Warrington and from Chester to Congleton will be more familiar to Cheshire residents. These wetlands are a legacy left by a subsequent glaciation that extended only as far as Whitchurch. It left a ridge of high ground just north of the town, which is actually the terminal moraine of mineral debris that piled up at the glacier's leading edge.

As the glacier advanced, funnelled between the high ground of the Pennines to the east and the Clwyd Hills to the west, everything in its path was pulverised beneath it, flattening the frozen landscape and laying down a blanket of boulder clay. When the ice-sheet melted back, a ghost-like image of the channels of former major rivers was all that remained of the old landscape, onto which the pattern of meltwater channels running under the retreating glacier had etched themselves. A new landscape was then fashioned in its wake. Streams of meltwater carry away the debris locked within the ice, from sand-sized particles to enormous boulders (properly named 'erratics') the size of a minibus. These erratics still litter the landscape, with some of the largest deposited in central Staffordshire. While the smaller examples might be of interest to geologists, they are a serious nuisance to farmers who would break their ploughs while cultivating. Consequently, rounded (and often chipped!) cobbles of granite from Cumbria or Scotland lie discarded along hedge bottoms where they will cause least harm to future generations.

The face of the melting glacier would occasionally shed lumps of ice, which embedded themselves into the wet sand and clay surface left behind. These 'icebergs' would then melt quietly in their own time leaving deep, water-filled hollows. At this point, the formation of meres and mosses as we know them today becomes more complicated. Many indeed originated in ice-formed 'kettle-holes', but others have developed in valleys and depressions left in the landscape by the swirling meltwater. The whole landscape was in a state of flux – as quickly as one meltwater channel formed, another would cross it, cutting off its flow by blocking the original channel with material dropped from its own sediment-laden water. Water would become impounded in land-locked channels and either be held by a clay bed or simply drain away into sand.

Gradually, as the climate warmed, vegetation would start to recolonise the new landscape. Initially opportunist plants, those spreading by spores or windblown seed moved in – the lichens, mosses and primitive plants such as horsetails. The

Figure 5.4. Round-leaved Sundew at Black Lake.
© Colin Hayes

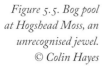

Figure 5.5. Bog pool at Hogshead Moss, an unrecognised jewel. © Colin Hayes

Figure 5.6. Schwingmoor, a superb example, South Moss, Abbots Moss SSSI/SAC. © Colin Hayes

newly formed lakes were no exception, forming margins of swampy vegetation in the shallower water. How each mere or moss continued to develop from this stage would depend on its position in the landscape, the substrate in which it had formed and the type of water running in from its catchment. At one extreme might be an overflowing lake, fed by a large catchment of predominantly clay land. In such cases, there would be a steady through-flow of mineral-rich water, allowing vegetation to grow rapidly, but also allowing decomposition processes to take place, so that the lake remained with only a fringe of marshland. At the other extreme, an enclosed lake might sit perched high above the surrounding landscape within a small sandy catchment. Nutrient inputs to such lakes would have been much lower and considerably more acidic. Vegetation would grow and decompose much more slowly under these conditions – an environment only specialist plants such as the *sphagnum* mosses could tolerate. Peat accumulated steadily over millennia, eventually filling the basin and lifting the vegetation surface so it received only rainwater. Our raised bogs formed in this way. In some of our deepest basins, this process continues today, but our lives are too short for us to witness more than a tiny fraction of this succession. Clearly, some basins have not yet filled with peat – sites such as Wybunbury Moss (where underlying salt subsidence has deepened the kettle-hole) and South Moss, Abbots Moss have only a skin of moss covering the surface of a yet unconsolidated lens of peaty soup. Beneath these quaking bogs ('schwingmoors', as they are properly named) peat formation continues today, and at some time in the future, climate permitting, the peat in these basins will finally become consolidated.

The water flowing through most meres continues to carry away decomposition products, so we can expect open water conditions to prevail for many

Figure 5.7. Transitional Willow/Alder carr with Marsh Marigold at Hatch Mere. © Colin Hayes

centuries to come. At one extreme, a shallow basin might have accumulated virtually no peat; at the other, a deep basin could have filled with up to 12 metres of peat that is firm enough to walk over. Between these extremes, every intermediate form exists. These would include the many swamps that are gradually succeeding to bog, as rainfall from above begins to influence their vegetation more than the groundwater below (Oakhanger Moss, near Alsager), and those lakes where the shallow margins have already developed peat bog while the deepest core remains as open water (Hatch Mere, with Norley Moss on its edge).

Adverse impacts

With all the levels of protection, detailed in the box on p. 106, one could get the impression that recognised sites of importance might have a secure future. Unfortunately, this is not always the case, because many changes have occurred on and around them over the last 50 years, which continue to make it difficult to maintain these sensitive wetlands in good condition. There are many cases where improved productivity of catchment land, through increased fertiliser applications and ploughing for arable production has increased the sediment and

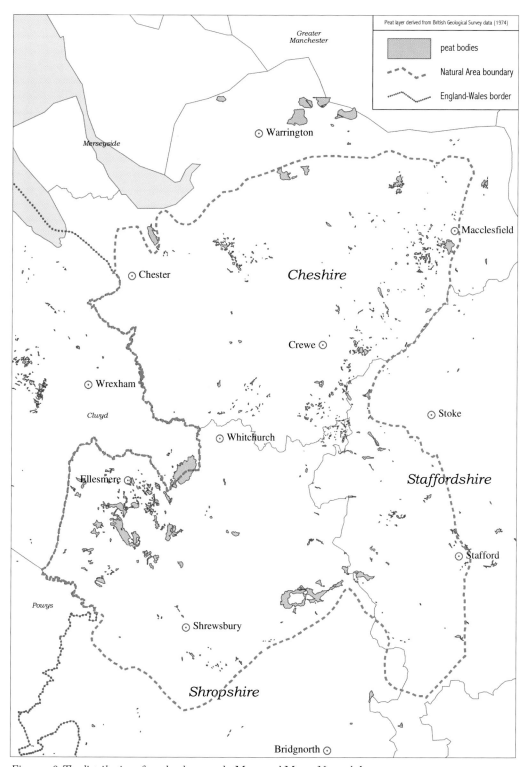

Figure 5.8. The distribution of peatlands across the Meres and Mosses Natural Area.

Conservation designations

Figure 5.9. Lily Pool at Abbots Moss SSSI/SAC. © Colin Hayes

Such diverse and arguably irreplaceable ancient areas of natural vegetation have not escaped the notice of conservation agencies and organisations, with their confusing array of site designations. In Cheshire, 22 glacial wetlands considered to be of national importance benefit from Site of Special Scientific Interest (SSSI) designation (9 mosses, 8 meres and 5 sites where mosses sit next to meres). European legislation prioritises the conservation of wetlands, with 'raised bog' (even if degraded, but capable of restoration), 'quaking bogs (schwingmoors)' and 'aquifer-fed open water with fluctuating water levels' habitats receiving special protection. In the early 2000s, Special Area of Conservation (SAC) status was conferred on three candidate sites in Cheshire – Abbots Moss, Wybunbury Moss and Oak Mere. The Ramsar Convention on Wetlands of International Importance now gives additional protection to a selected subset of SSSIs, an 'archipelago site', which includes the best examples of all the successional stages to be found across the Meres and Mosses Natural Area (Fig. 1.6). These special designations do not mean that other sites received no protection, because about 100 additional glacial wetlands have Local Wildlife Site (LWS) status (originally Sites of Biological Importance or SBI). This recognition of county-based importance ensures that local planning authorities more rigorously consider planning applications for any development that might adversely affect a Local Wildlife Site.

nutrient load on meres, turning their water more eutrophic and speeding up the process of succession. Drainage of mossland has largely ceased now that peat cutting on an industrial-scale is no longer permitted. However, even when the old drains on the moss are blocked, succession to scrub and woodland continues, in many cases too quickly for conservation management to control it. Drainage of peripheral land causes a lowering of local groundwater levels (after all, this is its specific purpose to benefit development or agriculture) making it very difficult to maintain mosslands in wet condition, especially during the times of drought such as we have experienced in recent years. There is also evidence that groundwater abstraction has drawn down water tables causing levels to drop in meres, and mosses to dry out, even when the abstraction has been some distance from the wetlands themselves. Drier sites are likely to succeed more rapidly to woodland, with the colonising trees eventually sucking further water from the peat, spoiling it for the specialist plants and animals that have evolved in the open conditions that have persisted for thousands of years. Instead of wet, open sites, we now have an increasing number of dry and heavily shaded peatlands. As if enrichment and desiccation were not problems enough, changes that are more serious still occur quite frequently. For example, landowners excavate peat deposits to create lakes to improve fishing or shooting or plant conifers or fast-growing broadleaves such as Poplar. Some peatlands have disappeared completely, subsumed in the relentless pursuit of nationally important sand deposits, a conflict of interests that has been particularly acute across the sand-sheet to the south of Delamere Forest. Fortunately, the Environment Agency is now more aware of the water

Figure 5.10. Peat extraction has exposed ancient pickled pine at Lindow Moss, Wilmslow. © Colin Hayes

table changes that can be associated with large-scale mineral extraction and sand-winning companies now have to complete all their working dry, from above the ambient water table, with no pumping permitted to remove accumulating water.

The prospect of these threats persisting does paint a rather bleak future for our glacial wetlands, with the meres possibly under greater pressure of change than the mosses, a good proportion of which man substantially modified many years ago. This is all against a background of a widely felt antipathy towards our 'bleak' and 'dangerous' 'quagmires', compared to the public's love of silvery-blue, reflective-surfaced, open waters. Climate change presents its own set of uncertainties: our glacial wetlands may benefit if the trend is towards higher rainfall, more akin to the conditions that prevailed during their formation, but if hot and dry conditions become the norm, the consequences could be terminal for these sites as we know them today.

What is it then that makes naturalists so keen to put so much effort into their conservation? There are many reasons. Some simply appreciate the relaxing atmosphere of such sites, where they offer a seclusion that is difficult to find these days – a quiet wilderness in which to walk or simply appreciate nature in its element. Others, more interested in the detail, find a wealth of plants and animals to study – beautiful butterflies like the Green Hairstreak, fascinating insectivorous plants such as Sundew and Bladderwort, as well as a confusing diversity of aquatic plants and *sphagnum* bog mosses. Threatened animals such as Water Vole and Adder find refuge, alongside Palmate Newts, Eels and other rarer fish species. Meres and mosses provide habitats for birds of prey such as Hobby as well as the smaller aerial predators, the dragonflies. While considering those creatures that it would be hard to miss, we should not forget the less-noticed aquatic invertebrates – the beetles and spiders in particular. The list of rare species is long, and unfortunately, it is growing both longer and shorter as more plants and animals become rare and eventually extinct.

Figure 5.11. Hatch Mere reflections. © Colin Hayes

Figure 5.12. Freshly emerged female Four-spotted Chaser at Hogshead Moss. © Colin Hayes

Figure 5.13. Black Darter male at Danes Moss. © Colin Hayes

Positive effects

In a determined effort to conclude my review on a brighter note, a few of the more positive achievements from the last five decades might offer a little encouragement. Any site of importance for wildlife owned or tenanted by a conservation organisation is likely to have a more secure future because nature conservation will be fundamental to all land management objectives. Rostherne Mere and Wybunbury Moss are Cheshire's only National Nature Reserves. Both were declared just over 50 years ago, so Nature Conservancy, followed by its various reincarnations as Nature Conservancy Council, English Nature and lately Natural England, has been able to refine the management of these wetlands exclusively for wildlife for more than half a century.

Since its formation, Cheshire Wildlife Trust has played an important role in mere and moss conservation, not least through its reserve acquisition programme, and currently owns or manages ten mere/moss nature reserves, seven of which are SSSIs. Abbots Moss had been included in 1915 among the 284 UK sites listed as 'worthy of preservation', noted as a 'piece of typical primeval country' with sundews and a breeding colony of Large Heath butterfly, then known as the Marsh Ringlet. Charles Rothschild described Abbots Moss as 'a place we should make every effort to secure' and his vision was finally realised in 1965 – albeit long after the Cheshire extinction of the Large Heath, last known to have bred in 1929 – when CWT signed a nature reserve agreement with its owners the Forestry Commission. Also in 1965, Saltersley Moss near Wilmslow and Black Lake in Delamere were amongst the Trust's first reserves, soon followed in 1967 when the Trust became responsible for managing a significant portion of Danes Moss near Macclesfield. More recently, CWT has acquired or been entrusted with the stewardship of Holcroft Moss, Hatch Mere and a particularly important part of Bagmere where the rare Small Pearl-bordered Fritillary

Figure 5.15. Green Hairstreak on Bog Rosemary at Shemmy Moss, Abbots Moss. © Colin Hayes

Figure 5.14. Brimstone feeding on Bilberry at Hatch Mere. © Colin Hayes

butterfly has its only known Cheshire site, laying eggs on the Marsh Violet and Dog Violet plants. The Trust is continuing to pursue further opportunities, with its anniversary year 2012 seeing acquisition of Blakenhall Moss and extensions to the reserve at Danes Moss.

Conservation organisations own or manage only a small proportion of meres and mosses; the majority are in private ownership. Countryside/Environmental Stewardship agreements have specifically targeted the influential catchment land of glacial wetlands for a number of years. Natural England is available to offer management advice and financially assisted management agreements to owners of SSSIs. Cheshire Wildlife Trust or agricultural consultancies can advise LWS owners how they could best manage their land to conserve and benefit wildlife and can assist them if they wish to apply for agri-environment support. Until recently, only 'agricultural land' qualified for these environmental subsidies, but under the Wetland Vision initiative, the wetlands themselves can finally benefit from financial support. Following a survey funded by Natural England to identify those relict mosses with the greatest potential for restoration, moneys have been made available to cover capital works, such as tree felling and ditch blocking or fencing to enable controlled grazing.

After the completion of capital works, landowners with Higher Level Stewardship agreements can receive additional funds to assist them with the cost

Figure 5.16. Black Lake, Delamere SSSI – after 30 years of asking, the shading and seeding conifers are soon to be removed (June 2011). © Colin Hayes

Figure 5.17. Part of Cheshire Wildlife Trust's reserve at Danes Moss. © Colin Hayes

of any ongoing management required. Ecological consultants have assessed more than 60 relict mosses across Cheshire, Shropshire and Staffordshire over the last five years and a tailor-made restoration management plan now guides towards recovery about one-third of these non-SSSI areas of county importance.

Delamere Forest mosslands

The concentration of old mosses in Delamere Forest has received particular attention. Formerly a hunting forest, the remnants passed to the Crown at the time of the Enclosures Act in the early 1800s. The need for greater timber production brought even the wettest basins into silvicultural use. Teams of prisoners from the Napoleonic wars laboured to dig trenches which breached the natural sills of mineral ground that impounded the water, emptying all of Delamere's wet hollows into the nearest of the many streams draining off the Forest. The discovery of fast-growing coniferous species imported from North America and elsewhere in the early 1800s enabled the planting of Delamere: Western Hemlock proved to be particularly well suited to the damp peaty conditions in the basins. For decades, naturalists visiting the forest could only gaze frustrated into the dense shade of serried ranks of planted trees that were continuing to suck the last vestiges of water from the drained peat.

About 15 years ago, the first signs of a change in Forestry Commission policy became evident with the damming of a small number of pools throughout the forest. A survey in 2003 revealed that about 130 basins were hidden beneath the trees, rather than the couple of dozen whose existence was known about! The team of consultants who undertook 'The Lost Meres and Mosses of Delamere Project' made inventories of terrestrial and aquatic invertebrates and of any relict bog plants still present. Patches of *sphagnum* survived in many of the basins, lifting hopes that restoration could still be possible, so the team prepared rehabilitation plans for those basins where it appeared easiest to block the outfall ditches. Visitors to the forest will have noticed the implementation of these plans over the last few years, with gaps appearing in the forest canopy where conifers have been felled, but not replanted. Peat and plastic piling dams now stem the flow of water from the basins, which instead fills the holes created in the peat during dam construction. Patience is all that is needed now while we wait for bog vegetation to re-establish across the re-wetted peat. Early signs are very encouraging, but the recovery process is quite slow, initially at least, and the luxuriant flush of young Birch trees that flourishes dispiritingly for a time, survives only until the peat becomes fully saturated.

The restoration of Blakemere Moss at the heart of the Forest has been particularly impressive. In late 1996, the Forestry Commission felled 41 ha of trees and installed a large sluice, allowing the area to flood naturally. At Blakemere's western end, where inundation is not so deep, a fascinating mosaic of moss-filled ditches with Heather with Bilberry on the dry mounds between has formed.

Figure 5.18. Wounded and dying: Hunger-hill Moss in Delamere Forest, where bog restoration is being planned using landfill tax grant money. © Colin Hayes

Sundew and Cottongrasses abound, several clumps of Royal Fern are regenerating, all these growing up from spores and seed lying dormant for almost 100 years beneath layers of needles in the shade of tall Pines and Hemlock. Unfortunately, two worrying problems have accompanied the re-wetting of Blakemere. In the rush to dam the outfall to create the lake, it was not appreciated that much of the water entering the basins originated from the north-facing slopes of Eddisbury Hill, land used for agriculture. Whilst the water was wanted, the nutrients it carried were certainly not, and where these flowed round the edge of moss before, damning impounded these enriched waters. The moderate eutrophication is

*Figure 5.19. Impressive
bog regeneration at
Blakemere Moss, Delamere
(August 2011). © Colin Hayes*

evident from the stands of Reedmace round the lake margins. The vast numbers of Black-headed Gulls and flocks of Canada Geese visiting the site add to the nutrient enrichment. These birds are also unwittingly the most likely importers of fragments of alien plants, which now carpet the shallow water and wet peaty margins. Wide swathes of Australian Stonecrop (*Crassula helmsii*) and Water Fern (*Azolla filiculoides*) (see Rivers, Chapter 6) now grow where *sphagnum* mosses should dominate. In the long-term, nobody knows which of these opportunistic colonisers will out-complete the other; in the meantime, a seed-bank of pervasive aquatic weed species now exists in the middle of the forest, and fears that these plants could spread to other forest wetlands have already been realised with the serious Stonecrop infestation found recently at Oak Mere SSSI. Most worryingly,

*Figure 5.20. Blakemere
Moss, the largest restoration
project (March 2012).
© Colin Hayes*

Figure 5.21. A young plant of Royal Fern regenerating on Blakemere Moss. © Colin Hayes

we do not appear to have found a way to halt the rapid spread of this plant. Attempts to remove it physically leave behind thousands of tiny plant fragments which are quickly able to regenerate; nor can herbicide treatment achieve 100% removal – while much of the Stonecrop is killed, so too are many non-target native plants.

Before leaving Delamere, the most concentrated area of glacial wetland restoration in the county, the 'White-faced Darter Reintroduction Project' deserves special mention. This rare dragonfly lives only on peatlands, or to be more accurate, it requires peaty pools with aquatic *sphagnum* where its larvae can

Figure 5.22. Australian Stonecrop and Water Fern invasion and current dominance at Blakemere Moss (August 2011). © Colin Hayes

*Figure 5.23. Common
Cottongrass at Gull Pool,
Abbots Moss. © Colin Hayes*

feed, and emergent Cottongrass so they can climb out of the water when ready to
metamorphose into adult form. The species was present at two sites in Delamere
until the early 2000s (see p. 205), but a significant change in the water chemistry
at both sites has almost certainly brought about its extinction. At Black Lake, the
thoughtless laying of a limestone track down to the water's edge to provide access
for film crews caused soluble calcium to run into the peaty pool, raising its pH to
near neutral and killing all the aquatic *sphagnum*. At Gull Pool, the pH has also
risen significantly, but the cause is less clear because there is no obvious surface
enrichment. Adjacent land receives applications of lime and fertiliser, so on such
sandy soils it is quite possible that these have drained down enriching the local
groundwater system. Whatever the causes, the dragonfly needs new homes until
its original ones can recover their natural acidity: the peat hollows under restoration across the forest provide a possible solution. However, creating wet peaty
pools and the right surrounding habitat is not enough, because the dragonfly
is known to travel only very short distances (a few hundred metres), so natural
colonisation will not occur. Fortunately, populations of White-faced Darter
thrive at Chartley Moss in Staffordshire and at Whixall Moss in Shropshire,
following highly successful re-wetting programmes on both these National
Nature Reserves. Eventually, when the most promising of Delamere's basins have
matured sufficiently to provide for the dragonfly's very specific requirements,
they will receive dragonfly larvae from the donor sites. Cumbria Wildlife Trust
attempted a similar reintroduction of White-faced Darter to re-wetted parts of
Foulshaw Moss last year, so Delamere's Steering Group will be looking for as
much guidance as possible from the Cumbria project to ensure they adopt best

practice when the project moves to its next phase. Once re-established, without further help, White-faced Darters should be able to find new breeding sites as they become available because the Delamere basins lie sufficiently close together, so there are excellent prospects that reintroduction will be successful.

Re-wetting programmes

Several other re-wetting initiatives scattered across the county are showing a great deal of promise. For example, at Cheshire Wildlife Trust's reserve, Holcroft Moss, ditch blocking and tree clearance is largely complete and part of the Trust's flock of Hebridean sheep have now controlled tree regeneration for almost a decade. This last remaining 20-hectare block of uncut peat now sits more than a metre above its surroundings, flat Upper Mersey catchment, and is all that remains of an enormous tract of raised bog that used to stretch from Warrington to Manchester before the ravages of commercial peat cutting progressively drained and removed it. Risley Moss is also part of that once extensive bog, where fortuitously a sufficient depth of peat remained when cutting ceased for ditch blocking to flood many of the old cuttings and initiate widespread bog regeneration.

Likewise, on Danes Moss, where peat cutting continued commercially until the early 1960s, ditch blocking by Cheshire Wildlife Trust and Natural England has kick-started bog regrowth over wide areas. The waste recycling company who gained planning permission to tip on the northern part of the moss 20 years ago, when landfill capacity was desperately needed, are also very successfully using

Figure 5.24. Regenerating bog in flooded cuttings at Risley Moss SSSI, Warrington. © Colin Hayes

Figure 5.25. Bog Myrtle in flower at Hatch Mere.
© Colin Hayes

peat dams to hold back precious rainwater on the SSSI-protected part of the bog they manage. Rare species of *sphagnum* are beginning to grow at scattered locations across the whole site and the future of the county's largest stand of the rare Bog Myrtle now appears secure. Unfortunately for older readers, only today's younger generation will live long enough to see bog mosses growing over the entire surface of Danes Moss, as they properly do on pristine raised bogs. Ironically, it will only be possible to claim that re-wetting has been successful when bog regrowth is so extensive that it is difficult to get around the site to monitor how widespread the rare species have become!

Meres and Mosses Nature Improvement Area

It is unlikely that the wildlife interest of our meres and mosses would survive without the help of nature conservation agencies and interest groups. In turn, these official and unofficial bodies will only survive if the wider population and the governments they elect continued to believe that conserving our natural assets is important to our future. So alongside all the surveying of sites, drawing up of safeguarding plans and effort involved in their implementation, it has been essential to maintain the interest of research students, local and national politicians and the wider public. Best practice and experiences are shared at an annual 'Meres and Mosses Forum' when pleas are made for university research departments to continue their invaluable work behind the scenes. Over the years, this has been an important informal get-together, where successful schemes have become the more usual topic of conversation rather than the downward trend in water quality and water levels.

Each year an association between Cheshire and Shropshire Wildlife Trusts promotes a 'Meres and Mosses Festival', when nature reserves are opened-up for guided walks so that young and old can become more aware of the importance and beauty of the natural lakes and peatlands dotted across the countryside in which they live.

Finally, in 2012 came the welcome news that 'The Meres and Mosses of the Marches' have been selected as one of the first twelve Nature Improvement Areas (NIAs) in the UK. This project, led by the two county Wildlife Trusts, covers an area of 40,000 ha and will see substantial funding applied to improve the network of habitats across south Cheshire and north Shropshire, and to inspire people about the unique value of our meres and mosses.

*Figure 5.26. Enclosed and tranquil –
Norbury Mere SSSI. © Colin Hayes*

Further reading

English Nature. 1998. *Natural Area Profile #27: Meres and Mosses.* English Nature, Peterborough

English Nature. 1998. *A Strategy for the Conservation of the Meres and Mosses of Cheshire, Shropshire and Staffordshire.* English Nature, Peterborough

Sinker, C. A. 1962. The *North Shropshire Meres and Mosses – a background for ecologists.* Field Studies Vol. 1 No. 4. Reprinted Headley Brothers Ltd., London

University of Lancaster Archaeological Unit: Leah, M. D., Wells, C. E., Appleby, C. and Huckerby, E. 1997. *North West Wetland Survey: The Wetlands of Cheshire.* Lancaster, UK

University of Lancaster Archaeological Unit: Leah, M. D., Wells, C. E., Stamper, P., Huckerby, E. and Welch, C. 1998. *North West Wetland Survey: The Wetlands of Shropshire and Staffordshire.* University of Lancaster, UK

About the author

Colin Hayes first savoured ecology when he became vegetarian at Sussex University in 1970! This conversion changed his potential career path from biochemistry and genetics to one that finally found fruition contributing to the conservation of semi-natural habitats across the West Midlands and North-West England. After a spell teaching 'Modern Agriculture' in southern Africa as a volunteer during the mid-70s, he worked on farms, pot-banks and short-term conservation contracts, including spells as an RSPB warden at Peregrine Falcon and Red Kite nest sites.

Having tasted the excitement of working on nationally important wildlife areas during part-time work, his full-time appointment as Conservation Officer for Cheshire with English Nature in 1986 was a personal career milestone achieved. For 12 years, all Cheshire SSSIs were his responsibility and he played a pivotal role in the initial notification of Holcroft Moss and Oakhanger Moss and the extension of several existing sites, including Danes Moss, where notification forced landfill proposals to retreat. During his time in post, he also prepared the cases for the designation of The Meres and Mosses Ramsar Site and the candidate Special Areas for Conservation, Oak Mere and The West Midlands Mosses.

Finding that his role had become pre-occupied with targets, planning and reporting, prompted another career change in the late 1990s. Born and schooled in Stoke-on-Trent, he returned to North Staffordshire to make it the base for his own ecological consultancy business, 'Ecology-first', in 1998, which has kept him fully occupied to the present day. As an independent consultant, he has contributed to several of the mossland restoration projects referred to in his chapter, using every opportunity to put his camera to good use.

Rivers

Duncan Revell

WATER IS OUR MOST PRECIOUS NATURAL RESOURCE, ESSENTIAL TO OUR LIVES, livelihoods and wildlife. Without it, life on Earth would cease to exist. Water is constantly changing from one form to another, above and below the surface of our planet, through a process we call the hydrological cycle. As a solid, water is stored as ice in our glaciers and polar caps. Water vapour, a gas in our atmosphere, condenses to form liquid, which falls as precipitation to our oceans, lakes and rivers.

Britain's exposure to westerly North Atlantic air masses makes it one of the wettest places in Europe, and this climate has created the diverse landscape we see today. Cheshire's annual rainfall is around 800 mm. Although this amount of rain appears quite significant, it is actually a quarter of the rain that falls in the upland Lake District. Cheshire is relatively drier primarily due to the rain shadow effect of the Snowdonian mountains in North Wales, which capture much of the moisture from incoming Atlantic weather fronts.

The vast majority of the rain that falls in Cheshire finds its way into the many river systems of the county, which eventually flow into the Irish Sea through the Mersey and Dee estuaries. These rivers are amongst the county's greatest natural assets. They provide essential habitat and food for a wide variety of flora and fauna, some of which are nationally rare. They also provide drinking water and are a vital resource for industry and tourism.

Rivers vary widely in the type of habitat they provide for wildlife. In natural and semi-natural rivers, the type of habitat is dictated by fluvial processes. As river water moves downstream via gravity, energy is expended on the transport and rearrangement of materials in the channel and on to the floodplain. Gravel beds are usually found in the upland streams and support an array of invertebrates, such as mayflies and stoneflies. They also provide essential spawning grounds for salmonid fish species, such as Brown Trout. Gravel bars, depositional features along river banks, are home to beetles, flies and shrimp that can withstand flooding and drought conditions by burrowing into the substrate. Natural eroding cliffs along river banks offer ideal nesting opportunities for Kingfishers and Sand Martins. Other habitat types include pools, backwaters, floodplains and riffles. The last usually have the highest biodiversity, as almost all orders of macro-invertebrates inhabit riffles (Dobson & Frid 1998; Edmunds *et al.* 2004).

Figure 6.1. Water Vole.
© Tom Marshall

Flood risk

A large proportion of the watercourses in Cheshire are designated *main rivers* by the Department for the Environment, Food & Rural Affairs (DEFRA). The Environment Agency (EA) has legal powers, under the Water Resources Act (1991), to maintain and modify main rivers to reduce flood risk and protect people, homes and industry from the adverse effects of flooding. To ensure that development does not increase flood risk, the consent of the EA is required for most works in, or near, the bank of a main river in Cheshire.

The EA prioritises river catchments in terms of flood risk. High priority rivers tend to be those in urban areas where homes and industry are at greater risk of flooding. In these areas, the EA usually removes weed and silt from the centre of river channels, cuts vegetation along the river bank and repairs flood defences. This is done in a sensitive manner so as not to harm wildlife. Some of this work can be regarded as habitat management, providing a benefit to wildlife. For instance, the removal of scrub vegetation from river banks is likely to benefit Water Vole, a species which requires grasses and reeds as food. It is important to note, however, that the EA is not *responsible* for river maintenance. This remains the duty of the landowner and this applies to all rivers in Cheshire.

Many people think of Cheshire as a county of flat agricultural plains as far as the eye can see. Although this image is indeed true for much of the county, the western part includes the Sandstone Ridge of the Peckforton hills, and the eastern parts are characterised by the steeper moorland of the South Pennines. This upland area is the watershed, a divide that separates one river catchment, the Mersey, from another, the Trent.

Mersey and Manchester Ship Canal

The River Mersey is arguably the best known river in Cheshire. People often associate it with the city of Liverpool, although this famous watercourse actually begins in Greater Manchester, sixty miles upstream of Liverpool at the confluence between the River Tame and River Goyt in Stockport. From here, the river weaves its way in a westerly direction, past the conurbations of Gatley, Northenden, Sale and Urmston. The Mersey at this point is the historic boundary between Cheshire and Lancashire. At Carrington, the river flows into the Manchester Ship Canal.

The Manchester Ship Canal is an iconic feat of Victorian engineering, and was one of the last canals to be built in Britain. The idea of joining Manchester to the sea dates back to the mid-17th century. The feasibility of such a project was shown by the Bridgewater Canal (www.bridgewatercanal.co.uk), built to transport coal from Worsley to the Mersey to fuel the Industrial Revolution, and opened in 1761; this canal is now popular with holidaying narrowboat users, partly because it follows contours and has no locks, and is a designated Local Wildlife Site (LWS), mainly for its interesting assemblage of aquatic plants. It was 1894 before the Manchester Ship Canal (www.shipcanal.co.uk) was eventually opened by

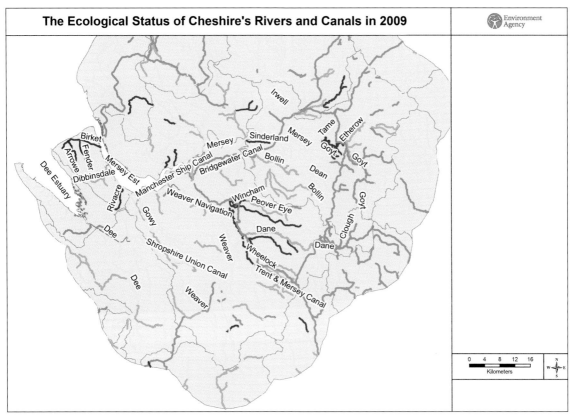

Figure 6.2. Map showing all the rivers and canals mentioned in this chapter, with their ecological status under the Water Framework Directive (Environment Agency (2009) The Dee and North West River Basin Management Plans www.environment-agency.gov.uk/wfd). Environment Agency copyright and/or database right 2009. All rights reserved. This map includes data supplied under licence from: © Crown Copyright and database right 2009. All rights reserved. Ordnance Survey licence number 100026380. Some river features of this map are based on digital spatial data licensed from the Centre for Ecology and Hydrology, © CEH. Licence number 198 version 2.

Queen Victoria, having been built despite strident opposition especially from the Liverpool Port Authority and the railway companies, who stood to lose considerable revenue, and at massive cost in money (£15 million) and lives (more than 100 fatalities and countless injured workers). The Canal stretches thirty six miles, from the Quays at Salford, to Eastham on the Wirral and collects water from a large number of rivers, including the Mersey, Irwell, Bollin and Weaver, thus inadvertently providing an important flood alleviation function.

Two other unintended impacts of the Manchester Ship Canal bring substantial wildlife benefits. The canal has to be dredged frequently, with the dredgings pumped into deposit lagoons where the water drains off and the silt and sand settle. The deposit lagoons at Woolston Eyes – named after the Saxon word *Ees* meaning *land near a meandering watercourse* – are a legally-protected Site of Special Scientific Interest (SSSI), primarily for its birds and amphibians.

Figure 6.3. Some of the characteristic riverine species. (a) Bullhead; (b) White-clawed Crayfish; (c) Otter; (d) Banded Demoiselle damselfly; (e) Dipper; (f) Sand Martin. (a) and (b) © Environment Agency, (c) © Elliot Smith, (d) © David Kitching, (e) © Margaret Holland and (f) © Duncan Cooke

A diverse array of wildfowl breed at the reserve, including Gadwall, Pochard and the nationally-rare Black-necked Grebe. Woolston Eyes is also home to one of the largest populations of Great Crested Newt in Europe. The other dredging deposit lagoons of the Ship Canal, the now-disused site at Moore and the operational site at Frodsham Marsh, are also significant wildlife habitat. The other inadvertently beneficial effect of the Ship Canal comes where it passes along the south side of the inner Mersey Estuary and isolates the area from human access, allowing thousands of wintering waterfowl to feed and roost close to the bank without disturbance.

For four miles westward from Irlam the Manchester Ship Canal is the canalised river Mersey, and the river separates again at Bollin Point near Rixton. The Mersey remains heavily modified and engineered as it meanders through Warrington, the largest town in the county. Howley Weir, near the centre of Warrington marks the tidal limit of the River Mersey, although spring tides often over-top this structure as in February 1990, when a tidal surge caused the Mersey to burst its banks, flooding parts of the town. From Warrington, the Mersey flows into the estuary and out into the Irish Sea between the Wirral Peninsula and the city of Liverpool.

Today, more than five million people live and work within the Mersey catchment. Water has played a vital role in the growth of Cheshire's towns and cities, through manufacturing industries that have shaped history. Once portrayed as *the river that changed the World* (Wray 2007), the Mersey fuelled the Industrial Revolution in the North West. The river supplied the energy required for the cotton mills and factories, and became the trade route for goods to be transported to Liverpool and the rest of the World.

During the eighteenth and nineteenth centuries, the industries thrived and the population soared. The pressure upon Cheshire's rivers was immense and their health suffered dramatically. Chronic pollution from industrial discharges and raw sewage led to a catastrophic decline in water quality, and this had an equally damaging impact on wildlife dependent on our rivers. The once thriving fishery on the Mersey became an ecological dead zone and by the 1940s all commercial fishing had ceased (The Mersey Life Project, Environment Agency, 2008).

Mersey Basin Campaign

In the 1970s, the River Mersey was the most polluted river in the whole of Europe. Toxic chemicals such as mercury were routinely discharged, and in 1978 and 1979 flushes of organic lead compounds (then used in leaded petrol) killed thousands of wading birds (mostly Redshank and Dunlin) in the estuary. Michael Heseltine, a senior Government 'Minister for Merseyside', in 1982 described the river as *an affront to a civilised society* with *water conditions…that are perhaps the single most deplorable feature of this critical part of England*. (The Mersey Life Project, Environment Agency, 2008). This led to the formation of the Mersey Basin

Campaign, a multi-billion pound investment from central government, the EU, industry and utility companies especially United Utilities, to facilitate the clean up of the River Mersey and its tributaries over a twenty five year timescale. It was hoped that a cleaner environment in the Mersey basin would lead to the regeneration of derelict land to benefit the local economy. The Mersey Basin Campaign created twenty two River Action Partnerships, covering the tributaries of the Mersey catchment, made up of local communities, volunteers, businesses, local authorities and regulators, with a range of projects such as waterside litter picks in Manchester and the Salford Quays Oxygenation Project. Unique to Britain in its administrative practice, the campaign was internationally recognised in 1999 when it became the first winner of the International Thiess River Prize for its partnership efforts in the Mersey catchment (Ekos Consulting, 2006).

The EA, and its predecessor the National Rivers Authority, has also played an essential role in river water quality improvements in Cheshire. Sewage treatment and industrial processes have improved considerably through stringent environmental legislation, regulation and enforcement, resulting in cleaner discharges to our rivers. The River Mersey is now cleaner than it has been in over a century, and better able to support life (Fig. 6.4). Important bio-indicator species, like Atlantic Salmon, River Lamprey and European Otter, have returned. The EA-led Mersey Life project has led to the construction of several fish passes in the Mersey catchment. This has enabled migratory Atlantic Salmon and Sea Trout to reach upstream spawning gravels that were cut off when weirs were built during the Industrial Revolution (The Mersey Life Project, Environment Agency, 2008); EA research shows that Salmon have successfully spawned in the rivers Bollin and Goyt in recent years. From 2001 to 2011, the EA have caught

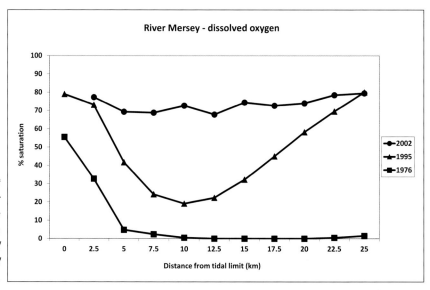

Figure 6.4. The improvement in the health of the tidal river Mersey is illustrated by this plot of the dissolved oxygen saturation in 1976, 1995 and 2002. Data from EA, adapted from Langston et al. 2006.

217 Salmon at Woolston weir fish trap, taking scale samples for genetic testing to establish the origin of the fish. Contrary to popular belief, only a small number of the sampled Mersey Salmon are from the nearby catchments of the Dee and Ribble. The vast majority originate from a wide range of rivers along the west coast of the British Isles, such as Cumbria, west Wales and Devon.

The Mersey tributaries – Bollin, Goyt, Etherow and Tame

The main tributaries of the River Mersey having their source in the uplands of the South Pennine hills are the Bollin, Goyt, Etherow and Tame. Of these, only the River Bollin lies entirely within Cheshire with its source at Macclesfield Forest. As it leaves the forest, the river flows through Trentabank, Ridgegate, and Bottoms reservoirs. From here the river enters Macclesfield and into numerous culverts. Between Prestbury and Wilmslow, it becomes semi-natural and dynamic, meandering through farmland and having more of a sandy substrate. Downstream of Wilmslow the river widens, as it meets the River Dean confluence, and meanders through a steep-sided valley of deciduous woodland at the National Trust's Quarry Bank Mill. Passing over several weirs, the river winds through Styal Country Park before disappearing under Manchester Airport's second runway. The 250 m long culvert was built in 1997 and was designed to try and incorporate features to be found in a natural river, with pools, glides and riffles. The same approach was adopted for the culverting of Sugar Brook, a tributary towards the end of the runway.

Downstream of the airport, the Bollin passes under the M56 motorway and meanders in a westerly direction past Hale and Dunham Massey SSSI. As it reaches Little Bollington, the river becomes more modified with flood embankments protecting agricultural land either side. After passing over Heatley weir, the site of a fish-pass for Atlantic Salmon and Sea Trout, the river discharges into the Manchester Ship Canal opposite Bollin Point. As with an increasing number of our rivers in Cheshire, the Bollin suffers from infestations of several invasive, non-native flora along its banks [see alien species box (pp. 130–131)].

Another upland tributary of the Mersey is the River Goyt. This river has its source within Derbyshire, close to its border with Cheshire just yards from the Cat & Fiddle pub between Macclesfield and Buxton. The river enters Cheshire twelve miles downstream at Disley, and flows past areas of deciduous woodland around Marple, before flowing into Stockport.

The Etherow also rises in the Peak District National Park in Derbyshire. The upper reaches are dominated by the Longdendale reservoirs, five consecutive reservoirs stretching five miles, providing public drinking water supplies. The river forms a four mile boundary between Derbyshire and the historic border of Cheshire between the mill towns of Hollingworth and Broadbottom. Downstream at Compstall, part of Etherow Country Park is an SSSI for its

Invasive alien species

Although these are a threat to terrestrial wildlife as well, many of the most destructive alien species affect, and are readily transported by, rivers.

Three large plants, Japanese Knotweed, Giant Hogweed and Himalayan Balsam were all introduced by the Victorians as ornamental species. In the absence of any of the natural predators found in their native countries, all three plants have a devastating impact on our native flora and fauna. They form large, dense areas along our river banks, excluding light and out-competing other plants that provide food for insects. Each Himalayan Balsam plant can produce two thousand seeds, with individual Giant Hogweed plants releasing up to fifty thousand. Giant Hogweed is a human health hazard as well, causing severe blistering of the skin if contact is made with a cut stem in sunlight. All the Japanese Knotweed plants in Britain are female, so the species does not spread through seeds. Instead, the plant can grow from tiny fragments of the plant's root, the rhizome; it can also regenerate from the nodes of cut stems. As the rhizome fragments are broken up during a flood, they are washed downstream colonising new areas of habitat (Environment Agency, 2011a).

Other invasive, non-native species of flora dominating our river habitats in Cheshire include Floating Pennywort *Hydrocotyle ranunculoides*, Water Fern *Azolla filiculoides* and Australian Swamp Stonecrop *Crassula helmsii* (also known as New Zealand Pigmy Weed). All three have been introduced as oxygenating plants for ornamental lakes and domestic garden ponds. Ironically, dense infestations on the water's surface prevent the penetration of light, causing a massive reduction in oxygen levels. The mats of vegetation may also block culverts, increasing the risk of flooding.

American Mink were first introduced to Britain in 1929 for the fur trade. They soon escaped into the wild where they have thrived, feeding on a variety of native wildlife such as nesting birds, chicks, eggs and Water Vole. Female Mink are small enough to enter Water Vole burrows and have a destructive impact, particularly during the Water Vole breeding season in the spring and summer months. Mink have spread extensively across Cheshire, and can be found along most of our rivers. Efforts to control their numbers through trapping have targeted catchments with known Water Vole populations. This has been successful on a local scale, but it would seem the American Mink is here to stay for the foreseeable future. They are often confused with the Otter, although half the size, at around half a metre long; some research shows that Otters are the dominant mustelid in aquatic habitats and, in their presence, Mink shift to a more terrestrial diet (Strachan & MacDonald 1999; Strachan & Moorhouse 2006).

Signal Crayfish inhabit the Bollin, Dane, Goyt, Etherow and Weaver. In the 1970s, farmers were encouraged to diversify and Signal Crayfish were introduced from the United States as a potential food species to generate additional income. Capable of travelling across land, they soon escaped from ponds and invaded our river network. The impact has been devastating for native fauna. They are aggressive, out-competing our native White-clawed Crayfish for food and habitat. They also feed on fish eggs, fry and invertebrates, including juvenile crayfish. Studies of sites where populations of White-clawed and Signal Crayfish occur together have found that, in all cases, Signals out-compete and totally eliminate native crayfish. This occurred on the River Dane in the late 1990s. Signal Crayfish also carry crayfish plague (*Aphanomyces astaci*), a highly invasive species of water mould native to North America. This fungus has been highlighted on the list of *100 of the World's Worst Invasive Alien Species* by the World Conservation Union

(IUCN) (Lowe *et al.* 2000). Crayfish plague can cause mass mortalities in White-clawed Crayfish populations, although it causes minimal damage to its original host (Holditch & Domaniewski 1995). Sadly, eradicating Signal Crayfish from our rivers is extremely difficult. Trapping tends to remove the larger, more dominant adult males, which provides greater breeding opportunities for numerous smaller males, causing a population explosion. Chemical control of Signal Crayfish in other parts of the country has largely been unsuccessful and this technique has a severe impact on native fauna within the treated stretches of river. Eradication has been achieved in some reservoirs, but all have been fully enclosed, with no outflow or inflow streams.

The Chinese Mitten Crab *Eriocheir sinensis* is another highly invasive, non-native species likely to have a negative impact on our native wildlife. Also included amongst *100 of the World's Worst Invasive Alien Species*, they devour fish eggs, invertebrates and burrow into flood defences.

Figure 6.5. Some of the invasive alien species. (a) Chinese Mitten Crab; (b) American Mink; (c) Signal Crayfish (with eggs); (d) Giant Hogweed; (e) Himalayan Balsam; (f) Japanese Knotweed; (g) Pond covered with Australian Swamp Stonecrop (New Zealand Pigmy Weed) Crassula helmsii; *(h) Pond covered with Water Fern* Azolla filiculoides. *All images © Environment Agency apart from (b) © Neil Phillips*

wetland habitats, and is managed by the Cheshire Wildlife Trust. The Etherow meets the Goyt at Brabyns Park south of Compstall.

The source of the Tame actually lies in West Yorkshire, and the river does not enter the historic boundary of Cheshire until it reaches Mossley, east of Manchester. The Tame meets the Goyt very close to the M60 motorway in Stockport, forming the Mersey.

Dane

The River Dane is one of the few remaining semi-natural watercourses in Cheshire. The river begins in Derbyshire's Peak District at Axe Edge Moor, close to the sources of the Bollin and Goyt. Some of the tributaries of the Dane, up on the high moorland areas, are the only places in Cheshire where Dippers breed, and are also home to a thriving Water Vole population, with deep pools and plenty of vegetation for food and cover. Water Vole numbers in Cheshire have fallen quite dramatically over the last fifty years, mainly due to habitat loss and predation by American Mink [see alien species box (pp. 130–131)].

The Dane enters Cheshire about a mile from its source and, like many rivers, forms a county boundary, as it steeply descends the South Pennine hills shared with Staffordshire. The surroundings alter from rugged moorland to deciduous woodland cloughs at Danebridge. This setting continues through to Hugbridge, following the Dane Valley Way.

Many of Cheshire's upland rivers have been heavily modified by human practices and development, which have had an adverse impact upon our wildlife. The utilisation of running water to power mills during the Industrial Revolution and rapid urbanisation has left a legacy of straightened rivers, culverts and weirs. This is pertinent to the Bollin, Goyt, Etherow and Tame. All of these river catchments have been impounded with dams to create reservoirs for drinking water. In many places, river habitat has effectively been fragmented by culverts, reducing its ability to provide the necessary light and food resource for flora and fauna. Weirs have prevented fish species from migrating upstream, and hard bank revetment has largely eliminated bankside vegetation and prevented birds and mammals from burrowing to create nests.

The Dane and a few upland tributaries, like Clough Brook, have retained a more natural form, however, only temporarily lost as the Dane flows through the town of Congleton. Several weirs have been constructed for mills and to try to tame the flow. Walls have also been built along the banks in an attempt to protect homes, factories and roads from flooding; even so, Congleton has suffered numerous floods, as in 1987 and 1998. As the river leaves the town, it returns to a more natural character and this has been formally recognised in its designation as an SSSI between Congleton and Holmes Chapel. This SSSI is one of the few relatively unspoilt stretches of river in Cheshire, exhibiting the physical form and flow of a natural river (referred to as hydromorphology). The channel is virtually free from human interference and exhibits all the features that you would expect to see under natural conditions: meanders, eroding cliffs, sand bars, berms and ox-bow lakes. This provides an important mosaic of habitats, which naturally leads to greater biodiversity. The river is ideal for fish with deep pools for feeding and refuge, and riffles and rapids for spawning. This provides food for larger predatory fish, Otters, Kingfishers and Grey Herons. Fallen trees within the river ('woody debris') add to the physical diversity of the river channel, providing a food source for invertebrates and cover for other wildlife, such as fish and Otters. The naturally eroding cliffs provide nesting sites for Sand Martins and Kingfisher. The sand bars are ideal refuges for sandy flies, in particular the rare Southern Silver Stiletto-fly *Cliorismia rustica*. Cheshire is one of the few places in Britain where this species is found. *C. rustica* was first discovered in Britain on the River Bollin in 1875 at Bowdon, near Altrincham. An EA-commissioned survey in 2005 confirmed its presence on the Bollin just downstream of Prestbury, and the Dane upstream of Holmes Chapel. Since then, further surveys have found the Stiletto-fly in other parts of Cheshire, including the River Etherow at Compstall, the River Goyt at Lower Bredbury, and the River Tame at Brinnington (Bates *et al.* 2006; Hewitt & Parker 2008).

Otters

Otters are very useful bio-indicators, showing the environmental health of a river system: their presence usually reflects good water quality, habitat and food supply. Otters almost disappeared from England in the 1970s due to the toxic effects of pesticides, later banned, allowing fish back to rivers that were once grossly polluted. In 2009 and 2010, the EA organised the fifth national Otter survey, in which Otters were found in every county in England apart from Kent. The survey showed that the number of sites with evidence of Otter nationally had increased tenfold in thirty years as the species has benefited from habitat enhancement and a significant improvement in water quality. In Cheshire, Otter evidence was found on the rivers Gowy, Weaver, Wheelock, Dane, Wincham, Bollin and Goyt.

Figure 6.6. An Otter spraint, the closest that most people come to finding this elusive species. © Environment Agency

The Dane weaves its way through farmland downstream of Holmes Chapel, before meeting the River Wheelock at the market town of Middlewich. The Trent & Mersey Canal runs alongside the Dane as it carves its way through farmland all the way to Northwich, where it flows into the River Weaver, one of Cheshire's most prominent watercourses.

Weaver

The Weaver takes its name from the medieval word *wefere*, meaning *winding stream*. Although some stretches of the river could be described in this way, most of the Weaver, like so many Cheshire rivers, has been heavily modified. This is a classic lowland river and one of the longest in Cheshire, at 50 miles. The flat Cheshire Plain forms the majority of the catchment, so the river responds slowly to rainfall events. The river starts at Stonehouse Farm just south of the picturesque village of Peckforton. On the map, from its source to the Mersey Estuary, the river forms a letter 'J' shape. It flows for several miles in a southerly direction before turning sharply north at Audlem. From here, it weaves its way to the historic market town of Nantwich, flowing through a straightened walled channel. Some of the old meanders of the river, cut off as part of the modifications, are still evident downstream of Shrew Bridge.

The river between Nantwich and Winsford is semi-natural, with features similar to that of the Dane SSSI. It winds past the village of Church Minshull and then around Top Flash, before entering Bottom Flash at Winsford. The flashes at Winsford are man-made, having formed as a result of subsidence caused by the pumping of brine in the salt mines underground. The flashes are designated LWSs for their marginal vegetation and open water habitat for birds.

At Winsford, the twenty mile long Weaver Navigation Canal begins, opened in 1732 mainly to allow export of salt and import of coal to fuel the evaporation of brine in the mines. Eleven locks and weirs cope with the 17-metre drop over the 20-mile stretch from Winsford to Frodsham. Competition from the Trent & Mersey Canal (completed in 1777) adversely affected the Weaver Navigation and eventually it was agreed to connect the two. Their nearest approach was at Anderton near Northwich and the only snag was the 15-metre vertical drop from the Trent & Mersey to the Weaver, beautifully solved in 1875 by an iconic feat of hydraulic engineering: the Anderton Boat Lift. This worked commercially for more than a century until reduced use of the waterways for trade forced its closure in 1983. However, a surge in leisure traffic on the canals in the 1990s, and Heritage Lottery Fund support allowed British Waterways to restore the lift and in March 2002, the Anderton Boat Lift was re-opened; it remains a popular tourist attraction (www.andertonboatlift.co.uk).

The confluence of the Weaver's largest tributaries, Wincham Brook and the Dane, is at Northwich. This is likely to be the reason the town developed, with the rivers providing good trade links. The Wincham Brook catchment includes notable rivers such as the Peover Eye, Smoker Brook and Wade Brook. Together, the Weaver, Wincham and Dane drain a massive area of Cheshire and it is no surprise, therefore, that Northwich has suffered historically from flooding. On 8th February 1946, following snowmelt and heavy rainfall, a large part of the town was inundated to a depth as much as 3½ metres, with less severe flooding in 1977 and 2000. The River Weaver remains heavily modified all the way down the lower Weaver valley, past Frodsham and into the Manchester Ship Canal at Weston near Runcorn. At this point some of the water from the river passes over the Weaver sluices into the Mersey Estuary.

The Weaver catchment is home to some of the Britain's rarest fauna, notably the White-clawed Crayfish. From the same family as the lobster, this legally-protected species is Britain's only native freshwater crayfish. Once widespread throughout Europe, recently its distribution has much declined and many populations have unfortunately been lost. The White-clawed Crayfish is found in a variety of habitats including rivers, streams, canals, lakes, reservoirs and water filled quarries. They are usually restricted to mineral rich and calcareous (slightly alkaline) watercourses with good water quality. This makes the species a good bio-indicator. Adult crayfish may dig numerous burrows in the soft mud of riverbanks and are largely nocturnal, although they can be seen foraging in shallow margins of rivers and lakes as dusk approaches on warm summer evenings (Holditch 2003).

One of the factors causing a decline in the White-clawed Crayfish population is the invasive American Signal Crayfish [see alien species box (pp. 130–131)]. Whilst competition and crayfish plague are thought to be the most significant threat to White-clawed Crayfish, they are also vulnerable to habitat destruction and pollution. In 2010, the White-clawed Crayfish was classed as globally endangered by the International Union for Conservation of Nature (IUCN).

Gowy

The River Gowy is another lowland river, typical of Cheshire. Comparatively short at 22 miles long, its source is just yards from that of the River Weaver, at Peckforton Moss. The river flows into the Mersey Estuary under the Manchester Ship Canal through a siphon at the Stanlow oil refinery. The Gowy's channel has been modified along its entire length, from source to estuary. During the Second World War, Italian prisoners were forced to carry out much of the river engineering. The Gowy has been dredged and straightened and the banks raised, to drain the land for agriculture and to attempt to reduce the likelihood of flooding of crops or livestock. In essence, the river has been disconnected from its natural floodplain. The Gowy has also been modified to reduce the risk of flooding to Stanlow oil refinery and Ellesmere Port sewage treatment works. A severe flood would not only threaten human lives, but could also result in chemical

Figure 6.7. The River Gowy at Cheshire Wildlife Trust's Gowy Meadows Reserve, with the Stanlow oil refinery in the background. © Environment Agency

pollutants entering the Mersey Estuary SSSI and Special Protection Area (SPA), an incredibly important habitat for wintering wading birds and wildfowl.

In 2001, an EA flood alleviation scheme was completed at Stanlow to reduce the risk of tidal and fluvial flooding from the River Gowy. Embankments running parallel to the river were raised further and the existing tidal flaps were refurbished at Folly Gates, a structure first installed in 1931. At high tide, the flow of water up the river causes the flaps to shut, preventing tidal flooding during extreme weather. When Folly Gates are closed at high tide, river water backs up behind the structure but is contained within the channel and between the embankments upstream. A relatively small flood occurred in 1997, when tidal flaps at the confluence between Thornton Brook and the Gowy in the refinery failed to operate correctly.

This scheme also delivered enhancements for wildlife at the Gowy Meadows. The works involved blocking off a culvert of Thornton Brook, where it crosses under the A5117 road and enters the refinery. Thornton Brook was diverted through the reserve and into the Gowy upstream of the refinery. In times of heavy rainfall, the reserve is flooded from Thornton Brook instead of the refinery, benefiting a wide variety of wildlife, in particular wading birds such as Snipe and Lapwing. The Gowy Meadows Nature Reserve is an area of floodplain grazing marsh, consisting of damp, unimproved acidic grassland. Shallow alluvial soils cover deep acidic peat, which was formed when the estuary infiltrated this area prior to the construction of the Manchester Ship Canal. The reserve is owned by Essar (previously Shell) but is leased to the Cheshire Wildlife Trust. It is one of their finest, supporting a number of nationally-rare species, such as Lesser Silver Water Beetle *Hydrochara caraboides*, Mud Snail *Omphiscola glabra*, Ground Beetle *Agonum piceum*, Great Crested Newt, Otter and Water Vole. The Gowy catchment is one of the best places in Cheshire to see Water Vole, owing to steep banks for burrowing and dense vegetation for feeding. Some of the side ditches off the main watercourses at the Gowy Meadows contain the locally-rare Water Violet *Hottonia palustris* and Bladderwort *Utricularia australis*, the latter a carnivorous plant feeding on invertebrates.

Floodplain grazing marsh is managed carefully using Dexter and Longhorn cattle suited to this scarce habitat. The relatively low numbers of cattle graze on the more common invasive plant species, creating a diverse tussocky structure enabling rare native flora to thrive. The trampling effect of the cattle creates an array of microhabitats, including shallow pools abundant with invertebrate life and ideal feeding grounds for wading birds. Grazing livestock also provide a supply of dung, which is important for invertebrates like the Ground Beetle.

The cattle are also important for maintaining biodiversity along the banks of the Gowy. Over-grazing is undoubtedly harmful to native flora, but it can also exacerbate erosion due to the excessive trampling of river banks. Across the country in recent years, considerable effort has been invested to address this problem, with the most common action being the fencing off of river banks to exclude all livestock. More recently, however, researchers have discovered that, in some instances, excluding livestock from the river corridor can actually reduce biodiversity dramatically (Alexander *et al.* 2010). Unmanaged scrub and invasive plant species out-compete other native species of flora. At the Gowy Meadows, a delicate balance is essential to ensure sufficient grazing to control dominant vegetation, without harming the important native species of flora in the river corridor.

In recognition of its ecological value, the Gowy Meadows has been designated a LWS. Although safeguarded through local planning policy, the designation is non-statutory, so the site has no legal protection. Many of Cheshire's naturalists argue that the Gowy Meadows should receive legal protection as an SSSI. The Gwent Levels in South Wales, which has been afforded SSSI status, is a remarkably similar site. Ironically, the diversity of species inhabiting the Gowy Meadows is equal to, if not marginally better, than that of the Gwent Levels (Harmer 2008). Consideration was given to designation as an SSSI in the early

1990s, when English Nature came to the conclusion that the botanical interest did not meet the qualifying standard. Unfortunately, this was before the diverse aquatic invertebrate community was discovered.

Upstream of the Gowy Meadows, south of the M56 motorway, lies the Gowy landfill site. Granted planning permission in 1986, the landfill occupies what used to be part of the Gowy floodplain. To offset the loss of flood water storage, the regional water authority widened and deepened a series of ditches on the opposite side of the Gowy around the village of Picton. The capacity of Stanney Main Drain, Stanney Mill Brook and Picton Uplands was increased dramatically to increase their ability to cope with additional floodwater.

The River Gowy also has a legacy of around twenty water mills, which were primarily constructed for flour production. Today, only four remain intact: Bunbury Mill near the source of the river, Bates Mill alongside the Shropshire Union Canal at Beeston, Walk Mill just south of Tarvin, and Trafford Mill at Mickle Trafford. Although the other mills are long gone, many of the weirs and sluices have remained and this has created a barrier to the movement of wildlife, particularly species of fish, such as Chub *Squalius cephalus*, Roach *Rutilus rutilus*, Dace *Leuciscus leuciscus*, Bullhead *Cottus gobio* and European Eel *Anguilla anguilla*. The EA has installed eel passes on most of the weirs on the Gowy following stringent European legislation brought in to try and reverse the catastrophic decline in European Eel numbers since the late 1970s. It is thought that numbers have declined by as much as ninety five percent in the last thirty years, with possible causes being over-fishing, pollution, parasites, physical barriers to migration and climate change.

Watercourses of the Wirral

The Wirral Peninsula – flanked by the only estuaries of the county, the Mersey and the Dee – is around seven miles across and 14 miles long, and so this relatively small area is unlikely to generate enough surface water to form larger rivers similar to those found elsewhere in Cheshire. The vast majority of rainfall on the Wirral flows into the Mersey Estuary, mainly via the River Birket, Rivacre Brook and Dibbinsdale Brook. The last is an SSSI along a quarter of its length, primarily designated for semi-natural broadleaved woodland, reed swamp, fen pasture and neutral grassland. Dibbinsdale Brook adopts a more natural character, meandering through the valley and inundating the SSSI floodplain habitats during spells of heavy and prolonged rainfall. Rivacre Brook, in its lower reaches through Rivacre Valley Local Nature Reserve, is also semi-natural, although the upper part is straightened and culverted through Ellesmere Port. The River Birket has been heavily modified by urbanisation, agriculture and flood defence. As with the Gowy, the Birket has been straightened along its entire length, from its source at Hoylake Municipal Golf Course to the Great Culvert at Wallasey with most of its flow being diverted via a United Utilities pumping station into West

European eel

The European eel has an intriguing lifecycle. The Sargasso Sea in the mid North Atlantic Ocean is believed to be the species' breeding place. The adults die after spawning and the eggs hatch to form larvae called *Leptocephalus*, which drift on the Gulf Stream towards Europe. Once the larvae reach coastal waters, they metamorphose into glass eels, a transparent larval form. Glass eels head for the estuaries and swim upstream, entering freshwater where they metamorphose again into juvenile eels called elvers. As they move upstream they grow to become yellow eels, so called because of yellow colouration on their underside. Eels remain in rivers or lakes for a considerable length of time, up to twenty years, before becoming sexually mature and changing to a silvery colour. At this point they make the long journey back to the North Atlantic.

Float dock. The main tributaries, Arrowe Brook and the Fender, have also been modified, the latter straightened during the construction of the M53 motorway. Raised flood banks have been constructed parallel to the Birket, from Meols to Bidston, in an attempt to contain floodwater as this heavily urbanised part of the Wirral has a long history of flooding, with the river and drainage systems struggling to cope with heavy rainfall.

The Great Float docks at Birkenhead occupy what was once the Birket estuary and saltmarsh. As part of the construction work in the mid-nineteenth century, the Birket was diverted back on itself at Bidston, creating a loop, now called the Birket Old Courses. Today, this diverted channel surrounds Bidston Golf Course, with water flowing, very slowly, into the Birket. The Old Courses are a designated LWS, primarily for the interesting aquatic flora and breeding bird assemblage. From here, the Birket flows under the M53 motorway and through Bidston Moss, another LWS. Once a saltmarsh, the site now consists of a mosaic of ponds, reedbeds and marshland, providing great habitat for Water Vole and migrating birds, such as Reed Warbler, Sedge Warbler and Whitethroat. Despite the modification and historic pollution, biodiversity in the Birket catchment is improving. In February 2011, a healthy male Otter was recovered by the EA from the West Kirby to Bidston railway line near Arrowe Brook which post-mortem revealed had been electrocuted by the live rail. In 2005, evidence of Otter was also found upstream of Arrowe Park and along Dibbinsdale Brook.

Dee

Although they are extremely elusive, arguably your best chance of seeing an Otter in Cheshire is on the River Dee. This iconic river is internationally-recognised for its value to wildlife, being a Special Area of Conservation and SSSI. No other river in Cheshire has more wildlife designations than the Dee. The species of importance on the river are the Otter, Atlantic Salmon, Bullhead, River Lamprey *Lampetra fluviatilus*, Brook Lamprey *Lampetra planeri*, Sea Lamprey

Petromyzon marinus, Club-tailed Dragonfly *Gomphus vulgatissimus*, Water Crowfoot *Ranunculus fluitans x aquatilis* and *Ranunculus peltatus*, and Floating Water Plantain *Luronium natans*. Around fifteen thousand Salmon and Sea Trout migrate up the Dee each year, making it one of Europe's premier Salmon rivers. Unfortunately, in recent years, the Chinese Mitten Crab has been found in the Dee and its estuary. The nature conservation organisations both sides of the border are monitoring the population of this alien species and carrying out research with a view to finding a suitable control method.

The Dee rises in Snowdonia National Park at a mountain called Dduallt, seven miles south west of Bala Lake. The river enters Cheshire sixty miles downstream at Shocklach Green and forms the border between England and Wales for 11 miles. The river is semi-natural along this stretch, and shifts gradually across its floodplain. This is clearly illustrated when referring to an Ordnance Survey map, with the boundary line out of sync with the river channel. Just like the Dane, this semi-natural character of the river between Shocklach and Farndon has been recognised for its nationally-important geology and hydro-morphology in the form of a separate SSSI designation. Meanders, abandoned

EU Water Framework Directive

The importance of protecting our rivers for public health and our wildlife has never been greater. With a rapidly growing human population, the anthropogenic pressure on our rivers is considerable. A recent survey to identify the five biggest environmental concerns of people in the European Union (EU), found that nearly half were fearful of water pollution. This is one of the reasons the EU has made the protection and improvement of river water one of its main priorities. The EU's Water Framework Directive (WFD) came into force in December 2000 and became part of UK law in December 2003.

Focusing on ecology, and encompassing rivers, lakes and coastal waters, the Directive is intended to deliver cleaner, more diverse and sustainable river environments in Europe. The aim is for all rivers to meet good ecological status by the year 2027. The EU defines good ecological status as being slightly lower than pristine natural river conditions, a theoretical reference point in the absence of human influence. Each EU Member State is required to create river basin districts, with Cheshire having two: the North West and Dee. Each of these has a river basin management plan, with actions that will hopefully enable every river to reach good ecological status.

The WFD is not only about improving water quality. Another important element of good ecological status is hydromorphology. The intention is to have more naturally functioning rivers, returning them to their historic natural state and restoring hydromorphological features, as seen with the Dee and Dane SSSIs in Cheshire. Setting back embankments from the channel, reinstating floodplains, introduction of in-channel habitat (like woody debris), opening up of culverts and removal of redundant weirs and hard revetment are some of the measures required for rivers to meet these targets. The aim is to work with natural river processes, not against them.

channels, gravel bars, ox-bow lakes and ancient cliffs are just some of the rare features found in the floodplain.

Cheshire's boundary with Wales continues along the Dee to just upstream of Aldford, where the border veers off to the west. The river now flows entirely within Cheshire, past the Duke of Westminster's Eaton Hall, the picturesque village of Eccleston, and into the city of Chester. With the exception of the Crook of Dee and the Earl's Eye, the river along this stretch is straightened and embanked in an attempt to reduce the risk of flooding. However, this does not prevent the Earl's Eye LWS from occasionally being inundated by floodwater in the winter, with the wetter conditions benefiting wildlife, such as waders. The river is also an extremely popular tourist attraction, with regular boat trips in the summer months. The Dee flows over Chester weir, which disappears at the highest tides, meanders around the racecourse and re-enters Wales at Saltney.

The Huntington and Heronbridge water treatment works south of Chester abstract vast quantities of drinking water from the Dee. Two hundred and seventy million litres of water a day are taken from the river at Huntington alone, supplying drinking water to two million customers in the Cheshire and Merseyside area. This is one of the reasons why river flow and water quality are constantly monitored, making the River Dee one of the most regulated rivers in Europe. Low-flow regulation is essential to ensure that the river's lower reaches do not dry up in drought conditions. This would have severe consequences for wildlife and the drinking water supply. Several water level control structures, such as dams and sluices, are located in the upper Dee catchment in North Wales. During the wetter winter months, water is held back in these reservoirs and used in the drier summer months to maintain sufficient flows downstream for the requirements of the water companies and wildlife (Environment Agency, 2011b).

The Dee has suffered numerous pollution incidents over the years. In July 2000, a hundred thousand fish were killed downstream of Bangor-on-Dee. In January 1984, the river was accidentally contaminated with large amounts of phenol, a compound used to make plastics and disinfectants. The pollution initially went undetected, which led to the contamination of the drinking water supply for several weeks and many reported illnesses. The incident led to the creation of a Water Protection Zone, to protect consumers and wildlife from the risk of pollution. Covering the whole of the Dee catchment, it is the only Water Protection Zone in Britain.

Sinderland Brook

In Cheshire, a pioneering project to re-naturalise Sinderland Brook in Altrincham to reverse the ecological impact of human interference, making it more like the Dee and Dane, was completed in 2007. The restoration of Sinderland Brook, as part of the Stamford Brook housing development, won the National Trust,

Figure 6.8. The Sinderland Brook before (top left), during (bottom left) and after (above) restoration works. © Duncan Revell, Environment Agency

Redrow, Taylor Wimpey and the EA a National Waterways Renaissance Award in 2008. The honour was given in recognition of the greatly improved river habitats for wildlife and the reduction in flood risk to the neighbouring housing estates near Broadheath in Altrincham.

In the late 1960s, Sinderland Brook was straightened, deepened and diverted by the local water authority. This was to provide additional land for agriculture, but was also an attempt to try to reduce flood risk. It was thought that increasing the flow of the brook would remove enough water at times of heavy rainfall to prevent flooding. However, this did not stop banks being breached and flooding to homes as recently as the 1990s. Due to the urbanised nature of the Sinderland Brook catchment in this part of Cheshire, impermeable surfaces such as roofs, roads, pavements and car parks increase the amount of surface water runoff into the brook, which is unable to cope after intense rainfall.

In the late 1990s, a proposal was put forward by the landowner, National Trust, to create a flagship sustainable residential development to the south of Sinderland Brook. The idea was to work with natural riverine processes to reduce flood risk by allowing the river to flood areas away from homes and businesses. This follows the recommendations given by Sir Michael Pitt in his comprehensive review of the damaging summer 2007 floods in England. A proposal was made to restore over a mile of Sinderland Brook to a diverse meandering river to improve the habitat for wildlife and extend the floodplain, reducing flood risk to nearby housing.

Permission was granted by Trafford council in 2004 and work began to return Sinderland Brook to its former glory. The newly constructed brook is up to half the width of the old canalised brook and this encourages more frequent inundation of the new floodplain away from the development. No bank protection work was deemed necessary along the length of the restored watercourse, permitting the river to adjust naturally. The lack of hard engineering bank protection allows species such as Water Vole, Kingfisher and Sand Martins to create nests and the natural erosion provides invaluable substrate for habitat features downstream, such as sand bars and in-channel islands. Intervention will only occur if erosion threatens the limits of the extended floodplain or serious instability is identified. An on-going hydrological monitoring programme is being undertaken by Haycock Associates, the National Trust's river restoration specialists. The construction of the new floodplain has resulted in an increase in floodplain storage area. The flood alleviation work has provided a high level of protection for the new and existing housing developments nearby, contributing to DEFRA's Making Space for Water initiative.

Monitoring

The way in which we classify our rivers has changed following the introduction of the Water Framework Directive. The last twenty years has seen the EA and its predecessors adopt a General Quality Assessment (GQA) scheme to monitor river water quality in terms of chemistry, biology and nutrients. GQA was designed to provide an accurate and consistent assessment of the state of water quality and changes in this state over time. The chemical aspect of GQA involves monitoring ammonia, dissolved oxygen and biochemical oxygen demand (BOD) at numerous sampling points. BOD is the oxygen consumed by micro-organisms when breaking down organic matter in the aquatic environment: the greater the BOD, the higher the pollution. Chemical monitoring usually identifies the common sources of organic pollution from industry and agriculture.

Biological monitoring compares species of macro-invertebrates. This system was originally devised by the Biological Monitoring Working Party (BMWP). Samples are taken from designated points along a river using the standard kick-sampling technique. A monitoring officer stands in the river and submerges a hand-held net downstream. As they disturb the river bed with their feet, macro-invertebrates are caught in the net. These are then analysed in a laboratory. The pollution tolerance of macro-invertebrates differs markedly between species. Stonefly nymphs and mayfly nymphs, for example, are extremely sensitive to pollution, so they are very useful bio-indicators. If species of stonefly or mayfly are found in a river sample, the water quality is likely to be very good. On the opposite end of the scale are the bloodworms (midge larvae) and leeches. These species can tolerate very low levels of dissolved oxygen. Large numbers of these species within a sample, in the absence of stoneflies or mayflies, indicates very poor water quality.

River samples are also analysed for two particular nutrients, nitrates and phosphates. High levels of these nutrients can often lead to eutrophication, a dramatic increase in phytoplankton that can reduce oxygen levels and disturb the balance of organisms in the river. Rivers often differ in their concentrations of nutrients, depending on a number of factors. However, a river with low nutrients can still contain good water quality.

GQA has been pivotal in delivering environmental improvements by highlighting many of the major point sources of pollutants, such as discharges from sewage treatment works or factories. However, a more refined and comprehensive method of assessing the entire water environment has been introduced for the Water Framework Directive. This will hopefully lead to direct action where it is most required. Rivers are now classified with an overall status, being either high, good, moderate, poor or bad. The overall status is a combination of chemical and ecological parameters. There is now more focus on other sources of pollution, with over thirty measures grouped into ecological status and chemical status, including macro-invertebrates, fish, invasive species, pH, ammonia, phosphorus, zinc, arsenic and hydromorphology. The principle of 'one out, all out' is adopted, meaning the poorest individual result drives the overall river classification. For example, a river may have a 'good' classification for invertebrates, pH, phosphate and dissolved oxygen, but if the fish classification is 'moderate', then the overall status of the river is 'moderate' (Environment Agency 2009).

As with many rivers in Europe, a large proportion of rivers in Cheshire are ecologically damaged. The main pressures upon them are contaminants from urban drainage systems, diffuse pollution from agriculture, and sewage discharges from, for example, septic tanks. By meeting the requirements of the North West and Dee river basin management plans, the hope is that, by 2027, all rivers in Cheshire will be much cleaner than they were in 2009. They will have higher quality habitats for wildlife, and will have more sustainable usage by industry. This cannot be achieved without the commitment of landowners, developers, utility companies, nature conservation organisations, charities and volunteers. Working in partnership is crucial to the success of the Directive.

Rivers are incredibly important habitats for wildlife, and some of Cheshire's rivers are testament to this. In the midst of a growing population, the challenge in Cheshire will be to protect and enhance these wildlife corridors as a valuable resource for our future generations.

References

Alexander, K., Foster, G. & Sanderson, N. (2010) 'Good Ecological Status' of inland waterbodies – fencing of riverbanks is not 'good for biodiversity'. *British Wildlife* 23: 326–332.

Bates, A.J., Drake, C.M. & Sadler, J.P. (2006) The *Coleoptera* and *Diptera* fauna of exposed riverine sediments (ERS) on the rivers Weaver, Dane and Bollin: a survey report. Environment Agency.

Dobson, M. & Frid, C. (1998) Ecology of Aquatic Systems. Longman. Harlow.

Edmunds, M., Mitcham, T. & Morries, G. (2004) Wildlife of Lancashire, Exploring the natural history of Lancashire, Manchester & North Merseyside. Carnegie Publishing, Lancaster.

Ekos Consulting (2006) Evaluation of The Mersey Basin Campaign Final Report Government Office North West. www.merseybasin.org.uk/archive/assets/57/original/57_EKOS_Consulting_2006_Evaluation_of_the_MBC_report_to_Govt_Office_NW.pdf

Environment Agency (2008) The Mersey Life Project. www.environment-agency.gov.uk/static/documents/Leisure/The_Mersey_Life_Project__Vision_Document_and_Outline_Plan_March_2008.pdf

Environment Agency (2009) The North West River Basin Management Plan. www.environment-agency.gov.uk/wfd

Environment Agency (2011a) Invasive Species. www.environment-agency.gov.uk/homeandleisure/wildlife/31350.aspx

Environment Agency (2011b) The Dee Regulation Scheme. www.environment-agency.gov.uk/homeandleisure/drought/38579.aspx

Harmer, A. (2008) Gowy Meadows Aquatic Macroinvertebrate Survey. Environment Agency, North West.

Hewitt, S.M. & Parker, J. (2008) Distribution of the stiletto-fly *Cliorismia rustica* on Cheshire rivers. Environment Agency and Buglife – the Invertebrate Conservation Trust, Peterborough.

Holditch, D. (2003) Ecology of the White-clawed Crayfish. Conserving Natura 2000 Rivers Ecology Series No. 1. Natural England, Peterborough.

Holditch, D.M. & Domaniewski, J.C.J. (1995) Studies on mixed populations of the crayfish *Autropotamobius pallipes* and *Pacifastacus leniusculus* in England. *Freshwater Crayfish* 10: 37–45.

Langston, W.J., Chesman, B.S. & Burt, G.R. (2006) Characterisation of European marine sites. Mersey estuary SPA. Marine Biological Association of the United Kingdom. Occas. Publ. 18: 185.

Lowe, S., Browne, M., Boudjelas, S. & De Poorter, M. (2000) 100 of the World's Worst Invasive Alien Species: A selection from the Global Invasive Species Database. Published by The Invasive Species Specialist Group (ISSG), a specialist group of the Species Survival Commission (SSC) of the World Conservation Union (IUCN). www.issg.org/database/species/reference_files/100English.pdf

Strachan, R. & MacDonald, D. (1999) The Mink and the Water Vole – Analyses for Conservation. Environment EA and the Wildlife Conservation Research Unit, Oxford.

Strachan, R. & Moorhouse, T. (2006) The Water Vole Conservation Handbook. Second Edition. The Wildlife Conservation Research Unit, Oxford.

Wray, I. (2007) Mersey: the river that changed the World. Bluecoat Press, Liverpool.

About the author

Duncan Revell is a Biodiversity Officer at the Environment Agency in Warrington, with over ten years experience in the field of ecology. A graduate of the University of Stirling, his career began in the Western Isles of Scotland as an ecologist for Marine Harvest, one of the largest Salmon farm companies in the country. He has also worked for BMT Cordah, an environmental consultancy based in Edinburgh. With a keen interest in riverine species, particularly the White-clawed Crayfish, Water Vole and Otter, Duncan has spent the last eight years at the Environment Agency, conducting ecological surveys and delivering a number of habitat creation projects along the rivers of Cheshire.

Ponds – Pearls in the Cheshire Landscape

Andrew Hull

DURING THE PAST TWENTY-FIVE YEARS INTEREST IN THE STUDY OF PONDS HAS grown considerably. In the United Kingdom, and elsewhere in Europe, scientific research has shown that these small water bodies are not only an extremely rich biodiversity resource but also have an important role to play in climate change and the provision of ecosystem services. In Cheshire we are still fortunate in having one of the densest pond landscapes in the country. However, the sustainability of this significant wetland resource is not guaranteed. Pond numbers in Cheshire, as elsewhere in the UK, are in decline and this trend is likely to continue into the foreseeable future despite significant conservation effort.

This chapter will trace the origins of the Cheshire pond landscape; attempt to quantify the number of small water bodies in the county and give reasons for their decline. Then, the focus will change to look at the biodiversity value of Cheshire ponds, and then examine the conservation effort which has been and continues to be expended on this important wetland resource. Finally, consideration will be given to future pond landscapes in the county and suggest that although pond numbers may fall over the next fifty years, the Cheshire pond landscape may well be significantly enhanced.

What Are Ponds?

Ponds are small and shallow, natural or man-made water bodies defined as wetlands by the Ramsar Convention on Wetlands of International Importance. They typically outnumber larger lakes by a ratio of about 100:1 and recent studies have revealed their importance for conservation because, despite their small size, they disproportionately contribute to regional biodiversity, when compared to streams, large rivers, or lakes. Thus, ponds challenge conventional approaches to conservation biology, where much attention has been directed towards large-scale ecosystems.

The definition of the term 'pond' varies across Europe and there is no universal agreement of what a pond is. In terms of their area, they can vary from

Figure 7.1. The mill pond in Tattenhall: such large and deep ponds offer a suitable habitat for the Common Toad. © Andrew Hull

about one metre square to water bodies covering a few hectares. The karstic pools in north eastern Italy and Slovenia and the copular pools on the island of Gavdos in Greece are less than one square metres, whilst in the Czech Republic some of the largest fish ponds are in excess of 450 hectares. In the UK the upper size limit that differentiates ponds from lakes is two hectares with the minimum size being one square metre. Apart from their differing area, ponds can also vary in depth. Mediterranean temporary ponds – amongst the most threatened freshwater habitats in Europe – are but a few cm deep whilst in northeast England, according to legend, Hell Kettles pond is reputed to be bottomless!

Cheshire Ponds – their origin, form and function

And what of their origin? Well, ponds can be natural or man-made. Natural processes over geological time have created high pond densities in northern Europe with the kettle-holes which run from Denmark through northern Germany and Poland to Belarus and the ponds which can be found at high altitudes along the Alpine Arc. In Cheshire the meres and mosses (Chapter 5) are examples of kettle-holes formed in glacial times by the melting of ice blocks embedded in debris left by the retreating glaciers and it may be that some of the field ponds in Cheshire have a similar origin. Nevertheless, historically ponds were man-made, being dug for a multitude of agricultural, industrial and domestic purposes and often having multiple uses (see box below).

In the UK, the digging of holes in the ground has always occupied the inhabitants of these shores. In many cases they were dug to 'empound' water which was then used for drinking purposes, stocking fish for food, as well as providing a

Some Cultural and Historical Uses of Ponds

Cooling ponds	Distillery ponds	Dye ponds
Forge/furnace ponds	Irrigation ponds	Mill ponds
Peat ponds	Sauna ponds	Swimming ponds
Curling ponds	Drinking water ponds	Extraction ponds
Hammer ponds	Laundry ponds	Moats
Pond bays	Silt ponds	Traction engine ponds
Decoy ponds	Droving ponds	Fish ponds
Heathland ponds	Livestock watering ponds	Old farm ponds
Reclamation ponds	Stew ponds	Watercress beds
Dew ponds	Duck ponds	Flax retting ponds
Ice ponds	Marl pits	Ornamental garden ponds
Retention ponds	Subsidence ponds	Wagon wheel soaking ponds

Source: The Pond Manifesto, EPCN (2008).

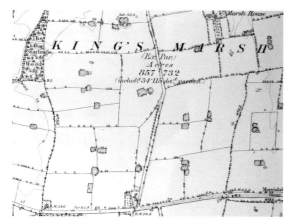

Figure 7.2. Section of the First Edition Ordnance Survey Series at 6 inches to the mile east of Farndon, Cheshire (c. 1870).

Figure 7.3. A recent (April 2009) satellite image of the same area east of Farndon. © Google Earth, Getmapping plc, Infoterra Ltd & Bluesky

means of defence. The number of ponds which were dug is difficult to ascertain, but it is estimated that today, in lowland areas of the country, there are perhaps half a million ponds, of which nearly fifty thousand were once in Cheshire; it is difficult to be more precise about actual numbers due to the problems of counting such small landscape features effectively and accurately. In any Cheshire parish, there will be more ponds in the winter months than the summer. Counting in July and August will almost certainly record ponds which are dry. In March and April, however, winter rain and flooding will not only fill existing pond sites, but will also lead to water retention elsewhere in the landscape as natural and man-made depressions may provide a temporary habitat for aquatic plants and animals.

By far the majority of ponds in Cheshire were formed by the extraction of marl, a mineral manure used widely during the eighteenth century to improve soil fertility. The practice of marling had been undertaken in Britain since Roman times and was widely adopted by the 13th century but died out in the early 19th century as more effective fertilisers became available. Because marl was plentiful in Cheshire it was often quicker to dig new pits than to cart quantities of the weighty substance far from the point of abstraction. The pits themselves were often located in the middle of fields, or at the highest point, or elsewhere where fields met so that the huge loads excavated could be carried a minimum distance with the least effort. Furthermore, many pits were dug in close proximity to each other – often two but sometimes as many as ten ponds or more – due, invariably, to inundation by rainwater which made excavation difficult due to waterlogging. Accordingly, pits became ponds, either through early rainfall or else when the seam of marl was exhausted. To remind us of their origin even today they are still locally referred to as 'pits' in Cheshire and in other parts of the UK. Marl pits

Figure 7.4. Cheshire's pond density is unrivalled in lowland Britain. These small biodiversity hotspots provide vital stepping stones across the county landscape. © Andrew Hull

were generally dug with a steep slope on one side and a gradual profile opposite to allow access for the marler's wagon and draught animals (Fig. 7.6).

Although other fertilisers (such as lime) were available during the eighteenth century, the prohibitive cost of transport did not allow their widespread use in Cheshire. However, with the development of canals, and later the railways, transport costs fell and more effective fertilisers were brought in from other parts of the country, sounding the death knell for marling. By 1870, with the publication of First Edition Ordnance Survey maps for Cheshire marl excavation had not been carried out for over half a century. Instead, what these magnificent large-scale Victorian maps show (Fig. 7.2) is a wetland landscape of water-filled pits, many of which remain today as a legacy to this ancient agricultural practice (Fig. 7.3). In addition to the thousands of marl pits, there is also evidence of other pond types in Cheshire including mill ponds, moated sites, dew ponds, industrial ponds and oxbow lakes but their numbers are limited across the county.

The loss of Cheshire ponds

Although they are still a characteristic feature of the Cheshire landscape, there has been a continuous decline in numbers due to the intensification of agriculture during the 1960s. This loss had not been quantified until detailed work was undertaken by the Ponds Research Unit at Liverpool John Moores University (LJMU). Although it was acknowledged that Cheshire (along with Lancashire)

Figure 7.5. The shallow water between two deeper ponds is characteristic of two marl pits that had been dug close to each other to exploit a particularly rich seam of the mineral manure. © Andrew Hull

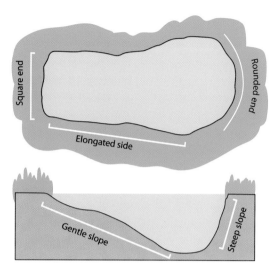

Figure 7.6. Schematic diagram of the profile of a marl pit. © Andrew Hull

Figure 7.7. A temporary pond holding water intermittently: the importance of temporary ponds cannot be overstated. They provide a valuable habitat for amphibians and invertebrates and, because they regularly dry up, exclude fish that otherwise would predate the other species. © Andrew Hull

contained one of the densest pond landscapes in lowland Britain, there was little attempt to account for actual numbers, consider rates of decline and conserve this impressive wetland resource. Also, there was little recorded information about the county's pond resource (with the exception of records from a few biologically interesting sites) and, importantly, the storage of biological records was poorly developed. Perhaps most importantly, there was no clear agreement on the actual number of ponds in the county and, on enquiry at Cheshire County Council and Cheshire Wildlife Trust, estimates ranged from 50,000 to a quarter of a million individual sites respectively. In order to address this issue the Ponds Research Unit, supported by Cheshire County Council, completed the first Cheshire pond audit in 1992 based upon map and aerial photographic evidence. This exercise was replicated at three dates to gain some idea about the continuing loss of ponds in the county (Table 7.1).

Results of the audit revealed that pond loss of over 59% was recorded in Cheshire between 1870 and 1985. The previous anecdotal evidence of pond

Figure 7.8. A characteristic Cheshire field-pond in good condition. © Andrew Hull

Figure 7.9. A fenced pond with a good buffer zone.
© Andrew Hull

Figure 7.10. A small pond in the latter stages of succession.
© Andrew Hull

numbers was clearly a gross overestimate and the reality of the situation was that the county's pond resource was indeed seriously threatened. Work elsewhere in the UK suggested that pond loss in lowland Britain was equally as dramatic with perhaps as many as 60% of all ponds having disappeared since the Second World War: the Cheshire pond audit provided additional evidence to reinforce these national trends.

From this important baseline, the reasons for pond loss in Cheshire were then considered. In other English counties the loss of ponds was due almost exclusively to the intensification of agriculture. In Norfolk, a county with probably a greater pond density than Cheshire at its peak, pond loss far exceeded the 59% decline recorded in Cheshire due to the drainage of land to support the expansion of arable production. Cheshire, in contrast, was more fortunate than counties in East Anglia as pastoral agriculture still dominated the agricultural landscape and ponds, in the short term at least, provided a valuable source of water for livestock. Whilst dairy farming still remains a significant enterprise in Cheshire, the gradual spread of piped water to fields meant that the ponds' primary agricultural function became largely obsolete. A piped supply of clean water meant that

Date	Number of ponds	% decline	Ponds/ sq km	Data source
1870	41,546	59.2% (1870–1985)	17.87	OS 1st Ed. 1:2500
1969	22,644	45.5% (1870–1969)	6.46	OS 1:10,000
1985	16,964	25.0% (1969–1985)	4.85	AP Cheshire CC
2008	16,611	Data not comparable	4.82	OS Master Map

Table 7.1. Loss of farmland ponds in Cheshire 1870–2008. (AP = aerial photography)

livestock were healthier and were protected from being trapped in the deep silt typical of so many of the county's ponds. Increasingly ponds were fenced and livestock were excluded from grazing the margins which meant that marginal vegetation had the ability to dominate the pond surroundings which over time has led to an increasing volume of plant and leaf litter being deposited into the water. So, although Cheshire's ponds are still highly visible in the landscape, many are in the latter stages of natural succession – moving gradually from an aquatic to a permanently terrestrial phase.

Apart from their individual value, ponds in the county form a distinctive visual landscape which can be perceived as a mosaic in which clusters of *local ecosystems* are repeated over a wide area. A significant aspect of this landscape is the density of ponds and their spatial arrangement, factors which may influence the distribution of species. Despite the decline in numbers, pond density in Cheshire still remains highly impressive. As the map (Fig. 7.11) shows, significant parts of the county contain over 5 ponds per km^2 and, in a few areas, a pond density of 15 ponds per km^2 is observed. Taken together Cheshire ponds contain 20.7 km^2 of open water covering almost 1% of the total surface area of the county (2,108 km^2). If all ponds were surrounded by a 1-km buffer zone, the total area of the resulting pondscape would be 2,069 km^2, 98% of the area of Cheshire.

Parts of the county exhibit a lower density, in particular the eastern parts of the county where the land rises to moorland above 300 m and along the Sandstone Ridge in mid-Cheshire where this mosaic is broken. In these areas, the underlying drift geology and the upland nature of the local landscape made marl extraction uneconomic.

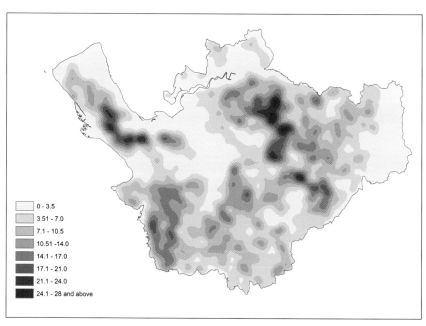

	0 - 3.5
	3.51 - 7.0
	7.1 - 10.5
	10.51 -14.0
	14.1 - 17.0
	17.1 - 21.0
	21.1 - 24.0
	24.1 - 28 and above

Figure 7.11. Pond density in Cheshire (ponds per sq.km). © Andrew Hull

Whilst much emphasis has been placed upon individual pond sites, it is vitally important to consider the pond landscape in totality. It must be remembered that ponds are not truly independent of one another. Instead they function as a network of habitats. First, ponds act as *stepping stones* and are explicitly recognised as such in Article 10 of the EU Habitats Directive which recommends their conservation. Such stepping stones help to improve the permeability of the landscape for aquatic and semi-aquatic organisms. Secondly, the semi-independent nature of individual ponds means that environmental perturbations such as pollution and disease are restricted in effect compared to freshwaters with larger catchments such as rivers. Thirdly, ponds act as refugia for biodiversity such that, should a population of a given species in one pond become extinct, there are more populations close at hand to recolonise that habitat. Importantly, it has to be acknowledged that the pond landscape of Cheshire is part of a much larger network of small water bodies which merges into north Shropshire, Staffordshire, south Lancashire and north east Wales.

Pond Conservation

Serious concern over the loss of ponds in the UK did not emerge until the start of the 1990s. Why ponds received so little attention before then is unclear, but it was widely assumed that they were:

- Abundant and not unduly threatened;
- Of little nature conservation value;
- Holding few species of regional importance;
- Of lesser nature conservation value than other habitats perceived to be more important; and,
- Relic landscape features of little value.

Over the past twenty years, these five assumptions have all been challenged and refuted. Importantly, evidence from Cheshire has been an important contributor to the argument supporting the urgent need for pond conservation and this was reinforced by the far-reaching impact of the Pond *Life* Project (see box (pp. 158–159)).

Biodiversity Value of Cheshire Ponds

Prior to the 1990s, there was little evidence that ponds in Cheshire were a rich biodiversity resource. Although the Pond *Life* Project had not planned to undertake a detailed biological survey of the pond resource in Cheshire, the Ponds Research Unit secured funding from the National Rivers Authority to undertake a Critical Pond Biodiversity Survey (CPBS). In four years (1995–1998) 488 ponds in the county were surveyed during the early summer months. Although only a single visit to each site was undertaken, the results represent one of the largest regional pond surveys ever undertaken in the UK. The results obtained remain impressive and suggest that Cheshire's ponds stand out as *pearls in the landscape* representing a significant biodiversity resource of national standing, as shown below.

The Pond *Life* Project

The profile of the Cheshire pond landscape was greatly enhanced by the award to the Ponds Research Unit of £1m over four years (1995–1999) from the *Life* Programme of the European Union. The Pond *Life* Project application was based first upon the knowledge that pond numbers in Cheshire and elsewhere in NorthWest England were in sharp decline and, secondly, the realisation that small water bodies were gradually being recognised as an important biodiversity resource. The Project developed and implemented a conservation model for ponds and other small water bodies in the farmed landscape of NorthWest England and in similar European locations. The multinational project involved fourteen organisations in NorthWest England and a partner in each of Belgium, Denmark and the Netherlands. Those in Cheshire included Cheshire Wildlife Trust, Cheshire County Council, Vale Royal Borough Council, Warrington Borough Council, Wirral Metropolitan Borough Council, Cheshire Farming and Wildlife Advisory Group and the National Rivers Authority, which became part of the Environment Agency in 1996.

As a demonstration model, The Pond *Life* Project tested a range of initiatives to raise awareness about the region's pond resource, the threats that it faced and ways in which it could be successfully managed and protected. From the outset, the project strongly promoted a *landscape ecological approach* to pond conservation in which the value of any one pond was influenced by its proximity to other ponds and the idea of ponds as *stepping stones* across a landscape became the underlying philosophy. By adopting this strategic, landscape scale approach the Project stressed the needs: for a comprehensive database of sites to allow an overall review of the status of the wetland resource; to develop actions for the *pond landscape*

as well as for individual ponds; to create new ponds to regenerate the resource, but otherwise respect the ecological integrity of ponds at various stages of natural succession; and to affirm the concept and principle of *no net loss* of the county's pond resource.

The Pond *Life* Project provided a model of how pond conservation should be undertaken in the UK. Over four years the project developed a series of initiatives including the Parish Pond Warden Scheme; County Pond Networks; Pond Warden Workshops; the Annual pond warden conference – *The Big Splash!*; the first national pond conference – *British Pond Landscapes: Action for Protection and Enhancement*, Chester (1997); and the first European pond conference – *Ponds and Pond Landscapes of Europe*, Maastricht, Netherlands (1998).

Of these, perhaps the most innovative was the Parish Pond Warden Scheme. Volunteer Pond Wardens, recruited from Parish Councils and by advertisements in the free press, were invited to a series of workshops focused upon different themes ranging from pond creation and restoration; amphibian surveys; dragonflies and damselflies; aquatic plants and invertebrates. These sessions stressed that pond conservation was best undertaken locally with community effort.

Every local group was provided with a base map and aerial photographs from which they walked their parish noting whether ponds still existed, then measuring them, identifying surrounding land use, distance to the next nearest pond and estimating the amount of open water. This was a major task in its own right as some parishes held more than 100 ponds. Volunteer pond wardens, of whom there were more than 60 across Cheshire, were not required to have any prior experience, and workshops provided local groups with training and expertise to undertake basic surveys, starting with amphibians. As well as an annual meeting for all volunteers, an international conference at the end of the Pond *Life* Project was held in Maastricht in the Netherlands, where four pond wardens addressed delegates from across Europe about their experiences in their Cheshire parishes.

The volunteers in Cheshire were coordinated by a full time *Pond Community Officer* who worked to raise awareness of the county pond resource through quarterly newsletters, organising pond warden workshops, dealing with local enquiries and so on. Pond warden schemes involving local volunteers were started elsewhere including in the south of England, run by the British Trust for Conservation Volunteers (BTCV), and in Europe, in north east Italy, Slovenia and northern France. In NorthWest England, however, the aftermath of the Pond *Life* Project was not met with the same degree of enthusiasm; after the end of the EU funding, the Pond Community Officer post was abolished, and

the Pond Warden Scheme and the County Pond Network were dissolved.

The Pond *Life* Project was influential in changing ways in which pond landscapes across Europe have been regarded and, in a number of cases, protected and managed. Local planning authorities have adopted many of the outputs of the Pond *Life* Project and the concept of *no net loss* for ponds in the county has been written into county and local planning documentation. The Pond *Life* Project was one of the first examples of nature conservation working in 'the wider countryside', a concept which had, until recently, not been widely acknowledged. Now, with the acceptance of climate change and the need to provide a means for plants and animals to move through a landscape, the wider countryside has assumed a new priority. For nature conservation organisations such as Cheshire Wildlife Trust the idea of working at the landscape scale, with local communities, is now fully embedded in A Living Landscape, of which the county's ponds form a key component.

Figure 7.12. Community volunteers removing rubbish from village pond. © Andrew Hull

Figure 7.13. Invertebrate sampling in a Cheshire pond. © Cheshire Wildlife Trust

Invertebrates

During the four years of the CPBS, a total of 277 species of invertebrates were recorded with a mean invertebrate species richness of 28 species per pond. Of the total, 38 species had an official designated scarcity status by the Joint Nature Conservation Committee (JNCC, the UK government's statutory nature conservation advisor), including one snail, three dragonflies, two water bugs, one caddis and 31 beetles. The pond with the most species with a 'Status' was at Rudheath which included nine listed species. In total, of the 488 ponds surveyed, 103 contained at least two species with a 'Status', and a further 134 ponds contained one species with a 'Status'. These ponds are randomly distributed across the county with no area being less well represented. During the 1990s, at the time of the survey work, the JNCC kept an Invertebrate Sites Register which incorporated an Invertebrate Index allowing sites to be scored depending on their interest. For the Register, some sites were single ponds while others are assemblages of adjacent ponds in a group. When the individual survey ponds are aggregated the CPBS identified 128 sites and of these 28 ponds (22%) were found to support four or more species with a JNCC scarcity Status. Some notable sites included ponds at Chester Zoo (12 spp.), Rudheath (9 spp.), Tattenhall (8 spp.), Wincham (8 spp.), Capenhurst (7 spp.). The results obtained from Cheshire (and Lancashire) showed that in terms of invertebrate species richness, ponds in both counties were some of the best in the country.

Of the scarce species perhaps the most notable discovery was the presence of the Lesser Silver Water Beetle *Hydrochara caraboides*, a Red Data Book Category 1 species (RDB1), in danger of extinction. This large beetle was first found in Cheshire ponds in 1990, having been restricted since 1938 only to the Somerset Levels. Today, a Local Biodiversity Action Plan has been drawn up for the Lesser Silver Water Beetle in Cheshire and a few new sites have been discovered including one at Cheshire Wildlife Trust headquarters at Bickley Hall Farm.

Another species of significance – the Mud Snail *Omphiscola (Lymnaea) glabra* was found to be present in three Cheshire ponds during the CPBS. Formerly fairly widely distributed in the lowlands of the UK, the species is believed to have become extinct over large parts of lowland England, and is thus now listed as vulnerable (RDB2) in the British Red Data Book. The highest mollusc count at any single pond recorded 14 species at two ponds at Marshall's Arm in Hartford. In total, sixteen Cheshire ponds contained 10 or more mollusc species.

Perhaps the most obvious invertebrates to see at a Cheshire pond are dragonflies and damselflies (odonata). Not surprisingly, with so many wet places in the county, they merit a chapter in their own right (Chapter 9, pp. 196–209). Nevertheless, it is worth noting that the CPBS identified two ponds (both in

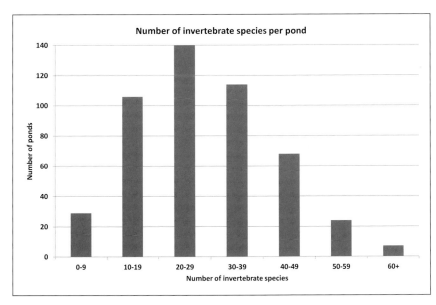

Figure 7.14. Invertebrate diversity in 488 Cheshire ponds surveyed during 1995–1998 in the Critical Pond Biodiversity Survey (CPBS).

Capenhurst) with odonata counts of 11 species. A further two ponds (in Whirley and Rudheath) recorded a count of 8 species and 26 Cheshire ponds (of the 488) contained more than 5 species. In all cases, these records include adult dragonflies not necessarily breeding within the ponds. At the time of the survey, four species of odonata had a JNCC scarcity Status: Hairy Dragonfly *Brachytron pratense*, Ruddy Darter *Sympetrum sanguineum*, Emperor Dragonfly *Anax imperator* and the Broad-bodied Chaser *Libellula depressa*.

Figure 7.15. A pond on Oxheys Farm, Rushton recording one of the highest invertebrate scores during the Pond Life Project surveys (1996). © Andrew Hull

Figure 7.16. The Lesser Silver Water Beetle Hydrochara caraboides. *© Andy Harmer*

Figure 7.17. The characteristic egg cocoon of a Lesser Silver Water Beetle. © Andy Harmer

Figure 7.18. The Lesser Silver Water Beetle favours heavily vegetated ponds as at Brook House Farm, Little Budworth. © Andrew Hull

The CPBS revealed significant invertebrate richness and highlights the great number of uncommon species which can be found in Cheshire ponds. Not all ponds support the same communities and this factor alone needs to be taken into consideration when undertaking pond management.

Plants

A total of 265 plants were recorded during the CPBS and the mean score per pond was 21 species. As is the case with invertebrates, many of the wetland plants in Cheshire ponds occur in other habitats including lakes, rivers, canals, flushes, rush pastures, and the apparent scarcity of a given species does not necessarily mean that the species is genuinely scarce throughout the county. Nevertheless, an impressive list of plants was recorded during the four years of the CPBS. At the surveyed ponds, all vascular plants, including aquatic species, were noted including all plants found in open water and up to the presumed maximum normal winter water level. Differentiation in reporting is made between 'submerged and aquatic plants' and 'plants' in general. Reference was also made to 'higher plants', that is, excluding liverworts, mosses and stoneworts. The maximum number of plant taxa recorded, of all descriptions, in any single pond in Cheshire was 58 and the most common number of plant taxa per pond was 22.

The 10% most botanically species-rich ponds in the county each held 35 or more taxa; the poorest 10% of ponds held 9 or fewer plant taxa. Of the nationally 'Scarce' species found during the CPBS, three species were found in Cheshire:

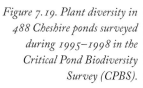

Figure 7.19. Plant diversity in 488 Cheshire ponds surveyed during 1995–1998 in the Critical Pond Biodiversity Survey (CPBS).

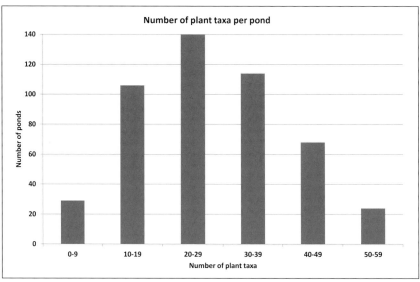

Fringed Water-lily *Nymphoides peltata* at 10 sites, Water-soldier *Stratiotes aloides* at 8 sites and Cowbane *Cicuta virosa* at 21 sites. The 21 records of Cowbane lie within nine 10-kilometre squares. Water-soldier was formerly native to Cheshire but now occurs only where introduced. This species has a restricted range chiefly in the Broads of eastern Norfolk but the Atlas of British Flora contains many records, pre 1930, from the Cheshire Plain (Perring and Walters, 1982). Another two species – Soft Hornwort *Ceratophyllum submersum* and Frogbit *Hydrocharis morsus-ranae* – were recorded at 3 and 15 Cheshire sites respectively. At the time of the survey, neither plant had a recognised rarity status, but their declining presence nationally suggested that at some time in the near future they would both be added to the list. For submerged and floating taxa, 51 species were recorded in Cheshire. Submerged pondweeds are becoming uncommon in the intensively farmed Cheshire landscape although Broad-leaved Pondweed *Potamogeton natans* was found in 144 ponds whilst Horned Pondweed *Zannichellia palustris* was recorded at six sites. Around 236 species of emergent plant were recorded. This term includes all species recorded (including trees) with the exception of those listed as aquatics. The common swamp dominants included Floating Sweet-grass *Glyceria fluitans* (44% of ponds), Common Sallow *Salix cinerea* (44% of ponds), Branched Bur-reed *Sparganium erectum* (46% of ponds), Reed Canary-grass *Phalaris arundinacea* (24% of ponds), and Greater Reedmace *Typha latifolia* (34% of ponds).

Of some concern, however, of the 51 aquatic species identified during the CPBS, no fewer than 11 had clearly been introduced to Cheshire. These include, for example, the water-lilies *Nymphaea alba* and *N. Lutea*, and other species stocked by aquarists, such as Common Hornwort *Ceratophyllum demersum* and

Curly Pondweed *Potamogeton crispus*. In total they make up 8% of the aquatic plant records for the survey. Of these highly invasive species one of the most well known is *Crassula helmsii* which is often sold by aquarists as New Zealand Pigmyweed or Australian Swamp Stonecrop. Occurring in 10 ponds at the time of the survey, this species can form large mats and can become a significant threat to native biodiversity (see also pp. 130–131).

Ponds and Amphibians

Before the advent of marling in the eighteenth century wetland features in the county were mainly rivers, streams, meres and mosses. We can conclude from this, however, that the Cheshire landscape was not particularly amphibian-friendly. However, this was all about to change. As a group of animals requiring standing water in which to breed successfully, the filling of marl pits with rainwater changed the situation for amphibians dramatically as it did, too, for the Cheshire landscape. Indeed this period, lasting for the next fifty years, might be considered as a 'golden age' for amphibians in the county. From being seriously localised in their distribution, the rapidly increasing number of water filled pits provided a fantastic opportunity for amphibians to increase their presence in practically all parts of the county. Amphibians are great opportunists and even the newts, which require aquatic plants on which to lay their eggs, will investigate new ponds well before suitable vegetation has grown. Unfortunately, the absence of amphibian records for the county from the 'golden age' means that we can only guess at colonisation and population size.

Figure 7.20. Human interference in ponds can lead to exotic and highly invasive species – such as Crassula helmsii – *out-competing native aquatic plants. © Andrew Hull*

Evidence today tells us that of the seven species of amphibian in the UK, five are to be found in Cheshire, Common Frog *Rana temporaria*, Common Toad *Bufo bufo*, Great Crested Newt *Triturus cristatus*, Smooth Newt *Lissotriton (Triturus) vulgaris* and Palmate Newt *Lissotriton (Triturus) helveticus*. Of the two remaining species the last recorded presence of the Natterjack Toad *Epidalea (Bufo) calamita* was in 2009 in the sand dunes at Red Rocks, Hoylake. Despite attempts to reintroduce the species with animals from the Sefton Coast, where Natterjack Toads are still abundant, all have failed due to the lack of suitable habitat and significant human interference. The seventh native species – the Northern Pool Frog *Pelophylax (Rana) lessonae* – has never been recorded in Cheshire and until the 1990s was generally believed to be absent in the UK. Four of the five Cheshire species still remain widespread in the county and only the Palmate Newt has a restricted range preferring the more acidic ponds in the north and east. Despite this, it has to be remembered that all of our amphibian species are declining and, like most species across the world, are suffering as a result of climate change, habitat loss and disease.

Of the 488 ponds surveyed in Cheshire during the Pond *Life* Project, none contained all five species. This compares to Lancashire, where two (0.4%) of the 512 ponds surveyed contained five species with only the Natterjack Toad being absent. Only five ponds (1.04%) in Cheshire contained four species compared to 13 ponds (2.5%) in Lancashire (Fig. 7.21).

Whilst the Pond *Life* Project enabled an assessment of the presence or likely absence of amphibian species in the series of ponds surveyed, resources were not available to estimate the population size of individual species at each site. In terms of their conservation, the size of a population (and how it changes

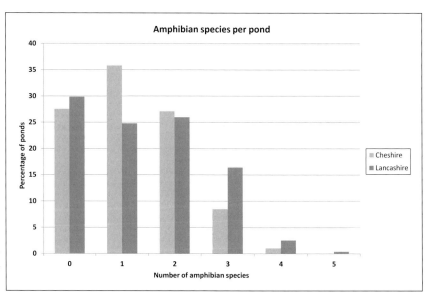

Figure 7.21. Amphibian diversity in 488 Cheshire ponds and 512 Lancashire ponds surveyed during 1995–1998 in the Critical Pond Biodiversity Survey (CPBS).

over time) is a vital part of the jigsaw. From other research, together with our observations, we do know that amphibians favour unshaded ponds and are particularly attracted to new ponds. We also know that most species (with the exception of the Common Toad) do not happily co-exist with fish. From this we can assume that Cheshire's increasingly shaded pond resource is becoming less suitable for supporting sustainable amphibian populations. This is often supported from field survey where shaded ponds often contain perhaps a single clump of frog spawn, or a few newt eggs compared to more open ponds, with

Figure 7.23. A male
Great Crested Newt.
© Andy Harmer

suitable marginal vegetation, containing sometimes hundreds of clumps of frog spawn, and thousands of newt eggs. A positive response to this situation is the creation of new ponds but once again, the temptation to stock with fish leads to diminishing returns as has happened in many new ponds created as part of planning mitigation schemes for the Great Crested Newt. In these cases, new ponds have been created in the wrong place close to areas of public access and have been stocked unknowingly by local anglers.

The Great Crested Newt is, for a number of reasons, the most noteworthy amphibian species in Cheshire. Despite being locally common in Cheshire, the Great Crested Newt is globally threatened across its north European range so this species is strictly protected under European and domestic legislation and the UK government has a legal obligation to report its conservation status every six years. In terms of its presence in Cheshire, the Pond *Life* Project revealed that 35% of ponds surveyed had the species present. Cheshire, then, remains a stronghold for this large and spectacular newt species which often grows up to 15 cm in length but once again, its decline is due to habitat loss as a result of agricultural intensification and development. From research across Europe it is unlikely that population numbers and the density of breeding sites is exceeded in any other country and it is quite likely that the Cheshire population represents the greatest concentration of the species across its range. The presence of Great Crested Newts in Cheshire brings with it a significant responsibility for local authorities in the county and also an intractable problem when it comes to development. It is this species which has brought conservation and development into direct conflict because the planning system requires that developers need to ensure that the species is unharmed during any building programme and this, if undertaken correctly, can be an expensive exercise. Failure to act responsibly can result in significant fines to developers if the species, at any stage of its life cycle, is harmed or destroyed. All ponds within 500 m of a development site, as a pre-requisite of any planning application, need to be surveyed for the presence or likely absence of Great Crested Newts. Now, as has been noted earlier, there are very few parts of the county that are more than 500 m from a pond and over a third of all Cheshire ponds have Great Crested Newts present. From this the developers' nightmare often becomes a reality and has to be dealt with effectively.

Nevertheless, there have been a number of successful developments in Cheshire over the past fifteen years which have put in place amphibian mitigation schemes to enhance Great Crested Newt habitat. Perhaps the most successful scheme has been the works associated with the development of the second runway at Manchester Airport. The loss of over 46 ponds, many of which held thousands of amphibians and 24 of which contained Great Crested Newts, was compensated by the restoration and creation of over 90 ponds set within 350 ha

Figure 7.24. A high-quality Great Crested Newt pond with excellent terrestrial habitat. © Andrew Hull

Figure 7.25. An uncared-for pond in Winsford, but still home to Great Crested Newts. © Andrew Hull

Figure 7.26. A new pond constructed as part of the Great Crested Newt mitigation scheme for the A34 by-pass, Handforth. © Andrew Hull

Figure 7.27. One of the group of ponds near Manchester Airport, especially important for their newt populations. © Andy Harmer

Figure 7.28. A pond created in mitigation for development at Chester Business Park. © Andrew Hull

of agricultural land owned by the airport authority. Before development started, all amphibians were captured and transferred to this new amphibian-friendly landscape which is subject to a 15-year management plan. Other schemes have also been successful, such as at Chester Business Park which has not only seen numbers of Great Crested Newt increase but the ponds created have also been attractive for Water Voles which have also increased in numbers. For a more detailed discussion on amphibians in the county, readers are referred to the *Atlas of the Amphibians of Cheshire and Wirral* (Guest & Harmer, 2006).

Temporal Changes in Ponds and Pond Biodiversity in Cheshire

The original survey work undertaken by the Pond *Life* Project was based upon a single visit to each site and whilst this approach illustrated the great diversity of pond life in Cheshire, it did not provide any insight into how pond life changes over time. In order to address this issue the Ponds Research Unit undertook a repeat survey of 51 ponds in 2006. The ponds were selected randomly from those surveyed in 1996 which had Great Crested Newts present. Using the same methodology and the same surveyor for both surveys, the results revealed some interesting changes. The ten year change revealed that only 31 of the 51 resurveyed ponds still had Great Crested Newts present, a 38% decline in recorded presence. Explanations for their absence in 20 ponds were successional change (51%), arrival of fish (15%), draining of or filling in of pond (9%), deterioration of terrestrial habitat (6%) and other factors (19%). The results for invertebrates were more positive, however, with 22 orders increasing in diversity without losing species. Interestingly, over the ten year period there was a high degree of turnover in insect orders, with a net increase in species richness particularly in beetles (coleoptera), bugs (hemiptera), dragonflies (odonata) and caddis flies (trichoptera). Botanical communities appear to be relatively stable, with ponds that were recorded as highly diverse in the first survey remaining highly diverse in the second. It has been acknowledged that pond communities tend to be higher than for other water body types and this research provided the first quantification

Figure 7.29. Recorded as a Great Crested Newt breeding pond in 1996, at the time of the second survey in 2006, this farm pond in Alvanley had been filled in. © Andrew Hull

Figure 7.30. A new, well designed pond, adjacent to Tattenhall Marina.
© Andrew Hull

of variation in plant and invertebrate communities within individual ponds over time, which provides an additional dimension to pond diversity. The issue of succession plays a far greater role in pond ecology than for other habitats, making them particularly vulnerable to loss through 'benign neglect' on the part of landowners and managers. The turnover suggests that some groups of species (e.g. grasses) become more prevalent at later stages of succession but that this comes at the cost of other species (e.g. charophytes – green algae such as stoneworts). The replacement of one group by another leads to a stable diversity with higher turnover. Late-succession ponds likely contain species that are not present in mid- or early-succession ponds, as demonstrated by the turnover in species. As a result, the maintenance of ponds through dredging of sediment, cropping of vegetation or fencing of banks may not benefit the pondscape biota. Instead, to manage for maximum diversity, ponds should be permitted to undergo succession to grassland, but new ponds must be created to maintain the continuum of successional states.

Pond Species in the Cheshire Region Biodiversity Action Plan

The Cheshire Region Biodiversity Partnership (CrBP) coordinates and delivers conservation action to help safeguard the Cheshire region's most vulnerable wildlife. It includes 21 Habitat Action Plans (HAPs) and action plans for 45 species with national plans and an additional 32 plans for locally significant species. Ponds are one of the 21 HAPs and there are a number of species attached to ponds which are found in the county and have a BAP status, either nationally or locally. In addition, others such as birds and mammals use ponds for at least part of their life: Reed Buntings, for example, were recorded at over 100 ponds during the CPBS.

Pond Species	UK BAP status
Great Crested Newt	National
Natterjack Toad (*)	National
Club-tailed Dragonfly	Local
Downy Emerald	Local
Lesser Silver Water Beetle	Local
Mud Snail	National
Variable Damselfly	Local
White-faced Darter (*)	Local
White-clawed Crayfish	National
Ivy-Leaved Water Crowfoot	Local
Other species using ponds	
Reed Bunting	National
Bat spp.	National
Otter	National
Water Vole	National

Sadly, the vulnerability of these species is starkly illustrated by the Cheshire extinction of two (*) during the last decade.

Future pond landscapes

Despite all the positive attempts at pond conservation that have been and continue to be made in Cheshire, there is little doubt that the number of ponds in the county will continue to decline. This is not due to infilling; rather, it is a result of vegetational succession. It has to be acknowledged that, unless ponds are managed, they are not built to last. Fifty years from now, the pond landscape of Cheshire will have changed noticeably with many fields losing their permanent wetland feature. Landscape connectivity as a result will be seriously disrupted as the *stepping stones* are gradually removed. However, it has to be remembered that many of the ponds which exist today have limited wildlife value. Ponds at this advanced stage of succession offer a habitat to only a few specialised aquatic creatures, none of which in Cheshire has any scarcity value. In many cases, these shaded out and often dry pond sites provide a habitat primarily for non wetland species – particularly birds who take advantage of the trees and shrubs which have encroached upon the small wetland. Invasive shrubby tree species such as Willow and Alder provide valuable habitat for Sedge Warblers and Grasshopper Warblers; Reed Buntings find a home amongst the dense swathes of Reedmace; and mature trees provide nesting sites for Great Spotted Woodpecker and Tawny Owl. As long as these characteristic 'dry patches' remain in the landscape, they will still remain as important stepping stones – but not for truly wetland species. Future landscape historians will note to students that the small patch of woodland in the middle of the field represents the original site of an 'old marl pit' which characterised the Cheshire landscape for three centuries.

But it is not all bad news. First, we know how to create ponds for wildlife. Over the past twenty-five years we have learnt what makes a good pond, whether it be for amphibians, dragonflies or for wildlife in general. The basic principles of wildlife pond design and creation have been tried and tested in gardens across the nation and have provided

Figure 7.31. A shaded, overgrown, pond at Bradley near Frodsham. © Andrew Hull

Figure 7.32. A shaded pond in Tatton Park with poor water quality and little biodiversity value. © Andrew Hull

Figure 7.33. Ponds on golf courses can be a valuable wildlife feature within a heavily managed landscape. © Andrew Hull

Figure 7.34. Garden ponds have provided a lifeline for wildlife, particularly for common amphibians such as the Smooth Newt and Common Frog, both of which breed successfully in this garden pond. © Andrew Hull

Figure 7.35.
A newly-created pond.
© Andrew Hull

a sanctuary, particularly for amphibians. To support these 'domestic' initiatives organisations like Pond Conservation (the national charity dedicated to protecting the wildlife of our freshwaters) with their on-line 'pond toolkit' provide a significant and readily accessible information source. Funding is also frequently available for community groups to support conservation work which includes ponds. Of these, Pond Conservation currently have a scheme – the 'Million Ponds Project' – which aims to create a network of ponds across the country. In the wider countryside farmers are creating ponds as part of government supported agri-environment schemes. The provision of grant aid for taking land out of production and payments for creating landscape features such as ponds is providing a vital buffer to pond loss. Of course, due to their small scale, ponds can easily be created and they have great potential for nature development plans. New ponds are rapidly colonised by a variety of organisms and well designed and located, pond complexes can be used to significantly enhance freshwater biodiversity within the Cheshire landscape. But it is not only wildlife gardeners, conservation organisations and the farming community that are creating new ponds. The emergence of ponds as useful ecosystem service providers is gaining much credibility. The Environment Agency value pond creation as an important part of flood defence, retaining water during periods of high rainfall; the Highways Agency use ponds to accommodate water run-off from new road schemes; urban planners see sustainable urban drainage systems ('SUDS') as a cheaper, more environmentally friendly way of dealing with unwanted water. These small reservoirs (ponds) not only provide an ideal water storage area, but can also be an integral part of the landscaping which now accompanies new housing and industrial developments. In all these cases, the water bodies that are created are often ideal for aquatic plants and animals and go some way to replace ponds lost in the wider countryside.

Conclusion

There is growing awareness in Europe of the importance of ponds, and an increasing understanding of the contribution they make to aquatic biodiversity and catchment functions. Ponds have been shown to contain a greater proportion of the regional biodiversity than other types of wetlands including lakes, ditches, rivers and streams and this pattern holds for agricultural landscapes across Europe. As well as having a greater diversity of flora and fauna, ponds also contain a greater proportion of rarer species and a greater proportion of unique species than other freshwater bodies. Furthermore, their function as stepping stones through a landscape is vital in times of rapid climate change. At a European level, ponds and pond landscapes are being promoted by organisations such as the European Pond Conservation Network. Influencing key decision makers at government and supra-government level is a key task of this organisation. In the UK, the pressure upon key stakeholders is the responsibility of Pond Conservation and, in the light of their advocacy, it is important that the conservation of the Cheshire pond

Figure 7.36. The ponds in Cheshire's eastern hills are usually quite acidic and hold the majority of the county's Palmate Newts. © Andy Harmer

landscape provides evidence of the value of these small water bodies. We have, therefore, a responsibility to raise awareness of the value of individual ponds and also the important function of the pond landscape in its totality. Key stakeholders in the region need to be informed about the fragility of this wetland landscape and every effort has to be taken by organisations such as Cheshire Wildlife Trust to disseminate this information as widely as possible. There is a need to embark on a rolling programme of pond creation in order to replace those ponds which are disappearing through natural processes. If this effort can be sustained then these pearls in the Cheshire landscape will remain a permanent jewel for future generations to enjoy.

Acknowledgments

Thanks to Jim Hollinshead of Liverpool John Moores University for the map (Fig. 7.11) and to Chris Hassall at Carleton University, Ottawa, Canada for analysing data collected by the Critical Pond Biodiversity Survey (1995–1998) and the re-survey of 50 ponds in 2006. Copies of the publications analysing both the original and resurvey of ponds in Cheshire (Hassall *et al.* 2011, 2012) can be obtained from the author. Much thanks must also go to Jonathan Guest who surveyed the vast majority of these ponds during the two survey periods. Tim Green supplied the marl pit diagram (Fig. 7.6) for which I am grateful.

References and Further Reading

Amphibian and Reptile Conservation www.arc-trust.org/

Boothby, J. (ed.) (1997) *British Pond Landscapes: Action for Protection and Enhancement*, Proceedings of the UK Conference of the Pond *Life* Project, 178pp, LJMU, Liverpool.

Boothby, J. (ed.) (1999) *Ponds and Pond Landscapes of Europe*, Proceedings of the International Conference of the Pond *Life* Project, 253pp, LJMU, Liverpool.

EPCN (2008). *The Pond Manifesto*, European Pond Conservation Network, Geneva (accessed from http://campus.hesge.ch/epcn/pdf_files/manifesto/EPCN-manifesto_english.pdf)

European Pond Conservation Network http://campus.hesge.ch/epcn/

Gabb, R. & Kitching, D. (1992) The Dragonflies and Damselflies of Cheshire. National Museums and Galleries on Merseyside, Liverpool.

Guest, J. & Harmer, A. (2006) Atlas of the Amphibians of Cheshire and the Wirral. Nepa Books, Frodsham.

Hassall, C., Hollinshead, J. and Hull, A. (2011) Environmental correlates of plant and invertebrate species richness in ponds. *Biodiversity and Conservation* 20: 3189–3222.

Hassall, C., Hollinshead, J. and Hull, A. (2012) Temporal dynamics of aquatic communities and implications for pond conservation. *Biodiversity and Conservation* 21: 829–852.

Hull, A.P. (1997) *The Pond Life Project: A Model for Conservation and Sustainability* in Boothby, J. (ed) British Pond Landscapes: Action for Protection and Enhancement, Proceedings of the UK Conference of the Pond *Life* Project, LJMU, Liverpool.

Perring, F.H. & Walters, S.M. (1982) The Atlas of the British Flora, 3rd edition. Botanical Society of the British Isles, London.

Pond Conservation: the Water Habitats Trust www.pondconservation.org.uk/millionponds/
   pondcreationtoolkit/

Rackham, O. (1994) *The Illustrated History of the Countryside*. Wiedenfeld and Nicolson,
   London.

The Million Ponds Project www.pondconservation.org.uk/millionponds

About the author

Andrew Hull is Emeritus Professor of Landscape Ecology at Liverpool John
Moores University. Having set up the Ponds Research Unit in 1990, the first
audit of Cheshire ponds was undertaken soon afterwards, demonstrating the
serious loss of ponds in the county. From 1995–1999 he was seconded from
the University to become Project Director of the EU-funded Pond *Life* Project
working in the UK, Belgium, Denmark and the Netherlands. Outputs from
this project have become a benchmark for pond conservation both in the
UK and beyond, including the need to work at a landscape scale; stakeholder
involvement and working with volunteers. More recently he has been involved
in the establishment of the European Pond Conservation Network (EPCN)
which, through the recently published *Pond Manifesto*, is seeking to influence
key decision makers of the need for greater recognition and support for the
conservation of these small but significant wetland features. He is currently the
first President of the EPCN.

Lichens in Cheshire

Mike Gosling

LICHENS ARE REMARKABLE DUAL ORGANISMS CONSISTING OF A FUNGUS WITH alga and/or cyanobacterium in a symbiotic relationship. This association results in distinctive morphology with unique reproductive structures and a wide range of lichen chemical products. Most lichens do not have consistent common names and are normally known by their binomial scientific name. The three main growth forms are crustose lichens that grow on a substrate and are firmly attached to it; foliose or leafy lichens that are flat to the substrate but can be lifted around the edges; and the fruticose lichens that hang off the substrate and can be easily detached. All three forms are well represented in Cheshire. On walls throughout the county the crustose *Porpidia tuberculosa* can be found. On walls and roofs the orange foliose genus *Xanthoria* is very common and the foliose *Parmelias* are common on the gritstones in the east of the county. The shrubby fruticose lichens are more sensitive to atmospheric pollution and are more restricted but in humid Willow carr such as at Hatch Mere, Budworth Mere and Oak Mere *Evernia prunastri* (Fig. 8.1) and *Ramalina farinacea* (Fig. 8.2) a few centimetres long hang off the trees.

Lichens are very adaptable and survive in a wide range of natural substrates from trees, rocks, soil, to unusual materials such as cast iron, glass, bricks, rubber, rope, rabbit droppings and old Wellington bombers. There are few habitats that they have failed to colonise and are found from the inter-tidal zone via the lowlands to mountain tops including places which are hostile to many life forms with extremes of temperature, rainfall, humidity and desiccation.

Lichens are very sensitive to atmospheric pollution and have been widely used as pollution monitors. The fortunes of lichens have varied greatly over the last 400 years. In Cheshire and other counties in NorthWest England the Industrial Revolution saw a catastrophic decline in their lichen flora that persisted well into the twentieth century. Now with the Clean Air Acts of the 1950s and '60s and the Control of Pollution Act of 1974 there have been significant declines in atmospheric pollution, as shown by the sulphur dioxide results for Warrington, Runcorn and Widnes shown in Fig. 8.3. This, together with shifting agricultural practices and new energy and transport strategies, has resulted in the lichen flora of Cheshire showing significant changes with increasing numbers of species and greater diversity.

Figure 8.1. The delicate beauty of Evernia prunastri, *a lichen with an economic use as a perfume fixative and common on trees in Cheshire. © Mike Gosling*

Figure 8.2. Ramalina farinacea, *the least pollution-sensitive member of the genus and now widespread on trees.* © *Mike Gosling*

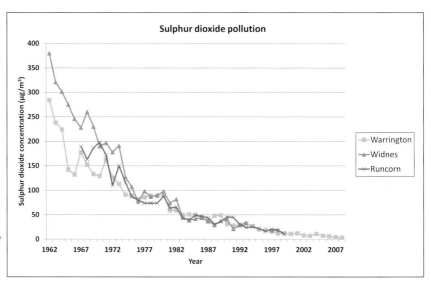

Figure 8.3. Annual mean Sulphur dioxide levels (μg/m³) in the three industrialised towns in northern Cheshire, 1962–2008.

Lichens in Cheshire have not been studied as much as they deserve, however, and more recording would be welcome. The only comprehensive lichen flora of Cheshire (Watsonian vice-county 58) is by Brian Fox and Jonathan Guest (Fox & Guest 2003). They record 291 taxa from the twentieth century with a further 10 taxa from the nineteenth century and another 21 that have become extinct in the county since 1900. This compares with 589 species in Northumberland (Gilbert 1980), 590 species in Hampshire (Brewis *et al.* 1996) and 487 taxa in Lancashire (37 not seen for a century or more) (Edmonds 2004).

The earliest vice-county records are from Turner and Dillwyn (1805). They list three *Lobaria* species and *Degelia plumbea*, characteristic of clean air and indicating SO_2 levels of under 30 µg/m^3 (Hawksworth & Rose 1970). They are also species in the Revised Index of Ecological Continuity which is used to grade ancient woodland (Coppins & Coppins 2002). Today only *Enterographa crassa* (Fig. 8.4) remains from the list of 30 species used to calculate the index – a measure of the almost total disappearance of 'ancient woodland' from Cheshire. Further sporadic records were added early in the twentieth century (Travis, 1915, 1922, 1925). Little lichen recording was the done until Brian Fox and Jonathan Guest began surveying the county in the 1970s until around 2000 with many other important records added by Oliver Gilbert, Ray Woods, Brian Coppins and other lichenologists.

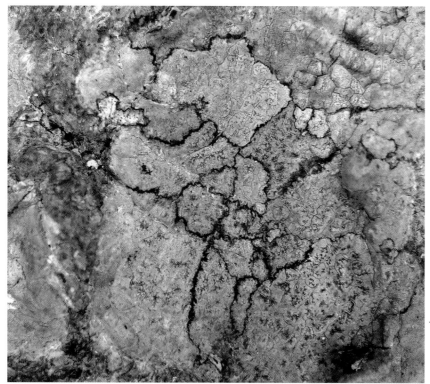

Figure 8.4. Enterographa crassa, *a woodland species used to calculate the R.I.E.C. (Revised Index of Ecological Continuity) and only known from Lower Wych Wood in the extreme south of the county. This shows a typical mosaic of thalli with small, innate fruits.* © Mike Gosling

Lichen Habitats

Woodlands

About 5% of Cheshire and Wirral nowadays is woodland. In the post glacial times 12,000 years ago much of Cheshire would have been wooded with a rich lichen flora of epiphytes (growing on the trees). Members of the *Lobarian* community – *Lobaria pulmonaria*, *L. virens* and *L. scrobiculata* – are recorded in Turner and Dillwyn (1805). Today these spectacular, foliose lichens are confined to areas of low levels of SO_2 and with ecological continuity such as NorthWest Scotland, North Wales and Devon and Cornwall. These lichens would have declined as trees were felled for fuel and timber. In Cheshire the salt, leather, glass and mining industries used wood as fuel (Smart 1992). But the industrialisation of the 18th and 19th century would have devastated the lichens with SO_2 being the main cause of decline. Since the Clean Air Acts of the 1960s there has been a decline in ground level concentrations of SO_2, and the recolonisation of many lichen habitats, particularly trees, began after a lag to allow spores and propagules to arrive perhaps on the wind or on birds. By the 1970s Fox found epiphytes returning to Cheshire but only to Willow carr around meres such as Hatch Mere and Rostherne Mere NNR (Gilbert 2000). In recent years there have been further changes particularly to epiphytic lichen flora. The once ubiquitous pollution-resistant lichen *Lecanora conizaeoides* which covered trees and sandstone has declined rapidly and is now difficult to find on trees and much rarer on the Millstone Grit in eastern Cheshire. Today an important change has been the rapid increase in species favouring eutrophication from farm spraying and pollutants from traffic with nitrogen-loving orange *Xanthoria* spp. and grey *Physcia* spp. now a common sight on roadside trees in rural and urban locations.

Today the ephiphytic flora reflects the age and structure of woodland, the degree of ecological continuity, microclimate, the effects of atmospheric pollution and changes in land-use.

Old Woodland

The Wych Valley in the southwest of Cheshire (Fig. 8.5) is a principal refuge for corticolous lichens (Fox & Guest 2003). Here in sheltered valleys, relatively remote from pollution, species such as *Arthonia spadicea*, *A. radiata*, *Enterographa crassa*, *Opegrapha vermicellifera*, *O. vulgata* and *Graphis scripta* can be found. It was here that in 1983, on an Ash tree, Brian Fox discovered *Fellhanera ochracea*, a species new to science although it was not so described until 17 years later (Sparrius & Aptroot 2000).

In areas of old woodland on the Cheshire Ridge the trees face the pollution from chemical works to the north and west. Despite some older trees and their semi-ancient status their epiphytic flora is poor. Many are devoid of any lichens and bear only a few bryophytes. However on the edges of woods and along roads in the Cheshire Plain the nitrogen-loving species are easily seen. Yellow

Figure 8.5. The steep-sided and sheltered Wych Valley in the southwest of Cheshire is probably the only site where some epiphytic lichens survived the industrial pollution. © Mike Gosling

Xanthoria parietina (Fig. 8.7) and cushions of *X. polycarpa* are common. The grey *Physcias* may form continuous sheets up the trunk and along branches and twigs. The common species is *Physcia tenella*, together with the greener *Phaeophyscia orbicularis* and the often fertile *Physcia aipolia*. On smooth bark occur the thin pale crusts and black fruits of *Lecanora eleochroma* elongating its thallus (body) with bark growth and the brown fruited *Lecanora chlarotera*.

The remains of the medieval woods such as Delamere Forest appear to have lost much of their lichen flora. These woods would have had a rich flora typical of the *Lobarian* alliance associated with climax woodland and with trees festooned with large foliose and fruticose species. In the 12th and 13th century the *Lobaria* spp. documented by Turner and Dillwyn (1805) would have grown alongside *Usnea* spp., *Leptogium* spp., *Degelia* spp., rarer *Parmelia* spp., *Sticta* spp. and *Nephroma* spp. This would have been a spectacular site now never seen in northern England. The pollution sensitive *Usnea articulata*, now confined to SouthWest England, Wales and the Isle of Man was last seen in Lancashire in about 1724 on trees near Burnley (Leighton 1872). This gives a brief glimpse as to the possible former richness of Cheshire's epiphytic lichen flora.

In the east of Cheshire on the fringes of the Pennines are incised valleys cut into Carboniferous gritstones and shales. Here lichens have managed to survive and the valleys retain some of their former lichen flora. The species found are typical of the western slopes of the Pennines from Yorkshire through Lancashire into Derbyshire. The lichens are acid-loving species, the grey-green *Parmelia sulcata* and *P. saxatilis*, the latter once used as a magical drug and worth its weight in gold, but only if collected from the skull of an executed criminal! Other common species are *Hypogymnia physodes* and *H. tubulosa* and the green/brown crisped thallus of *Plaismatisa glauca*. Around tree boles are *Cladonia coniocraea*, *C. macilenta* and *C. polydactyla*.

Roadside and Urban Trees

These often carry the species favouring higher levels of nitrogen from fertilisers and car exhausts mainly *Xanthoria* spp., *Physcia* spp. and *Ramalina farinacea*, the most pollution tolerant species in the genus. They are a common sight well into urban locations such as Chester, Northwich and Winsford. The trees also have more acidophilous lichens such as the grey-green foliose *Parmelia saxatilis* and *P. sulcata* often on boughs to a height of a few metres. Of more interest is the appearance of more pollution sensitive genera related to the *Parmelias*, *Flavoparmelia caperata*, a distinctive pale green lichen, the grey crisped thallus of *Parmotrema perlatum*, the shiny grey thalli of *Hypotrachyna revoluta* and *Punctelia*

Figure 8.6. Nutrient-enriched trees in town centres are now becoming an important lichen habitat with a good covering of species such as can be seen here in Winsford. © Mike Gosling

Figure 8.7. Xanthoria parietina and Physcia *spp. on nutrient-enriched trees at Knutsford Common. © Mike Gosling*

subrudecta. Some of these more pollution-sensitive genera have now become widespread. *Flavoparmelia caperata* occurs throughout Cheshire even in unlikely places such as Ellesmere Port; *Parmotrema perlatum*, recorded as occurring in sheltered sites such as Willow carr by Fox & Guest (2003), can now be found in more exposed sites in for example Northwich and Knutsford Heath. On the trees at Marbury Wood, part of the Northwich Woodlands and 3 kilometres from the centre of Northwich, all these *Parmelia* and related species can be found together with a brown relative, *Melanelixia glabratula*. On a few trees the shrubby species *Evernia prunastri*, still used by the perfume industry as a fixative, and the similar looking *Ramalina farinacea* are beginning to thrive. These woods are immature and secondary and include a planted avenue of Limes but perhaps indicate how in the future such wooded areas will become important sites for lichen epiphytes as pollution levels change and as the lichens reinvade from areas such as the Peak District and North Wales.

The response of lichens to levels of nitrogen in the air has recently been investigated by the OPAL survey (OPAL 2011). This survey has shown the common occurrence of nitrogen-loving lichens with numerous records on tree trunks and twigs in areas such as Birkenhead, Ellesmere Port, Northwich and Chester (OPAL 2011). This trend is no doubt now widespread throughout the county. The ammonia map for 2005 shows a particular hotspot around Cheshire with average NH_3 concentrations of 6 μg/m³, one of the highest concentrations in the country and reflecting the agricultural use of fertilisers. This together with increases in NO_x (NO and NO_2) from car exhausts have a major impact on the epiphytic lichens in Cheshire and the county reflects countrywide trends with many areas seeing an increase in nitrogen-loving species. On a score of +54 (air very clean) to -54 (very polluted air) the Cheshire records from OPAL give the county a score of -22 to 0, equivalent to air quality 'not good with nitrogen-loving lichens present but not abundant' (OPAL 2011).

Willow Carr

These are well known to lichenologists as good sites to record lichen reinvasion in response to lower levels of atmospheric pollution. They occur around the meres and in valleys where greater humidity, bark chemistry and the decumbent habit of Willows encourages colonisation. The first modern record of *Usnea subflor-idana* was made in 1977 at Rostherne Mere. By 1983 this lichen had become widespread in the county (Fox & Guest 2003).

The coincidence maps of six invasive epiphytic species in Willow carr in 1992 and again in 2002 show the significant spread throughout the county (Fox & Guest 2003). The early colonisation was of acidophilous species such as *Hypogymnia* spp., *Parmelia saxatilis* and *Platismatia glauca*. These are still there today but have since declined and been replaced with *Hypotrachyna revoluta*, *Parmotrema perlatum* (Fig. 8.8) and *Punctelia subrudecta*, three species that were not recorded anywhere in the county by Fox and Guest (2003). Similar recolonisation of Willow and Oak has also been noted in the adjacent vice-county (South Lancashire V.C. 59) at Longworth Clough near Bolton (Gosling 1993).

Fence Posts

Fence posts and railings made of timber with the bark removed develop a distinctive if limited flora. This lichen assemblage is found in Cheshire and throughout the country. In more rural areas where the posts have been allowed to rot they have crusts of lichens which blend in with the weathered post and need a lens to locate them. The blue-green granular *Trapeliopsis flexuosa* and *Placyhnthiella icmalea* with its chocolate brown coralloid granules occur on older posts and *Lecanora symmicta* and *Lecanora saligna* occur on less rotted wood. A minute but distinctive species on fence tops and wooden rails is *Micarea denigrata*: a search with the lens will reveal tiny extruded white pycnidia – the flask-shaped bodies containing conidia (asexual fungal spores) – typical of this species. This is a habitat often seen as unimportant but some lichens favour such places and in replacing old posts and rails if a few of the old ones can be incorporated into modern fencing this may allow the lichens to perhaps recolonise and flourish at that site.

Rock Outcrops

Cheshire is covered in superficial deposits of glacial till and sands. The bed rock where it does occur forms an important lichen habitat. The Triassic sandstones of the Cheshire Ridge and Carboniferous sandstones and shales in the east are acidic rocks with a flora typical of these substrates.

The Triassic rocks are poorly cemented deposits and rather friable and do not make a suitable substrate for lichen colonisation. The outcrops may bear only *Lepraria incana* in shaded niches though harder beds may carry *Cladonia* spp., yellow *Candelariella vitellina* and smaller white crustose species. Where these sandstones have been used to build church walls the flora may be rather more diverse and luxuriant.

The Carboniferous sandstone outcrops, screes and drystone walls in the east of Cheshire are a very different substrate. They are mainly made of quartz, like the Triassic, but are well cemented and durable and thus a suitable substrate for acidophile, saxicolous species. The steep road east from Macclesfield shows the rapid transition from Triassic to Carboniferous rocks. The walls soon become ones made of gritstone with *Parmelia saxatilis* (Fig. 8.10) forming a discontinuous but at times luxuriant covering on wall tops. This is further enhanced where nutrients drop from overhanging trees. Further into the foothills around Lamaload the walls carry a good variety of species. The grey crusts of *Porpidia tuberculosa*, the pale yellow green *Lecanora polytropa* and domed, black fruits of *Porpidia macrocarpa* are frequent. Also common are *Rhizocarpon reductum, Lecidea*

Figure 8.8. Parmotrema perlatum *on tree at Marbury, a species on the increase as air quality improves within the county.* © Mike Gosling

Figure 8.9. Punctelia subrudecta *on Willow carr at Hatch Mere. Such sites with their humidity and inclined Willows are an important lichen habitat within the county.* © Mike Gosling

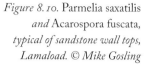

Figure 8.10. Parmelia saxatilis *and* Acarospora fuscata, *typical of sandstone wall tops, Lamaload. © Mike Gosling*

sulphurea and *Acarospora fuscata* looking like brown cracked mud. The walls have rarer species such as the bright yellow-green *Rhizocarpon geographicum* and *Lecanora epanora*, a lichen normally found on metal-rich rocks near old mines.

Where natural outcrops of sandstone and scree occur there are a wide range of micro-habitats for lichen colonisation. Here *Lecanora polytropa*, *Lecanora soralifera*, *Parmelia omphalodes*, *Parmelia saxatilis*, *Pertusaria corallina*, and *Porpidia tuberculosa* are common. On flat sandstone surfaces occur the neat rosettes *of Arctoparmelia incurva* and rarely *Fuscidea cyathoides* and *Ophioparma ventosa* with its blood red fruits. Between boulders the spiky *Cladonia portentosa* and *C. subcervicornis* occur and in deep shade the fine, black wires of *Cystocoleus ebeneus* can be found.

Calcareous Substrates

Cheshire has no significant limestone outcrops. Some limestones have been imported for ornamental purposes, for example the only county record for the very common calcicole species *Verrucaria baldensis* is in a rockery (Fox & Guest 2003). No doubt other such records exist! However lichens are adaptable organisms and a good substitute for limestone is mortar and concrete.

On concrete posts, rooftops in towns and villages the assemblage consisting of the fine yellow crusts of *Caloplaca citrina*, the orange fruited *Caloplaca holocarpa* and the minutely lobed *Caloplaca saxicola*, together with *Lecanora dispersa*, *Physcia* spp., *Rinodina gennarii* and *Xanthoria parietina* is ubiquitous. On mortared walls the small brown fruits with a frosted surface are *Sarcogyne regularis*, a calcicole rare on natural limestone and the finely cracked brown thallus is *Verrucaria nigrescens*.

Of special interest in Cheshire are the industrial lime beds such as at

Plumley and near Frodsham. These introduce a highly calcareous element into a county devoid of such habitats. The Plumley SSSI occupies 23 hectares, about 8% of the total UK area of 300 hectares of lime beds. The site is covered in immature woodland but calcicoles on lime waste and concrete include *Bacidea sabuletorum*, *Collema auriforme*, *Cladonia pocillum*, *Leptogium schraderi* and *Protoblastenia rupestris*. Further fieldwork in these habitats should reveal further species uncommon in the county. The trees here, whilst appearing to be of little interest, were examined by the author in 2011 and carry *Lecania naegelii*, the first county record, and *Caloplaca cerinella*, the second county record. Such finds remind us that lichens can live in unlikely places and such sites should not be neglected. Oliver Gilbert recounts the first time he saw anyone systematically recording from a tree looking at the roots, the bole, the trunk and peering into every crevice to make sure nothing was missed. The lichenologist was Brian Coppins, a lesson to us all that habitats may reveal many small species thought to 'not occur in our area' (Gilbert 2000).

Churches and Churchyards

These have been a favourite with lichenologists for many years. In areas with no natural outcrops they hold out the promise of finding saxicolous species on the walls, the gravestones and the church itself. An idea of their importance is seen in Northamptonshire where the occurrence of all but 10 of the 217 saxicolous species has been recorded in churchyards (Gilbert 2000). Whilst some churches have over 130 taxa, a total of 30–40 is more common (Gilbert 2000).

The churches in the north of Cheshire such as St Laurence Parish Church, Frodsham show the effects of pollution. The sandstones of the church are devoid of lichens and are blackened with soot. In the graveyard despite the stones being from the 18th century they have few lichens with many covered in green algae. On some horizontal slabs white crustose thalli of *Haematomma ochroleucum* occur with yellow *Candelariella vitellina* (Fig. 8.11) and *Lecidella scabra*. On smoother stones *Buellia aethalea*, *Lecanora polytropa* and *L. stigmatea* grow. There are no foliose species, their larger area of exposed thallus making them more exposed to pollution.

To the south and more distant from the pollution to the north and east the number of species and their diversity increases. At Little Budworth Church as well as a greater range of crustose species the foliose species *Melanelixia glabratula* occurs growing to a diameter of 10 cm.

Because lichens' requirements for light, moisture, shade are often critical a church such as many of those in Cheshire is an instructive place to study lichens. The orientation E-W gives four aspects with contrasting characteristics. The shaded north and east side may carry few lichens or only those tolerating shade but the well-lit south side may bear several species. At Little Budworth there is a spectacular demarcation of species from *Lecanora muralis* below the

Figure 8.11. Lichen colonisation showing the importance of microhabitats. The sandstone walls of the church at Little Budworth with vertical faces devoid of lichens but the inclined surfaces with crustose lichens such as the yellow Candelariella vitellina. *© Mike Gosling*

window, to *Candelariella vitellina* and *Tephromela atra* on curved and sloping surfaces to no lichens at all on vertical surfaces where the sun dries the surface and water retention is poor. Churches are excellent places to start the study of lichens and are where many of us first try to get to grips with this fascinating group. They are not too daunting in terms of species, there are lots of different niches and they often show the habitat preferences of lichens very clearly. There are excellent identification aids available such as the field key written by Frank Dobson (Dobson 2003).

Old Buildings and Stone Structures

The sandstones of the Pennine foothills and rocks imported from outside the county have been used as worked stone to build walls, roofs, old farm buildings, canals, railways and churches. This brings upland rocks into the lowlands and thus allows lichens normally found in the uplands to grow in the lowlands. Of note is the occurrence of *Xanthoparmelia conspersa*, a conspicuous, large upland species of acid rocks not found in the east of the county on natural outcrops but occurring in churchyards and on the roof of Nether Alderley Mill and at Stretton Mill (Fox & Guest 2003). The Stretton Mill (near Carden) is the only known county site for other rarities (Fox & Guest 2003): *Collema bachmanianum*, a nationally rare species with no other records in NorthWest England; *Xanthoparmelia mougeotii*, which has a curious distribution, widespread in Britain but with a wide gap in northern England; and *Physcia tribacia* which is common in southern England but decreases northwards with few records in northern England (National Biodiversity Network 2011). Such important records emphasise the possibilities of other upland species being found on old buildings in the lowlands. Species may be rare and occur at only a single location so that all likely sites are worth surveying.

Maritime Habitats

The rocks around our shores carry a number of distinctive communities. Some are able to withstand immersion in seawater while others tolerate inundation and salt spray above the high water mark. This has led to the three coloured zones on coastal rocks, the black zone dominated by species of *Verrucaria*, the orange zone above this where *Xanthoria* spp. and *Caloplaca* spp. are common, to the white zone furthest from the sea where species such as *Ochrolecechia parella*, *Lecanora* spp. and *Ramalina siliquosa* thrive.

The coastal Triassic sandstones on Hilbre and at Red Rocks are the only places where these maritime species can be seen. As in inland locations this rock is not a durable substrate and is prone to marine erosion and weathering. On Hilbre only *Verrucaria maura* occurs. It forms 'tarspots' on rocks but other related species could occur and the rocks need to be examined carefully since some can occur as patches amongst other *Verrucaria* spp. and in crevices and sheltered niches. A yellow/orange zone species found on Hilbre is *Caloplaca marina* consisting of yellow-orange granules with orange fruits. The grey zone species are represented by very rare *Ramalina siliquosa*, a lichen common round our coasts on hard rock where it can become established and reach 10 cm in length. In Lancashire it does not occur on the similar Triassic sandstone at Cockersands Abbey but on the Carboniferous sandstones at Heysham only 12 km to the north where is it is frequent and well established. Fox and Guest (2003) also record less common species, *Lecania aipospila*, *Lecanora helicopis*, *Lecidella asema* and *Collemopsidium halodytes*. The latter is a strange lichen normally appearing as minute black dots on barnacles, recorded all round Britain. The Cheshire record from 1917 is unusually from a clay bank (Fox & Guest 2003). *Lecidella asema* is a rare lichen in NorthWest England with only three coastal records from Anglesey to the Solway Firth. *Lecania aipospila* is an even rarer species with records all around the coast but only four in NorthWest England (National Biodiversity Network 2011). These data emphasise the importance of the few rocky shorelines from the Dee to Solway Firth and their occurrence helps to fill in the disjunct distribution from North Wales/Anglesey to southern Scotland.

Moorlands

In the east of the county the moorlands developed on the Carboniferous sandstones. Like many upland areas in Lancashire, Yorkshire and Derbyshire these habitats would have been open to atmospheric pollution which has led to a depauperate lichen flora. There are some common species of acid moorland, *Cladonia coccifera*, *C. furcata*, *C. macilenta*, *C. polydactyla* and *C. uncialis subsp. biuncialis* (Fox & Guest 2003). With time these moorland habitats should improve. In Lancashire these species occur together with *Coelocaulon* spp., *Cetraria islandica* and other typical moorland species.

Aquatic Habitats

These are challenging habitats for lichens since they must find firm substrates to colonise and cope with varying flow régimes including complete inundation to exposure and desiccation in periods of drought. The species in rivers within the Cheshire Plain have never been studied and are likely to be poorly developed due to lack of suitable stable habitats and water quality. But in the east where waters drain off the moors and water quality is not subject to agricultural run-off there may be interesting species waiting to be discovered. *Hymenelia lacustris* with its pale cream to orange thallus and deep orange fruits can be seen here and further field work should reveal aquatic *Verrucaria* spp. on sandstone boulders and outcrops.

Conservation and the Future

Lichens are remarkable organisms able to colonise a wide range of substrates ranging from trees, rocks and soil to more obscure ones such as rusting ironwork, rubber, thatch, old tractors, leather, rabbit droppings, antlers, glass and the shells of the Galapagos tortoise. Such adaptability means that diligent searching in the county will reveal further species. As habitats are destroyed and created, species may be lost and gained. A number of species in Cheshire occur at only a few sites or indeed at a single site. Such lichens are vulnerable to habitat destruction and the custodians of critical sites need to be aware of these species and include lichens in their management plans. In counties like Cheshire with such a small amount of woodland the trees in urban areas in parks and along roadsides may be critical to the future of some corticolous species. Knowledge and sympathetic management of such trees is needed and may cost little to implement.

As air quality changes lichens will respond: the dramatic changes in the flora on trees in response to the declines in SO_2 and increase in nitrogen compounds has already been commented on. Many areas have still not been explored or have been inadequately investigated. Lichens can be small and elusive so that much waits to be discovered in the county.

References

Brewis, A., Bowman, P. & Rose, F. (1996). The Flora of Hampshire. Harley Books, Colchester.

Coppins, A.M. & Coppins, B.J. (2002). Indices of Ecological Continuity for Woodland Epiphytic Lichen Habitats in the British Isles. British Lichen Society, London.

Dobson, F. S. (2003). A Field Key to Common Churchyard Lichens. Frank Dobson, New Malden.

Edmonds. M. (ed) (2004). Wildlife of Lancashire. Carnegie Publishing, Lancaster.

Fox, B. & Guest, J. (2003). The Lichen Flora of Cheshire and Wirral. Nepa Books, Frodsham.

Gilbert, O. L. (1980). A Lichen Flora of Northumberland. *Lichenologist* 12: 325–395.

Gilbert, O. L. (2000). Lichens. Collins, London.

Gosling, M.M. (1993). *Lancashire Wildlife Journal* 2 & 3: 1–6.

Hawksworth, D.L. & Rose F. (1970). Qualitative scale for estimating sulphur dioxide air pollution in England and Wales using epiphytic lichens. *Nature* 227: 145–8.

Leighton, W. A. (1872). The Lichen Flora of Great Britain, Ireland and the Channel Islands. Leighton, Shrewsbury.

Smart, R. (1992). Trees and Woodlands of Cheshire. Cheshire Landscape Trust, Chester.

Smith, C.W., Aptroot, A., Coppins, B.J., Gilbert, O.L., James, P.W., & Wolesley, P.A. (eds) (2009). The Lichens of Great Britain and Ireland. British Lichen Society, London.

Sparrius, L. & Aptroot, A. (2000). *Fellhanera ochracea* a new corticolous lichen species from sheltered localities in western Europe. *Lichenologist* 32: 515–520.

Travis, W.G. (1915). Cheshire Lichens. *Journ. Bot. Lond.* 53: 219.

Travis, W.G. (1922). The Lichens of the Wirral. *Lancashire and Cheshire Naturalist* 14: 177–190.

Travis, W.G. (1925). Additions to the Lichen Flora of the Wirral. *Lancashire and Cheshire Naturalist* 12: 152–154.

Turner, D. & Dillwyn, L.W. (1805). The Botanist's Guide through England and Wales. 2 Vols. Phillips & Fardon, London.

Websites

National Biodiversity Network. www.nbn.org.uk

Natural England. www.sssi.naturalengland.org.uk/citation/citation_photo/1001690.pdf

OPAL. www.opalexplorenature.org/AirSurveyAnalysis

About the author

Mike Gosling was a lecturer in Geology at Further Education Colleges in Lancashire and at the University of Central Lancashire; now retired and spends his time leading field courses, giving lectures in Geology and doing workshops and consultancy. He has been studying and recording the lichens in Lancashire for 30 years and in recent times has started looking at the bryophytes in the county together with the lichens in Cheshire and Yorkshire. His current interest is focused on the lichens of urban parks following the reduction of atmospheric pollution in towns.

Dragonflies and Damselflies

David Kitching

CHESHIRE IS A COUNTY OF GREAT CONTRASTS AS IT RUNS FROM THE COAST along the Wirral, across the plain and into the uplands of the western Pennines. This means that a very wide range of habitats is available for odonata (dragonflies and damselflies), ranging from slow rivers to fast running streams, lakes and meres, to mosses and bogs, and of course the enormous number of ponds and marl pits that characterise much of lowland Cheshire.

Odonata recording in Cheshire

In an age of easy communication and dissemination of information we know so much more about the odonata of Cheshire than we did back in 1960 when the New Naturalist volume 'Dragonflies' was published (Corbet *et al.* 1960). At that time there were twenty species known to have resident breeding populations in the county and there were perhaps two or three people regularly recording them. In fact, until the mid-1970s, much of the information was collected by the Lancashire County Recorder. The level of knowledge was significantly increased once Ian Rutherford agreed to become Cheshire County Recorder in addition to his existing role for lepidoptera. Ian ran a 10-km square-based recording scheme from then until 1984 when he handed over responsibility for odonata recording to Richard Gabb.

In 1985 the county was also very much at, or just beyond, the northern range of a number of species such as the Emperor Dragonfly *Anax imperator* and the Ruddy Darter *Sympetrum sanguineum*. Occasional sightings had been made of vagrant examples of these southerly based species, but there was no evidence of breeding.

Richard Gabb began the tetrad (2 kilometre square) based odonata recording scheme immediately after becoming County Recorder as he felt that this would give a clearer picture of distribution, especially if combined with the recording of breeding behaviour. This would point to the places that were essential to the survival of such mobile species. The scheme covered all of Cheshire as left in

Figure 9.1. A mating pair of the Hairy Dragonfly Brachytron pratense, *now fairly common on Cheshire marl pits.* © *David Kitching*

Figure 9.2. The Emperor dragonfly Anax imperator *(female) is now established across the whole county from the Wirral coast to the eastern hills.*
© *David Kitching*

1974, plus the Wirral and the 'new' parts of the county north of the Mersey in Halton and Warrington. The areas of old Cheshire in Stockport, Trafford, and Tameside were excluded.

The new scheme saw 628 records submitted by 31 individuals in the first year and this led to an annual report being produced to summarise the findings and encourage recording in new areas. By the end of 1992 there were already well over 5000 records from nearly 100 individuals for the period beginning with the 1980 season. This had been boosted from 1987 by considerable effort being made to survey the areas that had fewest records, mainly in the south and west of Cheshire away from the main centres of population. English Nature helped with funding towards the cost of travel.

It was in 1992 that the National Museums & Galleries on Merseyside published the results in the book *The Dragonflies & Damselflies of Cheshire* written by Richard Gabb and David Kitching. I had joined the survey programme in 1984/5 and taken on the computerisation of the records and introduced electronic plotting of the data. This provided a history of recording in Cheshire and a snapshot of the status of the different species of odonata in the county. 25 species had been definitely recorded up to 1992, although only 23 of these had been seen since 1980, including a single record of the Keeled Skimmer *Orthetrum coerulescens* at Risley Moss. The two species not seen since 1980 were the vagrant Yellow-winged Darter *Sympetrum flaveolum* and Red-veined Darter *Sympetrum fonscolombii*.

New species during the 1980s

It had become clear during the initial survey period that changes in the distribution of odonata nationwide were being reflected in the Cheshire fauna. New species were moving into Cheshire and scarce species were becoming more widely established. Indeed, it was seeing one of these, the Broad-bodied Chaser *Libellula depressa*, on the Middlewood Way at Bollington in 1984 that fired my interest in the odonata. This species was at the northern limits of its range with just the odd specimen being seen, mainly on the Wirral. With a preference for new water-bodies with plenty of bare and muddy margins it could appear and breed successfully for a year or two and then vanish as the site matured and more vegetation developed. The large breeding numbers at Bollington declined to nothing over 5 or 6 years but by then it was beginning to spread across Cheshire and by 1990 there was a possibility of spotting it almost anywhere.

The Hairy Dragonfly *Brachytron pratense* was only known from three sightings, one each at Hatch Mere (1943), Newchurch Common (1945) and Oulton Park (1961). Nationally it was considered to be in decline due to drainage

Figure 9.3. Broad-bodied Chaser Libellula depressa *male. © David Kitching*

of lowland ponds and drainage ditches and efforts were made to relocate it in Cheshire in the early 1980s. This search was successful in June 1985 when the first sighting of a Cheshire Hairy Dragonfly for 25 years was made at Hatch Mere and the following year another specimen was spotted at Gull Pool. It is an early season flyer, being seen from May to July and it is possible that it had been overlooked previously, but in the following years breeding colonies were discovered on the River Weaver at Vale Royal and Billinge Green Flashes near Davenham. Since then the Hairy Dragonfly has staged a recovery in numbers and has also expanded its range across Britain and Ireland. It is now fairly common on marl pits in central Cheshire and in the west.

The rivers Severn and Dee are only 13 miles or so apart at their closest and the Common Clubtail *Gomphus vulgatissimus* was known from the former,

Figure 9.4. Broad-bodied Chaser Libellula depressa *(female), a species that moved into Cheshire in the 1980s. © David Kitching*

Figure 9.5. The Common Clubtail Gomphus vulgatissimus *(female) is a speciality of the River Dee. © David Kitching*

so efforts were made to find whether the species might be in Cheshire. There were no historic sightings of this insect and yet the search was successful and in June 1985 an exuvia (the shed larval skin) was found on the Dee at Churton: the excitement of this discovery is described by Richard Gabb in *Cheshire's Favourite Wildlife* (Norman 2012). Next year an adult was found and since then the stretch between Farndon and Aldford has become a popular place to search for freshly emerged adults around the end of May. This is the most northerly population of this insect in Britain and it seems to be expanding. Insects have even been found in the centre of Chester in 2011. Mature adults are notoriously difficult to find and most people look for immature specimens, which are easy to watch and photograph along the banks in the last two weeks in May.

The Emperor Dragonfly *Anax imperator* is Britain's largest dragonfly and in the 1970s it was generally found only south of a line from mid-Wales to the Wash, although a breeding population was well established on the Lancashire coast at Ainsdale by the 1980s. The only historic record for Cheshire had been made by Cynthia Longfield at Oak Mere in 1955, but uncorroborated sightings in 1983 and 1986 led to hopes that this species might be moving northwards. Finally, in June 1989 a male was spotted on a cluster of marl pits in Handforth. Whilst I was watching this individual patrolling across the pond it suddenly flew straight up into the sky and kept going up until it was almost out of sight. When it returned it was followed by a second male that immediately began patrolling

another part of the pond, having occasional clashes with the original male when
their paths crossed. I can only assume that the first male had spotted it flying over
and flown up to investigate. 1990 saw adults appearing at a number of locations
in central Cheshire, including an ovipositing (egg-laying) pair at High Legh.
Breeding was proven in 1993 when a number of exuviae were collected from the
pond at Lower Moss Wood nature reserve in Ollerton. It has now become established across the whole county from the shoreline on the Wirral to the moorland
above Macclesfield and can be seen flying from late May to early September. It
has continued to expand its range to the north and west, being found in Scotland
and recently in Ireland.

New species since 1992

In 1992 Richard Gabb and I speculated as to which species might be next to
appear in Cheshire and to a large extent the predictions made then have come
true. Three species have moved in and are now known to be breeding.

   The first was the Migrant Hawker *Aeshna mixta*, a late season species that in
the 1970s had a southern and eastern distribution in England. It had become well
established as a breeding species in the earlier years of the century, having once
been thought to be just a frequent immigrant. It arrived in the Midlands in the
1980s and early '90s and, sure enough, the first Cheshire sightings came at Sound
Common close to the southern border with Shropshire and Staffordshire. Within
a week further insects were found on the Weaver at Vale Royal and Winsford.

Figure 9.6. The Migrant Hawker Aeshna mixta *(male) had not even been recorded here for the 1992 county Atlas but is now the commonest hawker dragonfly in many places, and is prone to visit gardens. © Andy Harmer*

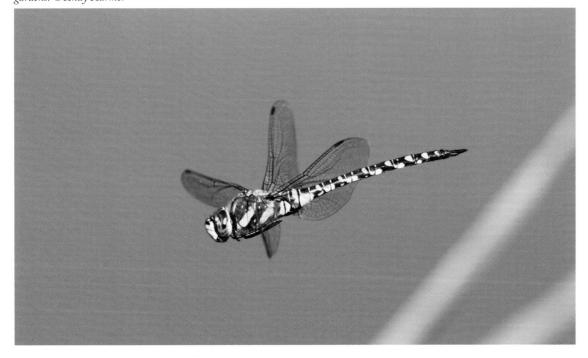

The next few years saw the Migrant Hawker spread across the whole of lowland Cheshire from Burton on the Wirral to Poynton Pool in the east, becoming the commonest hawker dragonfly in many places. The Migrant Hawker is not as territorially aggressive as most dragonflies and this means that the numbers of individual insects that can be observed on a particular waterbody can be as many as twenty. They are also prone to roosting for periods close together in trees and bushes if the weather turns cooler during the day. I have seen gorse bushes at Newchurch Common with six or seven adults hanging with a few feet of each other. The population of this species seems to have reduced since 2007, but this may be due to poor weather in recent years when the adults were emerging in August.

Next to arrive was the Black-tailed Skimmer *Orthetrum cancellatum*, a species that had never been recorded in Cheshire. This fast flying insect has, like the Broad-bodied Chaser, a preference for waters where there are margins of sand or mud on which the males often land. In the 1970s it was found in the southeast of England in increasing numbers. It was not until 1996 that the first confirmed Cheshire record was made when a rather bedraggled male was found on the bog at Risley Moss. The next year it became clear that this had not been a wandering vagrant when more adults were found on the Wirral and at Tatton Park. Breeding was confirmed in 1998 at Meols with a steady spread thereafter across the county. This was less rapid than that of the Emperor Dragonfly and it was not until 2009 that it reached Poynton in the east. The year 2011 saw a pair at Danes Moss SSSI with ovipositing taking place. The shallow waters at Plumley Limebeds seem to be particularly suited to the Black-tailed Skimmer and large numbers breed there every year.

It was speculated that if the Common Clubtail could make the jump from the Severn to the Dee then perhaps the White-legged Damselfly *Platycnemis pennipes*, which is a common insect on the Severn, could also find its way

Figure 9.8. A female of the dainty White-legged Damselfly Platycnemis pennipes, *first found breeding on the River Dee in 2007. © David Kitching*

northwards. Whilst it would be more difficult for a small and weaker-flying damselfly to make the jump between rivers it was considered that the flowing waters of the Llangollen Canal might make a useful conduit into Cheshire for this insect. Over the years a number of possible sightings were followed-up with no success although it was appreciated that such a small and insignificant insect could easily be overlooked. It was not surprising therefore, when the first record was made in 2007 at Farndon, that the species was already breeding well on the River Dee in that area. Since then the White-legged Damselfly has been found along the river from Crewe-by-Farndon down to Aldford. Numbers seen have fluctuated over the intervening years but it is clearly established and may have spread further. Searching amongst the grassy bankside vegetation in early June would probably yield new sites if anyone is interested in looking.

A further species to appear in Cheshire has been the Golden-ringed Dragonfly *Cordulegaster boltonii*. This is a large insect with yellow and black markings and the mature adults have brilliant emerald green eyes. Unfortunately it can be misidentified by inexperienced observers seeing examples of the Southern Hawker *Aeshna cyanea* which can have yellow and brown markings in some individuals, particularly immature females. This meant that, although a number of possible sightings were reported in the 1980s, it had been impossible to corroborate the identity of the insects. There were only two reported sightings before 1980; at Hale on the Mersey estuary in 1970 and at Chester in 1890. The presence of the Golden-ringed Dragonfly was finally confirmed in 2008 when a female was photographed on the Dee at Crewe-by-Farndon. A male was seen close to the same spot in 2009 and further adults were spotted at Farndon, Bickley and on the Forge Brook at Marbury in 2010. The regular sightings around Farndon, with further records from the Welsh bank, suggest that there may be a breeding colony somewhere in the vicinity, and a search along the rivers and streams feeding the Dee could prove fruitful.

White-faced Darter

The arrival of the new species has added much interest to the study of odonata in Cheshire. On the other hand the White-faced Darter *Leucorrhinia dubia* has been lost from the two sites where it had been long established. Black Lake in Delamere Forest, where it was last seen in 1997, has seen significant changes in the quality of the habitat. This has become much more shaded as trees have been allowed to grow near to the margins. Construction of limestone tracks nearby altered the water chemistry and the acid pool is now nearer to neutral these days. This is reflected in the vegetation, with little floating *sphagnum* to be seen, and this is essential to the survival of the larvae which are exposed to predation without it. There had been considerable resistance to removal of the shading on amenity grounds although some trees were finally taken out in January 2012; nevertheless, I do not see this habitat becoming suitable for White-faced Darter again in the foreseeable future.

The main stronghold of the species was Gull Pool near to Newchurch Common on which large numbers emerged from the *sphagnum* rafts every year. Once again rapid and catastrophic habitat change saw the species extinct here in just a few years. A change in groundwater levels saw a rise of at least half a metre in the surface level of the pool and this seems to have brought a change in water chemistry towards neutral or even slightly alkaline. Again the *sphagnum* has disappeared, and with it the dragonflies. The last adult White-faced Darter in Cheshire was seen here in 2002, and in 2003 a single exuvia was located.

In 2011 Natural England with the assistance of the Forestry Commission started to look at the possibility of reintroducing the White-faced Darter to Cheshire, following a successful start to reintroduction at some sites in Cumbria. Initial surveys suggest that there may be some locations in Delamere Forest that could be suitable for a reintroduction. Much more work to ensure the habitats are sustainable will be required before any attempt is made, but maybe one day the forest will see the return of the insect that has been adopted as the symbol of Delamere Forest Park.

Figure 9.9. White-faced Darter Leucorrhinia dubia *male (left) and female (right).* © David Kitching

The future

What of the future? There is no reason to believe that the northward spread of new species will not continue if temperatures continue to stay higher than they once were. There are many examples of continental species beginning to appear with greater regularity in southern England. Some of these, such as the Vagrant Emperor *Anax ephippiger* and Lesser Emperor *Anax parthenope*, have already made an appearance in Cheshire. Damselflies may take a little longer to reach Cheshire, but the Small Red-eyed Damselfly *Erythromma viridulum* has made a rapid advance since first appearing in south-eastern England in 1999 and it has already spread from Devon to Yorkshire. It is likely that this species will be in Cheshire in ten years or so, although the expansion of its range has slowed a bit in the last year or two.

The status of the Variable Damselfly *Coenagrion pulchellum* gives some cause for concern as it is limited to a few conglomerations of marl pits together with a large population at Hatch Mere. A number of new locations for the Variable Damselfly have been found since detailed recording began in the 1980s, but it does not seem to be expanding its range and has disappeared from former haunts on the Wirral. The specific requirements for this species are not well understood and it is not clear why it occurs at some ponds whilst not at others which appear superficially to be of equal quality and suitability. Any deterioration in the ponds where it is currently found can only have a serious effect on the overall population

Figure 9.10. A male Variable Damselfly Coenagrion pulchellum. *© David Kitching*

Figure 9.11. The rarest dragonfly breeding in the county, known from only one site, is the Downy Emerald Cordulia aenea. *This is a female.*
© *David Kitching*

and threaten its long term survival in Cheshire. It is well worth looking for, particularly in the west of the county and with a bit of practice can be differentiated from the very similar Azure Damselfly *Coenagrion puella* whilst flying.

The rarest dragonfly known to be breeding in the county is the Downy Emerald *Cordulia aenea* which definitely breeds at Gull Pool but there is no proof of breeding anywhere else. A consequence of the change in water quality has been that the population of the Downy Emerald at Gull Pool has increased significantly and I estimate that numbers in recent years have been up by a factor of four or five. The Downy Emerald does not appear to disperse widely or actively seek new breeding water and this is reflected in the scarcity of records away from the immediate environs of Gull Pool. There there are single records from Petty Pool at Whitegate in 1882, Wybunbury Moss in 1956, and Little Budworth Common in 1990. At Hatch Mere there have been sightings of this species on territory on several occasions since 2002 and it is just possible that it may be breeding there in low numbers. The larvae have a requirement for leaf litter in which to conceal themselves and this may be adversely affected by tree clearance works on the perimeter of the lake, and this needs to be considered in any management planning for Hatch Mere. If new breeding colonies are not established then the Downy Emerald is going to be in danger of extinction in Cheshire should another change in its breeding habitat occur such as that which eradicated the White-faced Darter.

Conservation

Climate change has, so far, been beneficial in bringing us a number of southerly species but habitat loss, particularly that of good ponds, is the greatest threat to all Cheshire's odonata. Whilst Cheshire is well known for the number of ponds, particularly the marl pits of the central area, there are not that many surviving ponds which can be considered to be of high quality for odonata (see Ponds Chapter, pp. 148–179). Far too many have been shaded by tree and shrub growth on the margins and I am still saddened when I find ponds, often newly dug, where trees have been planted around the edges. Within a few years these waters are rendered useless for dragonflies and damselflies and the floating and emergent vegetation is shaded out, whilst the water fills with leaf litter and the trees reduce water levels through their roots. Tipping into ponds is another significant problem on farms where they may be seen as useless space and a good place to dispose of unwanted materials at low cost; surplus big bales of straw seem to be particular favourites for this fate. Many of the marl pits were excavated at least two hundred years ago and natural succession is rendering them shallower and likely to dry out. Unless some means is found to dredge some of the better examples we shall lose a valuable resource. The successional changes that I have observed at some of the best marl pits in west Cheshire over the past 25 years suggest that action is needed as soon as possible before they are seriously degraded.

Modern recording

The recording scheme for odonata in Cheshire that Richard Gabb started continues to gather details of sightings made by a large number of individuals who submit records, mainly by e-mail. This is a complete change from the 1980s when lots of record cards had to be transcribed onto the computer database. The information is submitted to the national scheme and is helping towards the production a new national Atlas of odonata in 2013. The data are available online with details of all records submitted for the past two years together with pages showing current activity at www.brocross.com/dfly/dfly.htm. There are also maps showing the distribution of each species and photographs to assist with identification.

References

Corbet, P.S. (1999) Dragonflies: Behaviour and Ecology of Odonata. Harley Books.

Corbet, P.S., Longfield, C. & Moore, N.W. (1960) Dragonflies. Collins, London.

Ford, W.K. (1953) Lancashire and Cheshire Odonata (A preliminary list). *North West Naturalist* 6: 227–233. New Series No.2.

Ford, W.K. (1954) Lancashire and Cheshire Odonata (Some further notes). *North West Naturalist* 6: 602–603. New Series No.4.

Gabb, R., & Judd, S. (1985) Cheshire Dragonflies Annual Report 1985. Privately produced and sent to all individuals who submitted records.

Gabb, R. & Kitching, D. (1986 & 1987) Cheshire Dragonflies Annual Report 1986 & 1987. Privately produced and sent to all individuals who submitted records.

Darter Magazine (initially Darter Newsletter of the Dragonfly Recording Network), British Dragonfly Society, Issue 19–1999 to Issue 28–2011.

Gabb, R. & Kitching, D. (1992) The Dragonflies and Damselflies of Cheshire. National Museums & Galleries on Merseyside.

Hammond, C.O. (1983) The Dragonflies of Great Britain and Ireland. Harley Books, 2nd Edition.

Lucas, W.J. (1919) The Odonata of the Lancashire and Cheshire District. *Lancashire and Cheshire Naturalist* 12: 23–27.

Merritt, R., Moore, N.W. & Eversham, B.C. (1996) Atlas of the dragonflies of Britain and Ireland. HMSO.

Norman, D. (ed.) (2012). Cheshire's Favourite Wildlife. Cheshire Wildlife Trust.

About the author

David Kitching spent most of his career working for Cheshire County Council's Countryside Management Service, finally retiring as Countryside Management Officer with responsibility for managing the Ranger Service across the county. He was joint author of *The Dragonflies and Damselflies of Cheshire* and now runs a website covering the latest recording and sightings of odonata in Cheshire. As the Cheshire County Recorder for the British Dragonfly Society he is currently assisting with the national odonata recording scheme and the preparation of a new dragonfly and damselfly atlas for Great Britain and Ireland.

Mammals of Cheshire

Paul Hill, Penny Rudd and the Cheshire Mammal Group

THE FIRST MAJOR WORK ON THE MAMMAL FAUNA OF CHESHIRE WAS UNDERTAKEN by the Cheshire Mammal Group in the early part of this century, culminating in the publication of *The Mammals of Cheshire* (2008). A basic knowledge of the distribution of the mammals in the region was to be found in Coward's *The Vertebrate Fauna of Cheshire and Liverpool Bay* (1910) but so little survey work was undertaken in the time between these two books that the true changes in distribution are difficult to quantify. This said, there have been some major changes documented, with some species declining or vanishing from the region whilst others have been recorded for the first time (including several bat species). One species has actually vanished from the county and re-appeared in the last fifty years!

The variety of habitats in Cheshire, from the coast on the Wirral to moorlands in the Peak District in the east of the region, support some 50 species of mammal, including almost a dozen species of bat, most of the UK's small mammals, and our largest land mammal. Several other species, mainly marine, have been recorded only once or twice.

Marine mammals

Although Cheshire's coastline is relatively small, it still supports both Common Seal *Phoca vitulina* and Grey Seal *Halichoerus grypus*; large numbers of Grey Seal can be seen hauled out in the Dee Estuary (Fig. 10.2), with a record count of 825 off Hilbre Island on 24 June 2010. This population is made up of non-breeders, recently shown by satellite-tracking to be from colonies (rookeries) including Ramsey Island off southwest Wales and Colonsay in the Hebrides. Sometimes an occasional Common Seal is with them. A third species of seal, the Hooded Seal *Cystophora cristata*, has been recorded once from the River Mersey, a long way from its native area of Greenland or Northern Canada. The coastline of Cheshire is not really noted for cetaceans but sightings of sea mammals include Common Dolphin *Delphinus delphis* and Bottle-nosed Dolphin *Tursiops truncatus*, Harbour Porpoise *Phocoena phocoena* and Northern Bottle-nosed Whale *Hyperoodon ampullatus*.

Figure 10.1. Harvest mice, our smallest rodents. © Ben Hall

Figure 10.2. The haul-out of non-breeding Grey Seals on West Hoyle Bank, off Hilbre Island. © Steve Cumberlidge www.wirralcam.org

Rarer cetaceans recorded include Killer Whale or Orca *Orcinus orca* in 2001, Risso's Dolphin *Grampus griseus* and Minke Whale *Balaenoptera acutorostrata*.

Summer is the best time to see marine mammals from land, when Harbour Porpoise, Bottle-nosed Dolphin and Grey Seal tend to move inshore and into estuary areas. A visit to New Brighton, a trip on the Mersey Ferry or a stroll along the dockside may be rewarded by the sight of a fin, or even several, cutting the water's surface. Ferry journeys from Liverpool to Ireland and the Isle of Man provide opportunities to see a greater variety of species and a better chance of a good view. From shore, Hilbre Island is a good spot to look out for these elusive and appealing creatures. Occasionally whales and dolphins have been seen up the Mersey or Dee Estuaries, unfortunately these do not always find their way back out to the Irish Sea.

Farmland mammals

Dairy farming dominates in much of lowland Cheshire. This pastoral agriculture benefits many of our smaller mammals including the Brown Hare *Lepus europaeus* (Fig. 1.3) and Rabbit *Oryctolagus cuniculus*. During survey work as part of the Local Biodiversity Action Plan for the Brown Hare, the species was found to be distributed across most of lowland Cheshire, although at low densities. The Rabbit can be found throughout Cheshire inhabiting not just farmland but most rural and sub-urban locations including woodlands and heathlands. Some areas of Cheshire support small populations of melanic (all black) Rabbits, often smaller than normal specimens and apparently not surviving to adulthood as well.

Unimproved and semi-improved areas of grassland, including the uncut margins of fields in Environmental Stewardship, also support several small mammal species including Pygmy Shrew *Sorex minutus* and Common Shrew *S. araneus*, Bank Vole *Myodes glareolus* and (Short-tailed) Field Vole *Microtus agrestis*. The Field Vole tends to favour open grassland, whereas the Bank Vole is more regularly encountered in thick cover such as hedgerows, woodlands with good ground cover and young conifer plantations. If Field Voles are not present, then the Bank Vole will move out into areas with less cover; this shift is observed even from one year to another according to the cycle in vole populations. Traditional hay meadows were once the home of our smallest rodent, the Harvest Mouse *Micromys minutus*. This species has declined owing to the changes in agricultural practices. Now mainly found in rough wet grassland and reedbeds, it has also been the subject of a reintroduction programme in some areas, coordinated by Chester Zoo. Hedgerow boundaries and field margins can also be home to the Wood Mouse *Apodemus sylcaticus*, which despite the name, is not necessarily confined to woodland, often competing with Bank Voles for habitat occupation.

With a wealth of small mammals, predators are also to be found. The largest mammalian predator now found in the UK (apart from man!) is the Red Fox *Vulpes vulpes*, inhabiting farmland, woodland and even urban areas. Smaller predators include the Weasel *Mustela nivalis* and Stoat *M. erminea*; the larger Stoat quite capable of taking a full-grown Rabbit, whilst the Weasel's prey is mainly smaller rodents. During the 1950s outbreak of myxomatosis, the decline in the Rabbit population caused a shortage of food for Stoats, so this predator also declined. With the lack of grazing by Rabbits, the ground cover provided more

Figure 10.3. Fox, our largest and most widespread mammalian predator.
© Andy Harmer

habitats for small mammals which in turn led to an increase in the numbers of Weasels. With the decline in mxyomatosis the fortunes of the Weasel and Stoat were then reversed. Both species are widely distributed throughout the Cheshire region. The Badger *Meles meles* is also well distributed in Cheshire and although still illegally persecuted, the population appears stable. Most records, though, are from road casualties.

One of the species showing a dramatic increase in sightings during recent years is the Polecat *Mustela putorius*. Although many records refer to roadside casualties, this species is now regularly recorded. Persecution by gamekeepers in the 19th century led to the extinction of Polecats in many areas. During the First World War, the reduction in the number of gamekeepers (with many serving for King and Country), enabled the species to make a comeback in some areas, particularly in Wales. It is from this population than the colonisation of Cheshire from the mid-1980s would seem to stem, with records coming from many areas from 1993 onwards and by 2006 records were being received from semi-urban areas in Wilmslow, Stockport and Macclesfield.

Perhaps one of our most noticeable mammal species is the European Mole *Talpa europaea*. Whilst the mammal itself is not often seen, molehills are a common sight along the road verges in Cheshire – even being recorded from the central reservation of the Runcorn Expressway – and, to the dismay of gardeners, on nicely manicured lawns!

Figure 10.4. Records of Polecat – seen here eating a Rabbit – are increasing in recent years. © Andy Harmer

Woodland mammals

It is within our woodlands that we have seen most of the recent changes to our mammal fauna: in the last 50 years we have lost one species from our area, but have gained several others. The Red Squirrel *Sciurus vulgaris* was last recorded in Cheshire in the 1980s from Lymm and Rostherne, yet at the turn of the last century Coward described it as 'plentiful in wooded districts'. The decline in the Red Squirrel is well documented along with the increased spread of its American counterpart, the Grey Squirrel *S. carolinensis*, first introduced to Cheshire in 1876. It was not until the 1990s that the Grey Squirrel became widely recorded in Cheshire, where it is now a familiar sight in our parks, gardens and woodlands, often causing damage to young trees or destroying bird feeders.

Around the turn of the 20th century, the Hazel (Common) Dormouse *Muscardinus arvellanarius* was last recorded in the county, in 1910 at Wistaston near Nantwich. Eighty-six years later in 1996 a reintroduction programme for the species was started in the Wych valley. Over the following two years 54 animals were released. The population was thought to be over a hundred by 2007, having moved away from the release area and colonising adjacent linked woodlands. It is unlikely that the Dormouse will spread to other areas of the county since the species needs large areas of woodland, although recent study shows that they are more catholic than previously thought in their habitat requirements. The demise of the Hazel Dormouse in the county was probably caused by habitat loss and fragmentation, something which is still evident today.

In 2011 a new species for Cheshire was found during the Dormouse study when a Yellow-necked Mouse *Apodemus flavicollis* with young was discovered in one of the boxes! Continued monitoring of the Dormouse scheme may well reveal more records of this newcomer. The Yellow-necked Mouse is slightly larger than the Wood Mouse, with a complete yellow collar, and, as the Dormouse checker found out, much more aggressive when handled!

Aquatic mammals

Several species of mammal are associated with our freshwaters, rivers and ponds, the most obvious being the Otter. Prior to the 1960s the Otter *Lutra lutra* was almost extinct in England, the result of persecution, pesticides and pollution. The cessation of hunting in the 1960s, combined with the banning of organochlorine pesticides and improvements in water quality, has led to the Otter making a comeback, and the 2009–10 national survey showed Otters present in every county in England apart from Kent (see Rivers Chapter, pp. 122–147). With a male's territory covering up to 40 km of watercourse, then it will never be a common species but the survey found evidence of Otters in Cheshire on the rivers Gowy, Weaver, Wheelock, Dane, Wincham, Bollin and Goyt.

With the increase in Otter records and distribution there is some thought that American Mink *Mustela vison* is now declining, but there is no evidence to support this. Released by animal rights activists or escaped from fur farms, Minks established themselves on many watercourses and larger water bodies. Being a generalist predator, and equally at home on land as in water, they found no shortage of food and with no natural predators they soon expanded throughout the county, sometimes to the detriment of other mammals. The species was first recorded in the wild in Cheshire in 1952, but it was the 1980s before the number of records increased dramatically.

The Water Vole *Arvicola terrestris* was described by Coward (1910) as being abundant, often seen around the meres and marl pits in the county. Now, the Water Vole is Britain's fastest declining native mammal and UK wildlife legislation was changed in 2008 to afford it enhanced levels of protection. Locally, the NorthWest Lowlands Water Vole Project (2008–11) surveyed 257 sites in the northern half of Cheshire and found Water Voles present in 36% and possibly present in 13%, while 51% showed no signs of Water Vole (Powell & Milburn 2011). Results suggest that Water Voles may have been lost from up to 56% of previously occupied sites within the NorthWest Lowlands since 1998, indicating that the national decline in Water Vole populations is continuing to affect the project area significantly. Water Voles are not restricted to running water or larger water bodies and can be encountered in small ponds, even up in the eastern hills of Cheshire.

Sharing similar habitats to the Water Vole is the Water Shrew *Neomys fodiens*, the largest of the three shrew species to be found in the UK. Prior to 1980 Water Shrew was only recorded from Wirral and south and east Cheshire. Its distribution is now more widespread across the county, although it is probably

Bats

Of the 11 species of bat now recorded in Cheshire, several have been added in the last half a century, although some of these have been owing to developments in our understanding of bats and genetic research leading to taxonomic changes. In the 1970s Whiskered Bat *Myotis mystacinus* and Brandt's Bat *M. brandtii* were identified as separate species, but identification in the field to species level is not easy without specialist knowledge. Similarly, in 1997 the Pipistrelle Bat was separated into two species, Common Pipistrelle *Pipistrellus pipistrellus* and Soprano Pipistrelle *P. pygmaeus*. A third species of pipistrelle, Nathusius' Pipistrelle *P. nathusii* was recorded at Marbury Country Park in 2005 and again in subsequent years. This species was only identified following analysis of recordings made on a bat detector. Another new discovery, in January 2012, was of Lesser Horseshoe Bats *Rhinolophus hipposideros*, found hibernating in caves under Beeston Castle, and last recorded in Cheshire at the same site in 1948. Other species found in the county include Noctule *Nyctalus noctula* and Brown Long-eared Bats *Plecotus auritus* (Fig. 3.7).

Although bats forage over woodland, hedgerows and similar features, they require several roost sites during the year. Species such as the pipistrelles can form large maternity roosts in buildings during the spring and summer. Roosts in excess of 100 Soprano Pipistrelle Bats are not uncommon in houses, the bats occupying cavities or spaces between roof tiles/slates. The Brown Long-eared Bat will also occupy roof voids in older properties such as barns or large houses. Buildings with traditional roof structures may also support Natterer's Bat *Myotis nattereri*, Brandt's or Whiskered Bats. Larger species like the Noctule tend to favour trees for roosting, although very few roosts have ever been found in Cheshire, but the species is regularly recorded during activity surveys. As bats are offered full protection under the Wildlife and Countryside Act and the European Habitats Directive, we know more about them than most other mammal species because bat surveys are regularly undertaken to support planning applications for development proposals. The loss of mature trees, hedgerows and roost sites in buildings, without mitigation, would lead to a reduction in the population of our bats.

under-recorded. Most small mammal trapping is carried out in woodlands or meadows, habitats in which the Water Shrew is rarely found.

Another species associated with water bodies in Cheshire is Daubenton's Bat *Myotis daubentonii*. This bat can be found hunting for insects of larger water bodies in the county such as Budworth Mere, often in association with Soprano Pipistrelle which also hunt over water bodies. The pale underparts of the Daubenton's Bat help to differentiate them from other species.

Mammals associated with man

A selection of mammals is associated with man, either in industry or our homes. Naturally few people like to report such encounters, so it is difficult to assess population trends of species such as Common Rat *Rattus norvegicus* or House Mouse *Mus musculus domesticus*. Coward (1910) called the Common Rat the most destructive and abundant Cheshire mammal, and the same is probably true today.

The Common Rat and House Mouse are regularly encountered in grain stores on farms and both species can be found feeding under bird tables after dark. The Ship or Black Rat *Rattus rattus* has all but disappeared from Cheshire: the last recorded was a single individual disturbed during a survey at Bromborough docks in 2007, with the previous one in Northwich in 1996. The species was formerly fairly common around the docks at Birkenhead and Bromborough, and no doubt at other ports along the Mersey and Manchester Ship Canal.

Often associated with gardens, but not restricted to them is the Hedgehog *Erinaceus europaeus*. This familiar creature has declined in the last fifty years owing to the use of non-wildlife friendly slug pellets. The decline may also be due to our large population of Badgers, which prey on Hedgehogs. One of the best ways to monitor Hedgehog populations was from roadside corpses, but today this is not as reliable. Hedgehogs thankfully seem to have evolved to run away from bright lights, rather than curl up into a ball for protection! Recent winter weather may also contribute to poor overwinter survival rates for Hedgehogs who may wake during an unusually warm spell to find that they do not have their usual food sources available out-of-season, so use up preciously stored fat with no option to replenish prior to the next cold spell returning them into hibernation.

Mammals of the uplands

Whilst most of the mammals to be found in Cheshire can be encountered in the lowlands, some are restricted to the eastern hills. Here Red Deer *Cervus elaphus* (the UK's largest native land mammal) can be found, mostly escapes from deer farms or parks. Prior to 1910, Coward declared that the Red Deer was common in Cheshire Forests, but had all but vanished apart from in parks such as Tatton Park and Lyme Park. The deer at Lyme Park are thought to originate from wild deer roaming the Macclesfield area, whereas those at Tatton have been introduced from Scotland and elsewhere. Two populations of Red Deer (outside of those in parks) are considered to be present in Cheshire, one concentrated around Goyt Valley/Hoo Moor area, and the other in the River Dane/Bosley Minn area. The Goyt Valley population has spread west into Cheshire from Derbyshire, whilst the southern population, first recorded in the 1970s, is likely to be a feral herd derived from a captive population at Roaches House near Leek. The smaller Roe Deer *Capreolus capreolus* is becoming increasingly recorded in Cheshire, with only one record prior to the 1990s but almost annually in recent years. Smaller than the Roe Deer, Reeve's Muntjac *Muntiacus reevesi* has been recorded in recent years, with sightings focused around central Cheshire.

Another upland species in Cheshire is the Mountain Hare *Lepus timidus*, confined to the northeast of our region in the hills around Stockport and Disley. Only rarely seen, this species – the only truly native species of rabbit and hare in the UK – is best encountered in early spring, when its winter coat makes it stand out against the moors where the snow has melted.

Figure 10.7. Red Deer, the UK's largest native land mammal. © Ben Hall

Winners and Losers

Losers last 50 years	Winners last 50 years	Winners last 10 years
Red Squirrel	Grey Squirrel	Water Vole
Hedgehog	Otter	Nathusius's Pipistrelle
Water Vole	Mink	Lesser Horseshoe Bat
Black Rat	Hazel Dormouse	Yellow-necked Mouse
	Grey Seal	Serotine Bat
	Red Deer	
	Roe Deer	
	Muntjac	
	Polecat	
	Leisler's Bat	
	Brandt's/Whiskered Bat	

Mammal recording in Cheshire

Mammal recording is still very much in its infancy in Cheshire (except for those species offered special legal protection) and the next fifty years will undoubtedly see more changes. With cleaner watercourses, Otters may even spread to our canal systems, especially if conservation measures such as artificial holts are widely used to give the species a head start. National and European government policies such as Environmental Stewardship have helped many small mammals to keep a foothold and even expand in the county, payments for wide field margins being just one example. It remains to be seen what will happen when such payments stop, and whether landowners will continue to manage sympathetically when there is no financial gain for them. With more leisure time available to amateur recorders, it is likely that more records will be received to help increase our current knowledge of species distribution in the Cheshire region. Amateur and professional recorders have more resources at their disposal now than 50 years ago. Bat detectors (which 'translate' the frequency of a bat's echo-location so that it is audible to the human ear) are readily available, and combined with the ability to record to an MP3 recorder and then playback on a PC with specialist software, have made the secret world of bats more accessible to the general public. Many mammal groups have been successful in securing grants for equipment and have Longworth small mammal traps (a humane live trap for voles, shrews and mice) available for loan. Larger mammals – even Hedgehogs – can be detected using remote infrared motion detector cameras. These can be left in-situ for several weeks and then the recorded images viewed at leisure on a PC.

With the historic paucity of records, it is often not possible to determine whether apparent increases in distribution are due to recorder effort or actual range expansion. But the more that is known, the better our case for conserving them.

References and Further Reading

Cheshire Mammal Group (2008) The Mammals of Cheshire. Liverpool University Press.
Coward, T.A. (1910) The Vertebrate Fauna of Cheshire and Liverpool Bay. Witherby, London.
Powell, A. & Milburn, K. (2011) NorthWest Lowlands Water Vole Project Final Report. www.lancspartners.org/lbap/pdf/news_events/NWLWVP_Final_Report.pdf
Harris, S & Yalden, D (2008) Mammals of the British Isles: Handbook, 4th edition. Mammal Society.

About the authors

Paul Hill is a founder member of, and currently Chair of, the Cheshire Mammal Group. He is an avid naturalist whose main interests are birds, mammal and invertebrates, but if it moves it will grab his interest (these even extends to flowers that move in the wind!). Before setting up his ecological consultancy, Paul worked for the RSPB and the Cheshire Wildlife Trust.

Penny Rudd initially became involved with the Cheshire Mammal Group through her extensive knowledge of Harvest Mice. She has worked at Chester Zoo for over 30 years, in a range of office-based roles from Personnel Manager to Registrar, but has always maintained close contact with animal keeping teams, and has a large and diverse animal collection at home too. Her lifelong interest in animals started in childhood, stimulated by frequent travel between the UK and parts of Asia where her parents were working. Penny has served as a member of Cheshire Wildlife Trust Council.

Cheshire Mammal Group was formed in 2001 to encourage the study, conservation and awareness of mammal species in the Cheshire region. The aims of the Group are to provide information and practical help for national and local mammal surveys, to support and promote the work of the (national) Mammal Society and to interest new people in mammals. www.cheshiremammalgroup.org.uk

Birds

David Norman

CHESHIRE'S BIRDLIFE HAS CHANGED GREATLY IN THE LAST FIFTY YEARS. THE declines of some familiar birds have perhaps been emphasised, but there have been far more species gained in the county's avifauna than have been lost: 23 new species have started regularly breeding in the county since 1960, while eight have gone. Summer migrants make up a decreasing proportion of our breeding avifauna, but the avian biomass must have increased greatly, the rise in geese and other waterfowl, pheasants, pigeons and corvids far outweighing declines in small passerines.

This chapter is arranged in three sections covering ornithology in the county; changes in bird distributions or abundance over the last half-century; and some of the reasons for those changes. It does not list every species, but concentrates mainly on the breeding birds, with a few of the wintering ones, especially emphasising those that have undergone changes in their status.

Ornithological recording in the county

Birds are now perhaps the best-recorded aspects of our wildlife, with reasonable estimates for population as well as distribution, but it has not always been so.

The year 1962 saw the publication of *The Birds of Cheshire* by T. Hedley Bell, roughly half a century after Coward's massive *Fauna of Cheshire* (1910) and Coward and Oldham's (1900) *Birds of Cheshire*, so it ought to be easy to compare with the county's birdlife of that period. Bell's book, however, seems like an opportunity missed. For the commoner birds, Coward's species status statements were often copied, 50 years on, without consideration of whether they still held good. The book has little information about breeding birds, nothing about the wildfowl counts, and an over-emphasis on odd rarities, anticipating the modern cult of twitching. Bell produced a 1967 Supplement to correct some of the errors but the general style probably reflected the ethos of bird recording in the county around that time: the early Cheshire Bird Reports, following the formation of the Cheshire Ornithological Association, were slim booklets, also ignoring any common species.

Thus, despite the increasing environmental awareness, the 1960s and 1970s were the nadir of bird recording in the county but fortunately the national scene was much brighter, with the start of the BTO's Common Birds Census (CBC)

Figure 11.1. Cheshire and Wirral is by far the most important county in Britain for breeding Grey Herons. © Richard Steel

Recording area

Historical analyses of biological recording can be dogged by boundary changes, perhaps especially of birds whose recorders have seldom used the Watsonian vice-counties which have brought stability to botany and other taxa. The Cheshire bird recording area followed the local authority boundaries but in the 1960s and 1970s was treated as flexible, especially at the boundaries with Manchester and Flintshire, according to whether a recorder wanted to include a rare sighting. Following the 1974 major local government reorganisation, 'ornithological Cheshire' was agreed as the county of Cheshire, including Widnes and Warrington and the Metropolitan Borough of Wirral; this is largely Watsonian vice-county 58, with the addition of Widnes and Warrington and the exclusion of the northeastern Longdendale 'panhandle'. This recording area has remained unchanged ever since although sadly, even nowadays the Cheshire and Wirral Bird Reports contain a lot of Welsh records as most birds from the Dee Estuary are not differentiated between the two countries.

in 1962 and the extension of the Wildfowl Trust's wildfowl counts (started in 1947) to include waders in the Birds of Estuaries Enquiry (1969), plus a great rise in more widespread ringing following the introduction of mist-nets. Cheshire and Wirral did share in these nationally-organised developments, with one CBC started in 1962 (Bebington, Wirral), with another five in the next five years, full (year-round) counting of our two estuaries and some of the country's most active ringers including Merseyside Ringing Group (spreading far beyond their geographical name) from 1954, Hilbre Island Bird Observatory from 1957 and South Manchester Ringing Group from 1967.

Bird recording in the county was lifted out of the doldrums by the instigation of the first county breeding bird atlas, started in 1978, which caught the imagination of hundreds of volunteers who surveyed every tetrad (2x2 km square of the Ordnance Survey grid), of which there are 670 in Cheshire and Wirral. With hindsight it was unfortunate that the fieldwork took seven years to complete (1978–84) during a time of massive change especially in farmland birds, and in recording systems as the project was entirely paper-based at a time when personal computers were just starting to make their mark; but the First Atlas (as it is referred to in the rest of this chapter) was a seminal work and set the scene for a great leap in understanding of the county's birds.

The Cheshire Ornithological Association was replaced in 1987 by the Cheshire and Wirral Ornithological Society, one of whose early acts was to publish the book of the breeding bird atlas (Guest *et al.* 1992). CAWOS mainly concentrated on collecting records to compile the annual bird reports, which became ranked amongst the best in the country, whilst most of the systematic bird-recording in the county has been under the aegis of the BTO. Suggestions of producing a Millennium avifauna, 100 years on from Coward and Oldham, sadly foundered for lack of effort and fears of detracting from the annual report compilation. But CAWOS did then organise a new breeding and wintering atlas of birds, led by the present author, using the same methodology for distribution by tetrad, and also recording abundance and habitat. The fieldwork was completed in three breeding and wintering seasons (2004–07) and the book published in the following year (Norman 2008). The project also stimulated analysis to produce estimates of the county population for the most abundant 61 species, half of those regularly breeding in Cheshire and Wirral (Norman *et al.* 2012). This Second Atlas (as it is referred to in the rest of this chapter) provides much of the basis for the up-to-date knowledge.

Waterbirds

Most waterbirds have prospered in the last half-century, and this group includes several species for which the county is particularly significant in a national context. Cheshire played an important part in the history of the Great Crested Grebe, as has been reflected in its choice as the name for Cheshire Wildlife Trust's members' magazine. In the mid-19th century the species came close to extinction in Britain, driven by collection of the birds for use of their feathers in millinery. The national population in 1860 was estimated at just 42 pairs, with almost half (20) of them on the secluded lakes of private estates in Cheshire. Legal protection and a change in fashion allowed the species to come back from the brink and the national census in 1965 estimated 314 adults in the county (including non-breeders). Great Crested Grebes (Fig. 1.11) are now thriving and have spread to more waters, especially in the Mersey valley and Wirral.

Black-necked Grebes (Fig. 11.2) nested sporadically in the Delamere area in the first half of the 20th century, but none was known in the county from 1953 to 1980. The species then returned, with odd birds breeding from 1980, but the population took off from 1987 when they settled at the flooded dredging deposit lagoons of the Manchester Ship Canal at Woolston, which has become nationally their most important site. Up to 20 pairs, but more usually 10–15, breed here annually out of a national total of up to 50 pairs (Holling and RBBP 2011).

Cheshire and Wirral is the most important county in Britain for breeding Grey Herons (Fig. 11.1), probably linked to our status as the 'pond capital of the UK'. Grey Heron colonies have been counted in Britain since 1928, often cited as the longest-running census of any species other than man. Every known heronry has been visited every year and the total of apparently occupied nests in the county has risen threefold during the 32-year period 1980–2010 and now averages about 600 nests annually. Some of Cheshire's heronries are particularly large: in 2001–09 Budworth (Marbury) Mere held the largest heronry in the UK, with Eaton Hall the third largest, and three other Cheshire sites (Combermere, Rode Pool and Radnor Mere) among the top 50 in the country. Yearly fluctuations are mostly caused by mortality in hard winters, and Grey Herons have benefited from the warming trend of recent decades (Martin and Norman 2011).

Little Egrets have had an astounding story as a British bird. They were so scarce that records were scrutinised by the British Birds Rarities Committee until 1991 yet now winter flocks of over 100 birds can be found on the Dee estuary, and they breed here annually. A pair tried to nest at Frodsham Marsh in 1995, a year before their first confirmed breeding in Britain in 1996, in Dorset and Cornwall. Successful breeding in the county followed with single pairs in 2001 and 2004, then the year 2005 saw the establishment of a colony near the RSPB's Inner Marsh Farm reserve, which has grown to over 30 pairs out of a national total around 800 pairs (Holling and RBBP 2011). Cormorants similarly have colonised the county in the last decade, although with not as much excitement as accompanies most other species, with their first successful breeding at four sites simultaneously in 2004. They had increasingly moved inland as man overfished the seas and overstocked some inland waters; and the trigger for their breeding here has been a change in their habits to tree-nesting, common across the rest of its worldwide range, but not recorded in Britain until 1981. At Rostherne Mere the colony increased rapidly, to 134 pairs just five years later (Fig. 11.4).

Our largest waterbirds are now at probably their highest ever populations, not always to everyone's liking. In the national census of 1955, there were estimated to be 80 breeding pairs of Mute Swan in Cheshire but their population dwindled to a low of only 13 pairs in 1985, caused mostly by birds being poisoned after ingesting lead weights discarded by anglers. Responsible fishermen voluntarily changed to non-toxic weights, and legislation banning the use of lead became effective on 1 January 1987. The Cheshire Swan Study Group was formed in 1988 and monitored the rapid recovery of the population, topping 100 pairs in the county in 1996, and estimated in the 2004–06 Atlas to be around 200–250

Figure 11.2. Black-necked Grebes, a nationally rare breeder whose UK stronghold has been the Woolston Eyes SSSI near Warrington.
© Walter Soestbergen

Figure 11.3. Little Egrets are now a common sight flying over the Dee Estuary. © Damian Waters www.drumimages.co.uk

pairs breeding, with around 1,000 non-breeding birds. A pair of the non-native (Australian) Black Swan bred in mid-Cheshire in 2009 and 2010, causing havoc as they disputed the area with other waterfowl.

Canada Geese became established in the county early in the 20th century but were largely ignored by ornithologists. There was no mention of the breeding population in 1962 or 1967 by Bell, but in the First Atlas (1978–84) they were proven breeding in 136 tetrads, and in the Second Atlas (2004–06) this increased to 290 tetrads including almost every pond or lake in Wirral, from where they were absent only twenty years before. The national population doubled from 1991 to 2000, mostly from birds moving onto smaller waterbodies, as has happened here. At some sites their eggs are treated, under licence, in attempts to keep on top of their numbers. Outside the breeding season there are flocks of 1,000 or more Canada Geese, especially on the two estuaries, amongst the largest gatherings in the country, and some of our birds have moved to northern Scotland and back to join the moulting flocks on the Beauly Firth. Greylag Geese were seldom recorded fifty years ago but a breeding population had become established around the Eaton Estate by our First Atlas period; now they have spread to colonise much of the western half of Cheshire and Wirral.

In 1962, Bell wrote that small numbers of Shelduck nested around Hilbre and Burton Marshes, and on the Mersey around Ince. They have considerably increased, and changed their behaviour, since then. They now nest (usually in

Figure 11.4. Part of the Cormorant colony at Rostherne Mere. © Malcolm Calvert

Rabbit burrows) in any suitable site near to the tidal parts of the Dee or Mersey, and since 1977 have spread to breed, sparsely, at inland locations across lowland Cheshire. Post-breeding, they used to migrate to moult in the Heligoland Bight but from 1993 onwards they abandoned that habit and up to 20,000 birds gather in July to moult on the Mersey estuary, the largest flock in Britain. Brent Goose is another waterbird that has shifted its habits and there are now more wintering in the county than for at least a century, with a flock of 100 or more on the Dee, long-distance migrants of the burgeoning Light-bellied race that breed on islands in the Canadian Arctic and northern Greenland, spilling over from their traditional Irish wintering sites.

Amongst the ducks, Mallard has always been widespread but is now ubiquitous, with probably over 30,000 breeding individuals in the county. Tufted Duck is the commonest diving duck, having expanded its range greatly between the two county Atlases – in twenty years the number of tetrads with confirmed or probable breeding rose from 108 to 171 – and there are now few waters without the species, including almost every sizeable lake but also some small ponds and even narrow streams and ditches. Gadwall used to be scarce, and first bred in Cheshire in 1981; by the Second Atlas they had spread to give confirmed or probable breeding in 28 tetrads, mostly in or near the Mersey valley, and the county breeding population, although usually under-recorded, like most ducks, is at least 50 pairs. Mandarin was first found breeding in the wild in Cheshire in 1981, probably having spread from a colony of captive birds at Eaton Hall. They are now nesting in most of south-west Cheshire, all suitable waters in Wirral and parts of east Cheshire including the Langley and Trentabank reservoirs in the uplands, and the county population is probably 100 pairs. The diving duck Pochard started breeding here only during the 1970s, and is now clearly established with 15–20 pairs nesting annually although they only have one regularly occupied site, the Woolston Eyes SSSI. Ruddy Ducks have bred at most of the county's larger waters since their colonisation in 1968, and the Cheshire and Wirral population must have exceeded 100 pairs before reducing rapidly with the national eradication programme from autumn 2005, aimed at stopping them migrating south and inter-breeding with the Iberian stock of the endangered White-headed Duck. The fish-eating duck, the Goosander (Fig. 11.15), first bred in the county in 1995, and a few breeding birds are now established on three different river systems – the Dane, Weaver and Dee. Most of the other duck species are secretive during the breeding season but are present here in only small numbers. Across many species of waterfowl, there has been a general tendency for the larger birds to move on to smaller waters, as has happened with Coot as well, and perhaps as a result, species including Moorhen and Little Grebe have declined somewhat in the past fifty years, perhaps being squeezed out of some ponds.

Gulls

Modern man has made life easy for gulls, whose numbers have greatly increased; at sea by the wasteful discard of dead fish enforced by bureaucratic quotas, and inland by the easy availability of food at landfill sites, and edible litter carelessly dropped. Gulls are adaptable birds: in winter, until the late 19th century they merited the name of sea-gulls, as inland records were almost unknown, but by the 1960s they were commonly found following the plough, on slurried fields or flooded stubble or on damp grassland, with Common Gulls in particular favouring urban sports fields, and with some large roosts on meres and flooded sand quarries. Lesser Black-backed Gulls used to be almost exclusively summer visitors to Britain. From 1928 they started to be seen in Cheshire in some winter months, and by the 1960s the species was regularly here all-year round. In the January 1983 national survey, 10,190 of the 13,726 Lesser Black-backed Gulls recorded in coastal areas were on the Mersey estuary, although that site no longer has any special importance for them.

As breeding birds, Black-headed Gulls have had a long association with the Delamere area, nesting there since the Middle Ages, although they had ceased by 1965. So it was a nice return to history when the newly-flooded Blakemere Moss (pp. 112–114) was colonised by the species from 1999 onwards, with a population rapidly rising to at least 1,000 pairs in recent years. What was a surprise, however, was that Mediterranean Gulls chose this site for their first breeding in the county in 2004, after a decade of hanging around the other major Black-headed Gull colonies at Woolston and Inner Marsh Farm. Mediterranean Gull is another species that had not bred in Britain fifty years ago; their first nests were in Hampshire in 1968. The three large gulls have all nested in Cheshire and Wirral during the last half-century. Lesser Black-backed Gulls usually breed on the ground, on saltmarshes or moorland, and occasionally have been found nesting in the county, but a change in habits from 2003 saw a few pairs using the large flat roofs of commercial buildings in the north Wirral. Herring Gulls have a similar story of sporadic nesting, but more regularly on north Wirral rooftops in the last decade, some of them on residential properties where they incur the ire of householders. Nationally, at least 10% of these two species nest on rooftops, where they are safer from predators, and the habit is rapidly spreading. Unusually, an odd pair of Great Black-backed Gulls bred at Frodsham Marsh, on a tiny mud island just big enough for one nest, for five years from 1998 to 2002, but no others have yet followed their lead.

Raptors

Among the greatest success stories in the county's avifauna is the rise in breeding raptors. Fifty years ago there were only two species breeding in the county, Sparrowhawk and Kestrel, and the population of the former was severely depressed by what was later realised to be the effects of organochlorine agricultural seed dressings. Following the ban on these pesticides, the Sparrowhawk population recovered well, with confirmed or probable breeding in 181 tetrads in 1978–84 and in 235 tetrads in 2004–06; as Cheshire is not a well-wooded county, this is perhaps the natural extent of its distribution. In Bell's day Kestrel was 'widely distributed' and 'much the commonest' raptor; its status has probably not changed much in half a century but comparison of the two Atlases shows a subtle shift in distribution, with a loss of many urban Kestrels and an increase in rural birds. In the 1960s Buzzards occasionally summered, without evidence of breeding, but one or two pairs became established during the late 1970s, in woodlands in the Wych valley and the Lower Weaver valley. A 1994 survey found 5 confirmed and 14 probable breeding pairs, and a further census six years later recorded 56 confirmed and 128 probable breeding pairs. Now (2004–06 Atlas) there may well be 800 pairs or more and Buzzard has risen to become the commonest bird of prey in the county, a remarkable tale.

The Goshawk was never recorded in the county in the first half of the 20th century, but occasional sightings – apparently of birds escaped from falconers – were followed by breeding in the 1970s, which probably continues to the present day; proof is often difficult to come by, however, of this secretive bird that favours the dense and extensive forestry plantations. Merlins breed in the Peak District and occasionally choose a site in Cheshire rather than Derbyshire, and Hen Harriers could do likewise.

Peregrines (Fig. 3.1) had never been known to breed in Cheshire or Wirral, and nationally became scarce during the 1960s pesticide era. As the population recovered they spread to include Cheshire and first bred, on Beeston Castle, in 1989. They have continued to increase in the county and the pressure on breeding sites is such that in recent years they have nested on two sandstone natural cliff sites, a chemical works (pp. 43–44), a car factory and an oil refinery, a city-centre building, a clock tower, four road or rail bridges and inside a football stadium, incubating eggs above a largely oblivious Saturday-afternoon crowd!

Figure 11.5. In the last half-century Buzzards have risen from being a county rarity to the most commonly-seen bird of prey nowadays. © Chris Grady

Figure 11.6. Hobbies feed mainly on dragonflies and, as here, House Martins. They have moved north to breed in Cheshire only since the mid-1990s. © Simon Richardson

Figure 11.7. Aerial disputes between Ravens and Peregrines are now a common sight in Cheshire. © Jim Almond

Hobbies probably first bred in Cheshire in 1995 and have now increased to around sixty pairs, mostly in the eastern part of the county. Marsh Harriers have occasionally dallied here during spring, and have become increasingly common on autumn passage, but were finally proven to breed here in 2010 when I, with colleagues, went to ring three chicks in a nest in an extensive *phragmites* reedbed, and again in 2011 when two young were raised (Fig. 11.17). Red Kite has not yet been proven to nest in Cheshire, but a pair or two may be lurking undetected, and the species will surely soon be added to the list.

An honorary raptor, Raven, shares or competes for some Peregrine nest-sites, and re-colonised the county in 1991, their first confirmed breeding here since 1857. They first occupied the sandstone cliffs and, as their population rapidly grew, spread to nest in trees, usually Scots Pines, buildings including, famously, Chester Town Hall and Cathedral and recently Runcorn Water Tower, and several electricity pylons. Having adapted to this wide range of sites, there is probably no limit to the Raven's distribution other than availability of prey, and Rabbits seem to provide adequate substitute for their traditional sheep carrion.

Waders

Our breeding wader species have had differing fortunes. Fifty years ago, Little Ringed Plover was just colonising the county, with the first successful nesting in 1961. Since then, they have occupied most of the sand quarries and industrial sites at some stage, but the Cheshire breeding population seldom exceeds ten pairs in a year. Ringed Plovers bred on the north Wirral coast a few times in the first half of the 20th century but there was a long gap from 1954 until they started breeding at inland sites in 1975 and every year since, often at the same places that Little Ringed Plovers also use, but the larger bird is scarcer in the county. Avocet is a recent addition to our breeding list, birds producing chicks from 2002 onwards at several sites in the north of the county, although usually only one site per year. Oystercatchers nested on the Dee saltmarsh in the 19th century, then from the mid-1930s, with odd pairs on the Mersey as well, but their population alongside our estuaries was thought not to exceed 20 pairs a year in our First Atlas period. In the next twenty years they underwent a major shift in behaviour and now most birds breed inland, with perhaps 250 pairs recorded in over 100 tetrads during the Second Atlas. Redshank have gone the other way, with 'many records of its nesting inland by the meres, flashes and sewage farms' (Bell 1962) whereas now they are mostly found breeding close to the Mersey and, especially, the Dee. Snipe, Woodcock and Common Sandpiper have all declined greatly as breeding birds in the last fifty years and there may now be fewer than ten pairs of each. Lapwing is the commonest and most widespread breeding wader, but has declined nationally and locally since 1984, probably because their favoured mixed farming is now scarce. Curlews are retreating to the eastern hills, which used to be their sole breeding area but from about 1940 to 1965 they occupied much of southwest and central Cheshire as well. In the Second Atlas (2004–06) they were confirmed or probably breeding in only one-tenth of the tetrads in the county, probably a victim of early cutting of grass for silage, and continued drainage. The specialised breeding waders of the eastern moorlands are struggling: Dunlin has been lost, last known as a Cheshire breeder in 1985, and Golden Plovers still nest in small numbers, as in Bell's time (1962) although they have probably contracted their range to higher ground.

The main importance of Cheshire and Wirral for waders is in winter, when vast flocks, sometimes totalling 100,000 or more and mostly Knot, Dunlin, Oystercatcher, Redshank, Black-tailed and Bar-tailed Godwits, visit the two estuaries every winter, both of which have a suite of national and international designations for conservation of their wintering waterbirds.

The Grey Partridge is one of the farmland species whose population has crashed in the last quarter-century. Their distribution in the county reflects that decline, and they have been lost from two-thirds of their breeding areas since the First Atlas, down from 420 tetrads to 149. Red-legged Partridges have long been reared by shooting estates and odd pairs first started breeding regularly in the wild in Cheshire in the 1960s, but by 2004–06 they were found in more tetrads in the breeding season (152) than their native cousin. The breeding status of wild Pheasants is unknown fifty years ago, while now they are almost everywhere and certainly self-sustaining even without the annual release of thousands by shooting estates. Red Grouse depend entirely on the quality of heather moorland, needing extensive (and expensive) management, and there are still a few hundred pairs in our part of the Peak District. Black Grouse probably last bred in the county in 1960, at Danes Moss, and odd ones were seen in the eastern hills until 1980.

'Say goodbye to the Cuckoo' was the striking title of a 2009 book by a Cheshire-born environmentalist (McCarthy 2009), and many people in Cheshire have had to do so in recent years as we have shared in the species' rapid national decline. There is no shortage of their common hosts, Meadow Pipit, Dunnock and Reed Warbler – the latter seldom recorded being cuckolded in Cheshire until a flurry of activity in the county's reedbeds from 1988 to 1998 – but there has been a huge drop in the Cuckoo's favoured food of large hairy caterpillars, and no-one knew what happened to the birds on migration or in winter in Africa until recent satellite-tracking by the BTO. Nightjar is another species that feeds on moths, in this case their flying forms, and has been lost from Cheshire during our review period. They declined sharply in the first half of the twentieth century but fifty years ago probably a few bred in the Delamere area. In 1979 and 1980 pairs were found at Risley Moss, but these were the last known in the county.

Owls

The Barn Owl has become an icon for successful nature conservation. The Cheshire population was 240 pairs in 1932 but only 35 pairs in 1982–85 and just seven pairs in 1998 before local groups started working with landowners on creation of suitable feeding habitat in field margins and alongside watercourses (Fig. 2.12). The birds bounced back and the county now holds probably 150–200 breeding pairs. The other owls have differing fortunes. Little Owls appear to be slowly declining and our Tawny Owl population is probably only half of that in the 1980s. Odd Short-eared Owls breed near the eastern county boundary, and it is a puzzle why they do not colonise the saltmarshes of the Dee and Mersey, where they are common winter visitors. Long-eared Owls are under-recorded but have surely declined: a century ago Coward thought they were widely distributed but not very abundant, while now they breed only in the Mersey valley and Macclesfield Forest.

Of the woodpeckers, Great Spotted has long been the most common but has greatly increased its population in the last twenty years and spread way beyond woodland to breed almost anywhere; while Lesser Spotted has gone the other way to become one of the county's scarcest birds; its UK population has fallen by 75% in the last quarter-century. Green Woodpeckers have a patchy distribution and their numbers fluctuate largely according to the incidence of hard winters.

Cheshire is, and probably always has been, one of the most important counties in Britain for Swallows, who find abundant insects following the cattle. The Second Atlas showed that they had become scarce in the Mersey valley and east Wirral, for reasons unknown, and elsewhere in the county many of their former nesting-buildings have been renovated and made inhospitable, but it is still our most widespread and numerous summer migrant. Sand Martins dig their nests, as they always have, in river banks (Fig. 6.3 (f)) but most nowadays use commercial sand quarries. Their fortunes are largely determined by the rainfall in their west African winter quarters – in the drier years there are too few flying insects to support the population, so many birds starve – and the Cheshire population must be much lower now than half-a-century ago, following the Sahel droughts. Their close relative the House Martin is the second most abundant summer visitor, and must be one of our most familiar commensal birds, all of their nest-sites being on man-made structures. They, too, are probably somewhat less numerous than they used to be, with a net loss from 32 tetrads recorded between

Figure 11.8. Lesser Spotted Woodpeckers are now among Cheshire's scarcest birds. © Chris Grady

our two atlases, and nationally House Martin has been added to the amber list of species of conservation concern. There may be problems in their central African wintering areas, about which almost nothing is known, while they probably have fewer nesting opportunities here with modern building materials, for the birds cannot build their mud nests on plastic soffits and fascia boards. The supreme aerial feeder, the Swift, is certainly suffering for similar reasons. Most Swifts (Fig. 3.4) nest in the roof-spaces of buildings over 40 years old, especially the 1930s council estates and old Victorian and Edwardian houses, and renovation of older properties often leaves no access for the birds (pp. 42–43).

Wagtails and larks

In his New Naturalist monograph (1950) – based on his study at Gatley, in Cheshire until 1974 but now Greater Manchester – Stuart Smith declared 'Cheshire would appear to be *the* county for the Yellow Wagtail'; sadly, this claim could never be made today. They were contracting their range by the First Atlas period, although found then in 386 tetrads, but by our Second Atlas they were down to only one-third of that number, and virtually lost from Wirral, the western part of Cheshire and the eastern hills. Pied Wagtails are stable, well adapted to man's provision of close-cropped grass and flat tarmac or concrete areas, while Grey Wagtails have considerably expanded their range, being mainly a breeding

Figure 11.9. Cheshire used to be the *county for Yellow Wagtail, but not any more. © Tim Melling*

bird of the hill streams fifty years ago, but now nesting alongside most of our rivers and canals. In winter, they quit the highest land and northern haunts and spread widely across the county.

Kingfishers have had varying fortunes, suffering in the past from river engineering but now benefiting from cleaner water and warmer winters, and their population is reasonably secure. Dipper (Fig. 6.3 (e)) is the characteristic bird of fast-flowing rivers and streams in the eastern hills, clinging onto the riverbed whilst they walk underwater to find shrimps, mayflies and caddis or stonefly nymphs. Their breeding distribution contracted between our two Atlas surveys, perhaps because monitoring by the Environment Agency shows the biological quality of east Cheshire's watercourses to be deteriorating.

The decline of the Skylark in our agricultural landscape (Fig. 2.7) has been widely discussed. Fifty years ago they were almost ubiquitous in the county, with a similar distribution found in the 1978–84 Atlas although by then there were hints of the adverse effects of the switch from hay to silage. By the 2004–06 breeding bird survey they were found in only 480 of the 670 tetrads in Cheshire and Wirral. Meadow Pipits declined between our two Atlas surveys, but their present distribution, and numbers, sound similar to those of fifty years ago. They are now breeding mostly in the eastern hills, where they may be the most abundant bird, and in the Mersey valley and north and west Wirral. Tree Pipits, however, are close to extinction in the county, present in only 13 tetrads in the Second Atlas, with confirmed or probable breeding in only five, down from 82 tetrads in the First Atlas, with confirmed or probable breeding in 68. One hundred years ago Coward thought Tree Pipit an abundant summer visitor, although it had 'vanished from many of its former haunts' by Bell's time.

Pigeons and doves

The pigeons and doves have undergone major changes in their fortunes in our fifty year period. Who can now recall that the first Collared Doves in the county appeared in 1960, with breeding the following year, as part of their remarkable spread to the northwest from Turkey and the Balkans that started in the 1930s? Now they are almost everywhere except the eastern moorland, although they are seldom found far from man. Turtle Dove has gone in the opposite direction, last known to breed here in 2000, having been present in more than one-fifth of the county (144 tetrads) only twenty years before (1978–84). Woodpigeon is one of our commonest birds, as it was fifty years ago, although they are now an abundant breeder in towns and gardens, where they were formerly quite scarce. Stock Doves were virtually ignored until 1965 when it was realised how scarce they had become, as a result of poisoning from agricultural seed-dressings. Following the pesticide ban, Stock Doves bounced back quickly and were found in 70% of the county in both county Atlases. I wrote in our recent Atlas that Feral Pigeon holds the curious distinction of being the species most familiar to those who

Figure 11.10. Collared Doves, now common in all
Cheshire towns and villages, first bred here only in 1961.
© Neil Aiston

Figure 11.11. Turtle Dove underwent a precipitous decline
in Cheshire, last breeding in 2000. © Andy Harmer

know nothing about birds and most ignored by those who do. In keeping with
that comment, the species is not included in Bell's books of the 1960s but Feral
Pigeons now seem equally at home scavenging amongst shoppers' feet in a town
centre or foraging for seed in farmland.

Tits

Blue Tits and Great Tits were far too common and sedentary to have interested
the bird-recorders of the 1960s, but we now know that they probably breed and
winter in almost every tetrad, and both rank in the top ten most numerous species.
The status of Coal Tit has probably not changed much, either, breeding only in
the more wooded areas, especially with conifers, and spreading out somewhat
during winter. Long-tailed Tits are much more common now than, perhaps, they
have ever been. Bell commented that, following two or three winters with little
hard frost, the numbers in 1961 were probably higher than for many years. The
first detailed survey, the 1978–84 Atlas, found them to be a widespread breeder
but absent from the Mersey valley and north and east Wirral, probably because
of pollution inhibiting the lichens with which the birds bind their nests (Fig.
3.3). Since then, the combination of cleaner air and a long run of mild winters
has allowed them to colonise all of the county and in 2004–06 they were the
thirteenth most abundant breeding species. Willow Tit and Marsh Tit were not
realised to be distinct species until 1897 and the first Willow Tit identified in
Cheshire was one century ago, on 17 April 1912, by Coward at Rostherne Mere.

The distribution and abundance of the two species was not quantified until our First Atlas, when Marsh Tits were found in the breeding season in 160 tetrads and Willow Tits in 270. Since then, both species have undergone precipitous declines, to 30 and 49 tetrads respectively in the Second Atlas. Marsh Tit is the scarcer locally, but Willow Tits are so scarce nationally that they have recently been added to the list covered by the Rare Breeding Birds Panel, and the Mersey Valley, which holds the bulk of Cheshire's birds, is now among their national strongholds. The two species are now completely separated by habitat in the county, in the breeding season at least, Willow Tits in damp areas of scrub and carr woodland, while Marsh Tits are in mature old woods with substantial understorey.

Most small passerines are greatly under-recorded, but Wrens have always been ubiquitous and are probably commoner now than they have ever been, and this is likely to apply to Robins too. Dunnock has declined nationally to become Amber-listed, but in 2004–06 was the ninth most widespread species breeding in the county. Until about 1940, Song Thrushes outnumbered Blackbirds in Britain as a whole, and probably in Cheshire too, but now there are ten breeding Blackbirds for every Song Thrush. Mistle Thrush numbers have been slowly dropping but they are still widespread, breeding in 87% of the county's tetrads.

Redstarts were widespread in Coward's time, and found in most wooded areas fifty years ago, but now almost all the county records are in the eastern hills. Whinchats were declining fifty years ago and their last regular breeding here was in 1991, while Stonechats are much more common, and have undergone a

Figure 11.12. Redstarts have declined to become mostly a speciality of Cheshire's eastern hills. © Chris Grady

Figure 11.13. Whinchats stopped breeding regularly in Cheshire in 1991, but are still seen here on passage to and from Africa. © Tim Melling

fascinating shift in distribution from breeding on the coast and Mersey valley to now mostly nesting in the highest hills. There they meet the dwindling county population of Wheatears, a species which also, fifty years ago, used to breed in the lowlands. The moorland thrush, Ring Ouzel, is also disappearing; just two or three pairs still hang on at the highest altitudes.

Warblers

Our warblers share the habits of insectivory and long-distance migration but occupy such different habitats that it is not surprising that their fortunes have differed. Grasshopper Warblers are poorly recorded but are likely to have declined since the 1960s, like most species that winter in the Sahel, although their county population of around 120 pairs has probably been stable for the last quarter-century. Sedge Warblers are found in low-lying areas of western Cheshire and Wirral, mostly near waterbodies, and may now be back close to the numbers of fifty years ago. Reed Warblers have a similar distribution and a burgeoning county population, more than doubling between our two atlas surveys. *Sylvia* warblers divide themselves largely according to habitat – Blackcaps in woodland, Garden Warblers in scrub, Whitethroats in bramble and Lesser Whitethroats in hedges – but their demography has changed mainly according to where they spend their winter. Blackcaps now mostly winter around the Mediterranean rather than crossing the Sahara, and they have prospered; Whitethroats crashed in the Sahel droughts – 'Where have all the Whitethroats gone?' was the refrain in 1969 when the population dropped by four-fifths in one year – but are now recovering; Lesser Whitethroats, wintering in east Africa, are largely stable. Garden Warblers have waned somewhat, perhaps because of problems in west Africa but mostly from a reduction of their preferred scrub habitat, as also applies to the Willow Warbler, which half a century ago was our commonest warbler but now is found in only 80% of the county's tetrads. Bell (1962) wrote that Chiffchaff was 'far less abundant than the Willow Warbler' but now it is the opposite: in 2004–06 Chiffchaffs occurred in 92% of the tetrads (virtually everywhere except the highest, treeless, land) and its population may be three or four times that of its cousin. As with Blackcap, the warming climate is allowing more Chiffchaffs to winter around the Mediterranean, benefiting them in earlier spring returns and nesting. In the last national census in 1984 there were 90 singing Wood Warblers in Cheshire, but the species has declined rapidly since then, and may now be extinct as a Cheshire breeder. On the other hand, Cetti's Warblers have gradually spread north after first breeding in Britain in 1973, and I was pleased to confirm their first breeding in Cheshire in 2009. Goldcrests usually nest in conifers, even a single tree in a garden or woodland, and were found breeding in two-thirds of the county in the Second Atlas, a considerable rise from twenty years previously. Firecrests have been proven to breed just once in the county (2003) but are now regular winter visitors, having hardly ever been seen before the 1970s.

Figure 11.14. Wood Warbler is probably now extinct as a Cheshire breeder. © Steve Garvie

Pied Flycatchers probably first nested in Cheshire in 1948 and the county population rose slowly to 10–15 pairs by 1984, and now usually exceeds 50 pairs a year. Spotted Flycatchers have always been much more common but are in steep decline, found in 433 tetrads in the First Atlas and 226 in the Second.

A century ago, Nuthatch was a scarce bird, found mainly in south-west Cheshire but started spreading northwards in the 1930s and by Bell's time it was 'generally distributed throughout the county in suitable woodlands', quantified in our First Atlas with breeding season presence in 343 tetrads, rising to 457 by the 2004–06 survey. Treecreepers have a similar distribution but are now less widespread than Nuthatches, dropping from 475 to 407 tetrads in the two Atlases.

Four of the corvids (Carrion Crow, Jay, Magpie and Jackdaw) are common and widespread and still increasing their numbers. Periodic counts of Rook nests showed no significant difference between the Cheshire and Wirral totals in 1975 and 2009. The national decline of breeding Starlings and House Sparrows has been widely reported but one of the surprises of our 2004–06 Atlas was to discover that they had contracted their range locally: in the 1978–84 Atlas, Starling and House Sparrow were 1st and 4th in the number of tetrads occupied, but in the Second Atlas they fell to 16th and 17th. This was mostly because both species have been lost from our highest land, above 300 m in the eastern hills, for reasons that are not known. Tree Sparrows have shown a striking decline, common and widespread enough to be ignored by Bell (1962), present in the breeding season in 523 tetrads in 1978–84 but only in 321 during 2004–06.

Finches and buntings

Chaffinch has probably been the commonest breeding finch for the last century, with a small rise between our two Atlases as they colonised the last remaining gaps, in the Mersey Valley and north Wirral. Greenfinch similarly has long been common and widespread; between the two Atlases it moved to fill in most of farmland and the Peak District. In recent years it has become much less abundant as some local populations have been badly hit by a virulent disease, *trichomonosis*, from the mid-2000s onwards. Two finches, Hawfinch and Twite, have been lost as breeders in Cheshire and Wirral during this half-century, partially compensated by the arrival of Siskin, breeding in 1962 and 1964 then in 1990 and from 2004 on. Goldfinch was described as 'a rare resident' by Coward (1910) but by the 1960s it was a common breeder, especially on the urban fringes; now the species can be found nesting anywhere, encountered in 95% of the county's tetrads in 2004–06.

In arable areas, Linnet was one of the first species to suffer from changed agricultural practice from the 1960s onwards, perhaps because their favoured foods, small weed seeds, were among the earliest to be hit by modern herbicides. In Cheshire's largely pastoral landscape, the drop came later: Linnets were found in 587 of the county's 670 tetrads in the 1978–84 Atlas, but only 424 in the 2004–06 survey.

Crossbills breed sporadically in the coniferous plantations, but are very difficult to study. Lesser Redpoll, another 'woodland finch', was 'widely distributed' in the county fifty years ago but by 2004–06 was found in only 10% (67) of the county's tetrads, a massive drop from the 295 in 1978–84. They used to breed almost everywhere across the northern half of the county, but now are restricted mainly to the two areas of Forestry Commission coniferous plantations, Delamere and Macclesfield Forests, and the Inner Mersey valley. The status of the shy Bullfinch was essentially unknown until it was found in 497 tetrads in the First Atlas, dropping to 432 in the Second Atlas, perhaps not as big a drop as its national population decline might have suggested.

Cheshire can never have been particularly important for the Corn Bunting, as a bird primarily of arable land, but in the last twenty years the species has undergone a major contraction in range within the county, down from presence in 260 tetrads in our *First Atlas* to just 36 in 2004–06 and it is now one of our scarcest breeders. Fifty years ago Yellowhammer was common and widespread, and found in 571 tetrads in the 1978–84 surveys, but down to 371 in 2004–06. Reed Buntings have also dropped, from 542 to 427, but, as a partial migrant, are now much more likely to be found here in winter with the ameliorating climate.

The county's changing birdlife – some common trends and reasons

A variety of key factors underlie the changes described above, and these are condensed here, building on the summaries in the two county bird Atlases. Most of these effects are large-scale, not just relating to Cheshire and Wirral: of the 30 birds showing the biggest losses between our two Atlases, 25 of them are on the national lists of species of conservation concern. The natural world is complex, and the fortunes of many species are probably affected by a combination of causes, so the divisions given here are undoubtedly an oversimplification.

Climatic change in Britain

With the warming trend, it is perhaps not surprising that the county has been colonised by several species with a southerly distribution, such as Hobby, Little Egret, Avocet, Mediterranean Gull and Cetti's Warbler. Others have continued to spread northwards, including Reed Warbler, and the increased range of the Red-legged Partridge has probably been helped by the warmer weather. As species move in from the south, we have lost some northern species including Black Grouse, Twite and Dunlin. Red Grouse, the British race of the cosmopolitan Willow Grouse, is here at the southern limit of its range and the present warming trend is likely to affect them adversely. Golden Plovers have been returning to the Cheshire hills noticeably earlier in recent years, and breeding earlier in warmer

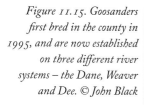

Figure 11.15. Goosanders first bred in the county in 1995, and are now established on three different river systems – the Dane, Weaver and Dee. © John Black

springs, although ultimately, the warming climate will probably put an end to their breeding in our area, and they are predicted to be lost completely from England as a breeding bird later this century (Huntley *et al.* 2007). Despite this general northward shift, it would be too naive to assume that southerly species are thriving: several have declined considerably, notably Turtle Dove, Tree Pipit and Wood Warbler, with Nightjar showing little sign of recolonising the county. And, further confounding the picture, Siskin has now spread from the north to establish itself as a regular breeder in Cheshire, as has Goosander.

At least as big an effect of the changing climate has been in winter, where the graph of winter temperatures (Fig. 1.12) particularly shows the relative infrequency of hard weather nowadays. This has changed the habits of some birds during winter itself, and also throughout the year. In winter, since the mid-1980s there have been no significant hard weather movements of species like Lapwing, some waterfowl and some thrushes. The milder winters have probably contributed to the increasing numbers of wintering warblers, especially the regular Chiffchaff and Blackcap, as well as the overwintering Cetti's Warblers. The wintering numbers and distribution in the county of partial migrants such as Stonechat, Goldfinch and Reed Bunting have undoubtedly increased.

Severe winter weather used to limit the populations of a range of resident species, which have not been restricted by this cause for over twenty years. The breeding numbers of fish-eating birds of fresh water, such as Grey Herons, are now at their highest recorded level in Cheshire and Wirral. Small insectivorous species have undoubtedly benefited from the mild winters: Long-tailed Tit and Goldcrest are much more widespread, and Wren is the most ubiquitous breeder. Grey Wagtails have probably prospered from the same cause.

Climatic change outside Britain

Many trans-Saharan migrants are decreasing in range and numbers, at least in part owing to conditions experienced on migration and in their winter quarters, and summer migrants make up a decreasing proportion of our breeding avifauna. The widening Sahara and reduced rainfall in western Africa, particularly from 1968 to 1984, severely reduced the overwinter survival, especially of species that winter in the Sahel including Sand Martin, Sedge Warbler and Whitethroat. Some of these species have adapted to their changed winter conditions and their populations are stable or increasing again, although others such as Yellow Wagtail are still declining, along with Turtle Dove and Whinchat, now lost as Cheshire breeders.

Some of the concern about conditions for our migrants in Africa is now shifting to those species wintering farther south including Redstart, Garden Warbler, Willow Warbler and Pied Flycatcher. Most of the longest-distance migrants have decreased greatly, notably Cuckoo, Tree Pipit, Wood Warbler and Spotted Flycatcher, although Swallows seem to be stable.

The warming trend has stimulated most resident species to nest earlier, and summer migrants to advance their arrival. Of 25 long-distance migrant species analysed for Cheshire and Wirral 1974–2009, the first individuals for all except Wood Warbler were arriving earlier, with an average date 12 days before that of 35 years ago (Eddowes 2011).

A similar effect is applying to some of our wintering birds, notably with a tendency for waterfowl to winter closer to their breeding grounds. Birds from the east, especially those breeding in Siberia, are reaching here in smaller numbers, such as Bewick's Swan, Pochard and Grey Plover. On the other hand, the numbers of some of the species breeding to the northwest (Iceland, Greenland and Canada) are increasing here, as fewer winter in continental Europe, such as Knot, Black-tailed Godwit and Redshank.

Land-use changes

The effects of modern agriculture on British birdlife are probably the best documented of all links between habitats and birds; as the farmed landscape makes up by far the largest area of the county, it is not surprising that agriculture has the biggest impact. 'Cleaner' fields, with more pesticides and herbicides but fewer weeds and insects, allied to a reduction in winter stubble and the practice of planting arable crops in the autumn, have led to massive falls in the numbers and distribution of many farmland species. Although our county has never had a high area of arable fields, many of those breeding species that have declined the most in this half-century in Cheshire are birds that eat small weed seeds throughout the year, with invertebrates essential for their chicks – Grey Partridge, Corn Bunting, Tree Sparrow, Yellowhammer, Linnet, Skylark and Reed Bunting – while Turtle Dove has been lost completely. There are some signs of a turn-around in the fortunes of some of these species in recent years where some farmers have taken up options under Countryside Stewardship or Environmental Stewardship, and the UK government is committed to halting the long-term decline in the index of farmland birds by 2020.

Other aspects of agricultural management have adversely affected birds. Drainage has left fewer damp areas suitable for Lapwing, Curlew, Snipe and Yellow Wagtail, all of which have declined in the county. The change from scythes to mechanical cutting meant the end of the Corncrake; numbers in Cheshire dwindled during the first half of the 20th century, with only odd breeding season records since the 1950s. Early, and repeated, cutting of grassland for silage means insufficient time for any species to nest in the fields, especially Lapwings and Skylarks. Pesticides now kill many of the farmland invertebrates, probably hitting the food supplies of species like Mistle Thrush, Rook and Starling.

Thankfully, agricultural chemicals are now extensively tested and none is known to be a direct poison to birds. The organochlorine seed-dressing used in the 1950s and 1960s hit birds like finches and Stock Doves and accumulated up the food chain to cause breeding failures in species including Peregrines and Sparrowhawks. The rise in these raptors is evidence that the pollutants are now only at low levels in the countryside.

In the hard winters of the 1980s there were sometimes flocks of thousands, or even tens of thousands, of Fieldfares congregating in the county's apple orchards. I followed them especially at the Daresbury Fruit Farm, where the neatly-pruned rows of pick-your-own apples provided opportunities to catch and ring this under-studied species, following which I wrote the book *The Fieldfare* (Norman 1994). But most of our orchards fell victim to changing EU subsidies, and the apple trees were grubbed-up.

Figure 11.16. Flocks of Fieldfares, sometimes with Redwings, gather in apple orchards in hard weather. © Bill Nevett

Provision of food and protection

Shortage of nesting sites is seldom a problem for most birds, but provision of nest boxes has certainly helped a few species. These include Pied Flycatchers, who return from Africa after the resident tits have appropriated most suitable holes, and Dippers, who may struggle to find a site; nest boxes may be used for breeding and for roosting in during winter.

Provision of food in gardens and feeding stations elsewhere may have helped with overwinter survival of some species, and perhaps encouraged wintering Blackcaps. Especially with finches, which otherwise have to delay breeding until there is sufficient natural seed available, man's actions may be allowing some finches to breed earlier, and have probably assisted the increased range of Greenfinch and Goldfinch in the county.

Some of the largest winter concentrations of farmland species of conservation concern, such as Tree Sparrow, Reed Bunting and Yellowhammer, have been found in planted areas of wildbird seed crops (Fig. 2.9), an industrial-scale example of food provision.

Reduction in persecution

Several species, particularly raptors and corvids, used to be held way below their natural population level by human persecution. Corvids, especially Carrion Crows and Magpies, were trapped or shot on many farms and estates, but fewer are taken these days; both species have spread to breed closer to man. In the last twenty-five years, Peregrines, Buzzards and Ravens have become established as breeding birds in the county. Ironically, now that some of these species are achieving a more widespread status, some individuals and organisations regularly argue for predatory birds to be killed, failing to understand the difference between the impact on individuals and species and often invoking the false equation between nests being robbed or small birds being killed and population declines amongst some prey species.

Improved quality of water and air

Pollution is now better understood as a hazard to humans and wildlife, and most pollutants are much reduced. The birds at the top of the aquatic food chain have prospered in the last twenty years, with Grey Heron populations rising enormously, and Cormorant and Little Egret now breeding in the county. Goosanders have also moved in and established themselves as breeders on three of Cheshire's river systems. On the other hand, Dippers have contracted their distribution in the county, and some watercourses are declining in quality. Detailed analysis of the results of our two Atlases has shown the beneficial effects on breeding birds of the cleaner air and water, and woodland planting, in Halton and Warrington, previously the most-polluted boroughs. From 1978–84 to 2004–06 four groups of birds have fared significantly better in the Mersey valley compared to the rest

Timeline of gains and losses of breeding species

Loss	Year	Gain
Black Grouse	1960	
	1961	Collared Dove, Little Ringed Plover
	1962	
	1963	
	1964	
	1965	Red-legged Partridge
	1966	
	1967	
	1968	Ruddy Duck
	1969	
	1970	
	1971	Mandarin
	1972	
	1973	
	1974	Pochard
	1975	Goshawk
	1976	
	1977	
	1978	
	1979	Greylag Goose
Nightjar	1980	Buzzard
	1981	Gadwall
	1982	
	1983	
	1984	
Dunlin	1985	
	1986	

Loss	Year	Gain
	1987	Black-necked Grebe
	1988	
	1989	Peregrine
Twite, Hawfinch	1990	
Whinchat	1991	Raven
	1992	
	1993	
	1994	
	1995	Goosander, Hobby
	1996	
	1997	
	1998	
	1999	
Turtle Dove	2000	
	2001	
	2002	Avocet
	2003	Lesser Black-backed Gull
	2004	Cormorant, Little Egret, Mediterranean Gull, Siskin
	2005	
	2006	
	2007	
	2008	
	2009	Cetti's Warbler
Wood Warbler	2010	Marsh Harrier
	2011	

Over the past fifty years some of the most extreme changes in the county's breeding birds have been the gains and losses of some species. The timeline (opposite) illustrates this, indicating the last year of known breeding of those lost, and the first year of regular breeding of those gained. Inevitably, there is an element of subjectivity in such a plot and it is not intended to contain every detail of the last half-century. Several of the species listed had previously bred infrequently, sometimes years before the major colonisation (Little Ringed Plover, Black-necked Grebe, Buzzard, Siskin, Cormorant, Little Egret), and some might have bred occasionally after their last listed year (Whinchat). Others are not listed here including some that have bred for a few years and then been 'lost' again (Common Tern, Great Black-backed Gull, Bearded Tit); some that bred sporadically, probably being under-recorded (Short-eared Owl, Merlin, Herring Gull); and some that have bred once only (Marsh Warbler, Black-winged Stilt, Black Redstart, Firecrest).

Figure 11.17. The Cheshire nests of two of the most recent colonists: Cetti's Warbler (left) © Richard Castell and Marsh Harrier (below) © David Norman

of the county: waterbirds (24 species), those feeding on invertebrates (16 species), woodland specialists (21 species) and the two species that decorate their nests with lichens (Chaffinches and Long-tailed Tits), while other groups (raptors (5 species), waders (7 species), farmland seedeaters (7 species) and aerial insectivores (5 species)) showed no difference between Halton and Warrington and the rest of Cheshire and Wirral (James, Norman & Clarke 2010).

Disease

Disease is probably ever-present in wild birds but sick individuals usually die, or are predated, quickly and are seldom noticed. Occasionally disease can affect populations and since 2005 *trichomonosis* (which has long been present in pigeons and doves) has crossed the species boundary and infected finches. The *trichomonas* parasite is spread mainly by infected water or sick birds spraying saliva, almost certainly at bird-feeders, the only places where doves and finches come close enough to transmit the parasite; garden populations of Greenfinches in parts of Cheshire have been hard-hit. Avian pox is afflicting some Great Tits in southern England, and is moving north and will surely be in Cheshire before long.

Unknown reasons

In a sense, understanding the decline in birds of arable farmland has been easy, with relatively straightforward prescriptions for action. Other groups of birds, however, are also dropping in population or decreasing their range, especially woodland species and summer migrants. Cheshire and Wirral is not a particularly well-wooded county, but the conifer plantations hold most of our breeding Crossbills, Siskins and Goshawks, none of them seen very often. A number of species associated with woods have decreased substantially in our review period, including Woodcock, Lesser Spotted Woodpecker, Spotted Flycatcher, Marsh Tit, Willow Tit and Lesser Redpoll. Another group of migrant species especially found in the Western Atlantic oakwoods – Tree Pipit, Wood Warbler, Redstart and Pied Flycatcher – are also in decline, for reasons that are largely unknown.

Although they all use woodland, their specific habitat requirements differ greatly and it is likely that different factors, probably acting in combination, are responsible. Elsewhere, especially in eastern England where most of the specialised ornithological organisations are based, browsing by deer is being increasingly blamed for modifying the woodland understorey. But probably nowhere in Cheshire and Wirral has yet suffered significant pressure from deer, and comparisons between the county and elsewhere in England could be fruitful.

References

Bell, T.H. (1962) The Birds of Cheshire. Sherratt, Altrincham.
Bell, T.H. (1967) A Supplement to The Birds of Cheshire. Sherratt, Altrincham.
Boyd, A.W. (1946) The Country Diary of a Cheshire Man. Collins, London.

Boyd, A.W. (1951) A Country Parish. Collins, London.

Coward, T.A. & Oldham, C. (1900) The Birds of Cheshire. Sherratt & Hughes, Manchester.

Coward, T.A. (1910) The Vertebrate Fauna of Cheshire and Liverpool Bay. Witherby, London.

Eddowes, M. (2011) Longer term trends in arrival timing of long distance migrants: the influence of abundance and population change. *Ringing & Migration* 26: 56–63.

Guest, J.P., Elphick, D., Hunter, J.S.A. & Norman, D. (1992) The Breeding Bird Atlas of Cheshire and Wirral. Cheshire and Wirral Ornithological Society.

Holling, M. and the Rare Breeding Birds Panel (2011) Rare breeding birds in the United Kingdom in 2009. *British Birds* 104: 476–537.

Huntley, B., Green, R.E., Collingham, Y.C. & Willis, S.G. (2007) A Climatic Atlas of European Breeding Birds. Lynx, Barcelona.

James, P., Norman, D. & Clarke, J.J. (2010) Avian population dynamics and human induced change in an urban environment. *Urban Ecosystems* 13: 499–515.

McCarthy, M. (2009) Say Goodbye to the Cuckoo. John Murray, London.

Martin, B. & Norman, D. (2011) Cheshire and Wirral heronries 1980–2010. Cheshire and Wirral Bird Report 2010, pp. 126–131.

Norman, D. (1994) The Fieldfare. Hamlyn, London.

Norman, D. (2008) Birds in Cheshire and Wirral: a breeding and wintering atlas. Liverpool University Press. www.cheshireandwirralbirdatlas.org/

Norman, D., Harris, R.J. & Newson, S.E. (2012) Producing regional estimates of population size for common and widespread breeding birds from national monitoring data. *Bird Study* 59: 10–21.

Smith, S. (1950) The Yellow Wagtail. Collins, London.

About the author

David Norman is a passionate bird-ringer, having handled more than 100,000 birds in Cheshire. The British Trust for Ornithology awarded him their Bernard Tucker Medal for outstanding contributions in ringing, nest-recording and bird surveying, only the second Cheshire ornithologist in sixty years to have been so honoured. He was a Council member of RSPB (Royal Society for Protection of Birds) (2004–09), and currently chairs the Merseyside Ringing Group and is a trustee of Cheshire and Wirral Ornithological Society and one of the two independent members of the UK's Rare Breeding Birds Panel.

David has published books or papers on a wide range of species and subjects including Fieldfare, Wood Warbler, Common Tern, Little Tern, Chaffinch, Sand Martin, Swift, Grey Heron, and the waders of the Mersey Estuary; and was instrumental in proving the first breeding in Cheshire of Marsh Warbler (1991), Cetti's Warbler (2009) and Marsh Harrier (2010). He co-authored the first breeding bird atlas of the county and led the project and wrote the book from the second atlas 'Birds in Cheshire and Wirral: a breeding and wintering atlas', published in 2008.

Index

— A —

Abbots Moss 102, 103, 106, 109, 110, 117
Acarospora fuscata 190
agrichemicals 5, 25, 27, 32, 246
agricultural land grades 25
agriculture 4, 25–37, 107, 113, 121, 135, 138, 143–145, 152, 155, 212, 245
air quality 13, 16, 41, 42, 181, 183, 184, 187, 189, 194, 238, 247
Alder 8, 10, 104, 174
alga 62, 85, 88, 89, 94–96, 173, 181, 191
alien species 1, 13, 20, 46, 67, 69, 71, 74, 81, 89, 92–94, 96, 114, 129–132, 135, 140
Altrincham 133, 141
Alvanley 172
ammonia 13, 14, 80, 144, 145, 187
amphibian 16, 18, 47, 125, 153, 158, 159, 165–169, 171, 174–176
ancient woodland 6, 7, 13, 183, 184
Anderton 134
anemone 59, 75, 83, 87–90, 92, 95
Arctoparmelia incurva 190
Arthonia spp. 184
Ash 7, 8, 10, 50, 184
Australian Swamp Stonecrop 13, 114, 116, 130, 131, 165
Avocet 233, 243, 248

— B —

Bacidea sabuletorum 191
Badger 6, 214, 218
Bagmere 20, 99, 109
Bank Vole 213

barley 27, 30
Barn Owl 6, 36, 234
barnacle 72–74, 81, 83, 85, 88–90, 92, 93, 95, 193
Bar-tailed Godwit 233
bat 15, 33, 47, 48, 54, 174, 211, 217, 220
Bearded Tit 249
bee 3, 26
Beech 7, 8
Beeston 24, 25, 44, 138, 217, 231
beetle 9, 10, 26, 46, 47, 49, 108, 123, 137, 160, 172
Bell, T.H. 223, 227, 238
Bewick's Swan 245
Bickley 20, 21, 36, 161, 204
Bidston 139
Bilberry 10, 110, 112
biochemical oxygen demand (BOD) 13, 144
Biodiversity Action Plan (BAP) 7, 8, 12, 161, 174, 212
Birch 7, 112
bird population index 32, 33, 36, 246
Birket 138, 139
Black Darter 109
Black Grouse 233, 243, 248
Black Lake 100, 101, 109, 111, 117, 205
Black Poplar 8, 9
Black Redstart 249
black sand 63
Black Swan 227
Blackbird 239
Blackcap 240, 241, 244, 247
Black-headed Gull 114, 229, 230
Black-necked Grebe 127, 225, 226, 248
Black-tailed Godwit 233, 245

Black-tailed Skimmer 203
Black-winged Stilt 249
Bladderwort 108, 137
Blakemere Moss 99, 112, 114–116, 230
Blakenhall Moss 110
Blue Tit 238
bog 3, 99, 102–104, 106, 108, 112–114, 118, 119, 197, 203
Bog Myrtle 119
Bollin 125, 127–130, 132, 133, 216
Bollington 129, 199
Boyd, A.W. 5
Branched Bur-reed 164
Brent Goose 228
Bridgewater Canal 124
British Trust for Ornithology (BTO) 32, 224, 234, 251
Broad-bodied Chaser 47, 162, 199, 200, 203
broadleaves 7, 107, 138
brownfield site 10, 39, 45, 46
bryozoa 71–73, 90
Budworth Mere 5, 181, 217, 225
Buellia aethalea 191
bug 160, 172
Bullfinch 243
Bullhead 126, 138, 139
bumblebee 20, 26, 39, 51, 52, 76
butterfly 3, 16–20, 22, 33, 51, 108–110
Buzzard 230, 231, 247–249

— C —

caddis 97, 160, 172, 237
Caldy 66, 77
Caloplaca spp. 190, 191, 193
Canada Goose 114, 227

Candelariella vitellina   188, 191, 192

Capenhurst   161, 162

carr   104, 181, 184, 187, 189, 239

Carrion Crow   242, 247

Cetraria islandica   194

Cetti's Warbler   241, 243, 244, 248, 249, 251

Chaffinch   42, 242, 250, 251

Chartley Moss   117

Cheshire and Wirral Ornithological Society (CAWOS)   42, 224, 225

Cheshire Ornithological Association   223, 224

Cheshire Wildlife Trust (CWT)   1, 3–5, 7, 9, 11, 20, 23, 37, 44, 46, 109–111, 118, 132, 136, 137, 154, 158–161, 178, 221, 225

Chester   4, 7, 9, 43, 83, 85, 100, 141, 171, 186, 187, 201, 204, 232

Chester Zoo   52, 161, 213, 221

Chiffchaff   241, 244

Chinese Mitten Crab   13, 96, 131, 140

Cladonia spp.   186, 188, 190, 191, 194

clam   57–59, 66

climate   1, 4, 14, 16, 17, 20, 22, 25, 30, 32, 34, 100, 101, 103, 108, 123, 138, 149, 159, 166, 177, 184, 208, 241, 243, 244

Coal Tit   238

coast   9, 13, 20, 44, 54, 56–97, 129, 139, 140, 166, 193, 197, 198, 201, 211, 229, 232, 240

cockle   60, 61, 63–65, 67, 77, 79

Coelocaulon spp.   194

Collared Dove   16, 237, 238, 248

Collema spp.   191, 192

Collemopsidium halodytes   193

Common Agricultural Policy (CAP)   5, 25

Common Birds Census (CBC)   17, 32, 33, 223

Common Clubtail   140, 174, 200, 201, 203

Common Cord Grass   95

Common Darter   47

Common Gull   229

Common Hornwort   164

Common Sandpiper   233

Common Scoter   59

Common Tern   249, 251

Congleton   49, 54, 100, 132

conifer   7, 50, 107, 111, 112, 213, 238, 241, 243, 250

Coot   229

Cormorant   80, 226, 228, 247–249

Corn Bunting   243, 245

Corncrake   32, 246

Corophium   78–80

corvid   16, 30, 223, 242, 247

cottongrass   113, 117

cow   26, 28–31, 137, 155, 212, 234

Coward, T.A.   5, 211, 215–217, 219, 223, 224, 234, 237–239, 242

Cowbane   164

crab   13, 59, 63, 68, 69, 72, 74, 78, 83, 90, 95, 96, 131, 140

Cranberry   100

Critical Pond Biodiversity Survey (CPBS)   12, 157, 160, 161, 163, 164, 174, 178

Crossbill   243, 250

crustacean   13, 75, 76, 78

Cuckoo   234, 245

Cumbria   101, 117, 129, 205

Curlew   233, 246

Curly Pondweed   165

Cystocoleus ebeneus   190

— D —

damselfly   14, 17, 18, 126, 158, 161, 174, 197–209

Dance Fly   47

Dane   10, 130, 132–135, 140, 141, 216, 219, 229, 244

Danes Moss   99, 109–111, 118, 119, 121, 203, 233

Danish Scurvy Grass   44, 45

deciduous   16, 129, 132

Dee   12, 13, 15, 58, 72, 76, 77, 79, 81, 85, 90, 95, 125, 129, 139–141, 145, 193, 200, 201, 203, 204, 228, 229, 233, 244

Dee Estuary   13, 57, 59, 76, 123, 138, 211, 212, 224, 226–228, 233, 234

deer   15, 218–220, 250

Degelia spp.   183, 185

Delamere   20, 109, 111, 112, 114, 116–118, 205, 225, 229, 234, 243

Delamere Forest   7, 107, 112, 113, 185, 205

Derbyshire   129, 132, 186, 193, 219, 231

Dibbinsdale   138, 139

Dipper   126, 132, 237, 247

disease   6, 9, 10, 26, 45, 157, 166, 242, 250

dolphin   211, 212

Dormouse   15, 215, 216, 220

Downy Emerald   174, 207, 208

dragonfly   14, 17, 18, 20, 47, 108, 116, 117, 140, 158, 160–162, 172, 174, 196–209, 232

drainage   1, 31, 47, 82, 95, 107, 112, 118, 135, 139, 145, 155, 172, 177, 199, 200, 233, 246

Dunlin   82, 127, 233, 243, 248

Dunnock   234, 239

— E —

Eastham   57, 93, 94, 125

Eaton   141, 225, 227, 229

ecosystem services   3, 149, 176

eel   81, 138, 139

Egremont   82, 85

Ellesmere Port   9, 43, 49, 135, 138, 187

Elm   9, 10

Emperor Dragonfly   14, 162, 197, 198, 201, 203

English Nature   7, 9, 23, 109, 121, 138, 198

Enterographa crassa   183, 184

Enteromorpha   73, 85

Environment Agency (EA)   13, 80, 107, 122–147, 158, 176, 237

Environmental Stewardship   6, 33–35, 110, 213, 220, 246

epiphytic lichens   184, 185, 187
Etherow   129, 130, 132, 133
Eurydice   75, 76
eutrophication   107, 113, 145, 184
Evernia prunastri   180, 181, 187

— F —

farm   4, 5, 6, 9, 12, 14–16, 25–37,
    46, 47, 129, 134, 150, 155, 158,
    164, 172, 176, 208, 212, 213,
    218, 219, 224, 233, 238, 242,
    245–247, 250
Farndon   140, 151, 201, 204
Fellhanera ochracea   184
Feral Pigeon   44, 237, 238
Field (Short-tailed) Vole   213
Field Maple   8
Fieldfare   53, 246, 251
Firecrest   241, 249
fish   47, 76, 78, 80–83, 90, 108,
    123, 127–133, 138, 141, 145,
    150, 153, 167, 168, 172, 226,
    229, 244
Flavoparmelia caperata   186, 187
Flaxmere Moss   99
Floating Pennywort   13, 130
Floating Sweet-grass   164
Floating Water Plantain   140
flood   3, 17, 25, 30, 34, 112, 118,
    123–125, 127, 129–132,
    135–141, 143, 144, 151, 177,
    225, 229, 230
flora   3, 11, 28, 39, 86, 95, 99, 123,
    129, 130, 132, 137, 139, 164,
    177
Foot and Mouth Disease (FMD)
    26
Forestry Commission   7, 10, 109,
    112, 205, 243
Foulshaw Moss   117
Four-spotted Chaser   109
Fox   213
Fringed Water-lily   164
Frodsham   127, 134, 135, 175, 191,
    226, 230
Frog   47, 166–168, 175
Frogbit   164
Fuscidea cyathoides   190

— G —

Gabb, R.   197, 198, 201, 202, 208
Gadwall   127, 229, 248
garden   10, 16, 18, 46, 47, 51, 52,
    54, 95, 130, 150, 174, 175, 202,
    214, 215, 218, 237, 241, 247,
    250
Garden Warbler   240, 241, 245
General Quality Assessment
    (GQA)   144, 145
Giant Hogweed   13, 130, 131
glaciation   11, 57, 66, 85, 99–101,
    106, 108, 110, 116, 123, 150,
    184, 188
goby   65, 75, 81
Goldcrest   241, 244
Golden Plover   233, 243
Golden-ringed Dragonfly   204
Goldfinch   51, 242, 244, 247
Goosander   229, 244, 247, 248
Goshawk   230, 248, 250
Gowy   8, 133, 135–138, 216
Gowy Meadows   136–138
Goyt   10, 124, 128–130, 132, 133,
    216, 219
Graphis scripta   184
grass   4, 5, 27, 28, 49, 124, 137,
    138, 173, 204, 213, 229, 233,
    236, 246
Grasshopper Warbler   174, 240
Great Black-backed Gull   230, 249
Great Crested Grebe   15, 80, 225
Great Crested Newt   12, 18, 47,
    127, 137, 166, 168–172, 174
Great Spotted Woodpecker   174,
    234
Great Tit   238, 250
grebe   15, 80, 127, 225, 226, 229,
    248, 249
Green Woodpecker   234
Greenfinch   242, 247, 250
Grey Heron   80, 133, 222, 225,
    244, 247, 251
Grey Partridge   32, 33, 233, 245
Grey Plover   245
Grey Squirrel   15, 51, 215, 220
Grey Wagtail   236, 244
Greylag Goose   227, 248
Guest, J.P.   18, 178, 183

Gull Pool   117, 200, 205, 207

— H —

Habitats Directive   59, 157, 217
Haematomma ochroleucum   191
Hairy Dragonfly   162, 196, 199,
    200
Hale (near Widnes)   57, 76, 82,
    204
Halton   4, 7, 9, 27, 42, 198, 247,
    250
Handforth   170, 201
hare   6, 33, 212, 219
Harlequin Ladybird   20–22, 52
Harvest Mouse   210, 213
Hatch Mere   99, 104, 108–110,
    119, 181, 184, 189, 199, 200,
    206–208
Hawfinch   242, 248
hay   5, 27, 28, 213, 237
Heather   112, 233
heathland   18, 20, 150, 212
hedge   6, 7, 8, 31, 33, 34, 101, 213,
    217, 241
Hedgehog   15, 218, 220
Helsby   44
Hemlock   111, 112
Hen Harrier   231
Herring Gull   230, 249
Higher Level Stewardship (HLS)
    6, 33, 110
Hilbre   13, 57, 59, 66, 67, 76, 81,
    85–94, 97, 193, 211, 212, 224,
    227
Himalayan Balsam   4, 13, 130, 131
Hobby   108, 243, 248
Hogshead Moss   102, 109
Holcroft Moss   109, 118, 121
House Martin   53, 232, 235, 236
House Mouse   217, 218
House Sparrow   51, 242
Hoylake   57, 138, 166
Hunger-hill Moss   113
Hydrobia   77, 79, 82
hydroid   71–75, 90
hydromorphology   132, 140, 145
Hymenelia lacustris   194
Hypogymnia spp.   186, 187
Hypotrachyna revoluta   186, 187

— **I** —

Inner Marsh Farm   226, 230
insect   3, 20, 45, 96, 130, 172, 217,
     234, 235, 240, 244, 245, 250
invertebrates   4, 6, 13, 20, 33, 34,
     46, 47, 51, 55, 58, 76, 79, 80, 82,
     91, 97, 108, 112, 123, 130, 131,
     133, 137, 138, 144, 145, 153,
     158, 160–163, 172, 173, 245,
     246, 250
Irish Sea   57, 63, 73, 123, 127, 212

— **J** —

Jackdaw   242
Japanese Knotweed   13, 130, 131
Jay   242
jellyfish   63, 69, 70, 94, 95

— **K** —

Kestrel   34, 230
kettle-hole   100, 101, 103, 150
Kingfisher   123, 133, 144, 237
Knot   58, 233, 245
Knutsford   54, 186, 187

— **L** —

ladybird   20–22, 42, 49–50, 52
lake   103, 104, 107, 113, 114, 120,
     123, 130, 133, 135, 139–141,
     149, 150, 152, 163, 177, 197,
     207, 225, 227, 228
lamprey   128, 139
Lancashire   16, 54, 124, 152, 157,
     161, 166, 183, 185, 186, 188,
     193, 194, 197, 201
Lapwing   6, 32, 33, 36, 137, 233,
     234, 246
Larch   7, 10
Leasowe   57, 60, 63, 89
Lecania spp.   191, 193
Lecanora spp.   184, 185, 188, 190,
     191, 193
Lecidea sulphurea   188
Lecidella spp.   191, 193
Lepraria incana   188
Leptogium spp.   185, 191

Lesser Black-backed Gull   229,
     230
Lesser Redpoll   243, 250
Lesser Silver Water Beetle   12,
     137, 161–163, 174
Lesser Spotted Woodpecker   234,
     235, 250
Lesser Whitethroat   240, 241
lichen   13, 14, 18, 40–42, 101,
     180–195, 238, 250
Lime (tree)   50, 187
limestone   43, 90, 117, 190, 191,
     205
limpet   88, 89, 91, 92
Lindow Moss   107
Linnet   242, 245
Little Budworth   163, 191, 192,
     207, 217
Little Egret   226, 227, 243,
     247–249
Little Grebe   229
Little Owl   234
Little Ringed Plover   232, 233,
     248, 249
Liverpool   94, 124, 125, 127, 212
Liverpool Bay   5, 9, 13, 57, 59
Liverpool John Moores University
     (LJMU)   152, 178, 179
Liverpool Museum   62, 67, 71, 73,
     80, 83, 97
Liverpool University   76, 82, 95
Lobaria spp.   183, 184
Local Wildlife Site (LWS)   4, 9,
     106, 124
Long-eared Owl   234
Long-tailed Tit   41, 42, 238, 244,
     250
Lower Moss Wood   202
Lugworm   58–60, 77, 80

— **M** —

Macclesfield   42, 43, 54, 109, 129,
     188, 202, 214, 219
Macclesfield Forest   7, 129, 234,
     243
Magpie   242, 247
maize   27, 30
Mallard   228

mammal   6, 15, 16, 18, 33, 34, 47,
     132, 174, 210–221
Manchester   4, 9, 39, 118, 124,
     128, 132, 224, 236
Manchester Airport   129, 169, 170
Manchester Ship Canal   124, 125,
     127, 129, 135, 137, 218, 225
Mandarin   229, 248
map   4, 9, 21, 105, 125, 151, 156
Marbury   5, 187, 189, 204, 217,
     225
marine   9, 13, 15, 56–97, 193, 211,
     212
Marine Conservation Zone (MCZ)
     13, 57, 59, 66
marine lake   13, 57, 71, 94
marl   8, 9, 150–153, 156, 165, 174,
     197, 200, 201, 206, 208, 216
Marsh Harrier   232, 248, 249, 251
Marsh Tit   238, 239, 250
Marsh Warbler   249, 251
mayfly   13, 123, 144, 145, 237
McMillan, Nora   86, 91, 97
Meadow Pipit   234, 237
Mediterranean Gull   230, 243, 248
Melanelixia glabratula   187, 191
Meols   62, 63, 139, 203
mere   9, 11, 54, 98–121, 150, 184,
     187, 197, 216, 229, 233
Mere Moss Wood   99
Merlin   231, 249
Mersey   67, 71, 74, 81–83, 85, 86,
     90, 92, 95, 97, 118, 129, 198,
     218, 225, 229, 233, 237–240,
     242, 243, 247
Mersey   10, 118, 124, 125,
     127–129, 132, 211
Mersey Basin Campaign   127, 128
Mersey Estuary   13, 23, 57–59, 76,
     80–82, 85, 123, 127, 134–136,
     138, 204, 212, 227–229, 234,
     251
Mersey Forest   7
Mersey Gateway   44
Mersey Narrows   59, 77
Merseyside   67, 71, 94, 127, 141
Merseyside Ringing Group   43,
     44, 224, 251
Micarea denigrata   188

Middlewich 134

Migrant Hawker 14, 202, 203

migration 16, 52–54, 65, 77, 80, 96, 128, 132, 138–140, 228, 229, 240, 245

milk 6, 26, 28, 29

millstone 184

Mink 13, 15, 130–132, 216, 220

Mistle Thrush 239, 246

Mole 214

mollusc 64, 77, 78, 89, 161

Moorhen 229

moorland 33, 124, 132, 156, 193, 194, 202, 211, 219, 230, 233, 237, 240

moss 9, 11, 98–121, 150, 163, 165, 197

moth 10, 17, 22, 39–41, 234

Mud Snail 12, 137, 161, 174

mussel 57, 59, 65, 67, 83, 85, 89, 90, 92, 93, 95

Mute Swan 226

— N —

Nantwich 134, 215

National Biodiversity Network (NBN) 17

National Nature Reserve (NNR) 11, 109, 117

National Rivers Authority 128, 157, 158

National Trust 7, 129, 141, 143, 144

Natterjack Toad 12, 18, 166, 174

Natural Area 9–11, 105, 106

Natural England 46, 109, 110, 118, 205

Nature Conservancy 86, 109

Nature Improvement Area (NIA) 9, 120

nature reserve 3, 5, 7, 11, 46, 54, 109–111, 117, 118, 120, 127, 136–138, 202, 226

neonicotinoids 26

Nephroma spp. 185

New Brighton 57, 85, 91, 92, 94, 212

New Ferry 59, 76, 77, 85

Newchurch Common 199, 203, 205

newt 12, 18, 47, 108, 127, 137, 165–172, 174, 175, 177

Nightjar 234, 244, 248

nitrate 5, 26, 27, 145

nitrogen 14, 27, 184, 186, 187, 194

non-native 45, 46, 129–131, 227

Norley Moss 104

Northwich 43, 134, 135, 186, 187, 218

Nuthatch 242

nutrient 3, 46, 95, 103, 107, 113, 114, 144, 145, 186, 188

— O —

Oak 3, 7, 8, 10, 50, 188, 250

Oak Mere 106, 114, 121, 181, 201

Oakhanger Moss 104, 121

oats 27, 30

Ochrolecechia parella 193

Opegrapha spp. 184

Ophioparma ventosa 190

orchard 27, 246

organochlorine 44, 216, 230, 246

Otter 13, 15, 126, 128, 130, 133, 137, 139, 174, 216, 220

oyster 64, 66, 72, 89

Oystercatcher 233

— P —

Palmate Newt 18, 108, 166, 177

Parmelia spp. 181, 185, 186, 187, 188, 190

Parmotrema perlatum 186, 187, 189

pastoral agriculture 4, 27, 31, 155, 212, 242

Peak District 9, 13, 31, 33, 129, 132, 187, 211, 231, 233, 242

peat 3, 25, 57, 59, 66, 99, 100, 103–105, 107, 112, 114, 116–120, 137, 150

Peckforton 7, 124, 134, 135

Peppered Moth 10, 39–41

Peregrine 11, 38, 43, 44, 231, 232, 246, 247, 248

Pertusaria corallina 190

pesticide 1, 3, 26, 34, 44, 46, 133, 216, 230, 231, 237, 245, 246

pH 117, 145

Phaeophyscia orbicularis 185

Pheasant 30, 223, 233

phosphate 5, 26, 145

Physcia spp. 184, 185, 186, 190, 192

Phytophthora 10

piddock 57, 59, 66, 68, 69

Pied Flycatcher 242, 245, 247, 250

Pied Wagtail 236

pig 29, 30

pine 7, 49, 50, 107, 113, 232

Pineapple Weed 45

Pink-footed Goose 53, 54

pipistrelle 33, 47, 48, 54, 217, 220

Placyhnthiella icmalea 188

Plaismatisa glauca 186, 187

plankton 58, 60, 63, 65, 69, 71, 78, 80, 87, 89, 145

Plumley 191, 203

Pochard 127, 229, 245, 248

Polecat 214, 220

pollination 3, 26

pollution 1, 10, 13, 27, 40–42, 63, 74, 80–83, 94, 127, 133, 135, 136, 138–141, 144, 145, 157, 181, 182, 184–187, 191, 193, 195, 216, 238, 246, 247

Polydora 90

pond 10, 12, 18, 34, 47, 95, 130, 131, 139, 148–179, 197, 200–202, 206, 208, 216, 225, 227–229

Pond *Life* Project 12, 157–159, 162, 166, 168, 172, 179

Ponds Research Unit 152, 154, 157, 158, 172, 179

pondweed 164, 165

Poplar 8, 107

Porpidia spp. 181, 188, 190

potato 27, 30

prawn 83, 95

Prestbury 129, 133

Protoblastenia rupestris 191

protozoan 62

Punctelia subrudecta 186, 187, 189

— **Q** —

quarries 135, 229, 232, 234

— **R** —

Rabbit 212, 213, 214, 219, 228, 232
Ragworm 78–80, 82
Ramalina spp. 181, 182, 186, 187, 193
Ramsar Convention 11, 106, 121, 149
raptor 16, 230, 232, 246, 247, 250
rat 217, 218
Raven 232, 247, 248
razor shells 63–65, 67, 68
rECOrd 17, 23, 49, 52, 97
Red Grouse 233, 243
Red Kite 121, 232
Red Squirrel 15, 51, 215, 220
Red-legged Partridge 233, 243, 248
Redshank 127, 233, 245
Redstart 239, 245, 250
Redwing 53, 246
Reed Bunting 34, 174, 243–245, 247
Reed Canary-grass 164
Reed Warbler 139, 234, 240, 243
Reedmace 114, 164, 174
reef 91, 92
reintroduction 14, 20, 116–118, 166, 205, 213, 215
restoration 9, 106, 110, 112–114, 116, 117, 121, 140, 141, 143, 144, 158, 169
re-wetting 11, 113, 117–119
Rhizocarpon spp. 188, 190
Rhododendron 10
riffle 123, 129, 133
Ring Ouzel 240
Ringed Plover 232
Rinodina gennarii 190
Risley Moss 99, 118, 199, 203, 234
Rivacre 138
river 4, 8, 10, 13, 25, 81, 100, 114, 122–147, 149, 157, 163, 165,

177, 194, 197, 200, 201, 204, 216, 229, 234, 237, 244, 247
Robin 47, 239
Rook 242, 246
Rostherne Mere NNR 5, 11, 109, 184, 187, 215, 226, 228, 238
Royal Fern 113, 115
RSPB 23, 79, 121, 221, 251
Ruddy Darter 162, 197
Ruddy Duck 229, 248
Rudheath 160–162
Runcorn 7, 40, 42, 44, 45, 54, 80, 81, 135, 181, 182, 214, 232
Rushton 162
Russell, G. 71, 85, 86, 94

— **S** —

Sabellaria 90–92
Salford University 76, 79, 80
Sallow 164
Salmon 13, 81, 128, 129, 139, 140
salt 44, 103, 134, 184, 193
Saltersley Moss 109
saltmarsh 13, 77, 95, 233
Sand Gaper 64, 67, 78, 80
Sand Martin 123, 126, 133, 144, 234, 245, 251
Sand Mason Worm 61, 62, 65
sandstone 89, 124, 156, 184, 188, 190–194, 231, 232
Sandstone Ridge 124, 156
Sarcogyne regularis 190
schwingmoor 102, 103, 106
Scolelepis 61, 77
sea squirt 86, 87, 94
seal 15, 211, 212, 220
seaweed 71, 73, 85, 86, 88, 93, 94
Sedge Warbler 139, 174, 240, 245
sheep 29, 30, 118, 232
Shelduck 227
shell 60–69, 72, 73, 74, 77–79, 81, 86, 89–91, 93, 97
Shemmy Moss 110
Short-eared Owl 234, 249
shrew 213, 216, 217, 220
shrimp 60, 65, 72, 75, 76, 95, 96, 123, 237
Shropshire 15, 99, 100, 112, 117, 120, 157, 202

Shropshire Union Canal 138
Shutlingsloe 31
Signal Crayfish 13, 130, 131, 135
silage 5, 28, 30, 233, 237, 246
Silent Spring 3, 26
Sinderland Brook 141–144
Siskin 242, 244, 248–250
Site of Biological Importance (SBI) 9, 106
Site of Special Scientific Interest (SSSI) 7, 9, 11, 57, 59, 99, 102, 106, 109–112, 114, 118–121, 125, 129, 132, 134, 136–140, 191, 203, 226, 229
Skylark 32, 33, 36, 237, 245, 246
Smooth Newt 18, 47, 166, 175
snail 64, 77, 96, 160
Snipe 137, 233, 246
Song Thrush 239
Soprano Pipistrelle 47, 48, 217
Sound Common 202
South Manchester Ringing Group 224
Southern Hawker 204
Sparrowhawk 230, 246
Special Area of Conservation (SAC) 57, 59, 102, 106, 139
Special Protection Area (SPA) 13, 57, 59, 136
sphagnum 100, 103, 108, 112, 114, 116, 117, 119, 205
spider 20, 42, 54, 108
sponge 72, 86, 94
Spotted Flycatcher 242, 245, 250
Staffordshire 6, 99–101, 112, 117, 121, 132, 157, 202
starfish 65, 74, 92, 93
Starling 242, 246
Sticta spp. 185
stiletto-fly 133
Stoat 213, 214
Stock Dove 237, 246
Stockport 4, 9, 124, 129, 132, 198, 214, 219
Stonechat 239, 244
stonefly 13, 123, 144, 145, 237
sub-littoral 63, 83, 85, 91, 94
Sugar Brook 129

sulphur dioxide (SO$_2$) 13, 181–184, 194
sundew 11, 101, 108, 109, 113
Swallow 53, 234, 245
swan 226, 227, 245
Swift 11, 42, 43, 236, 251
Sycamore 7, 47, 50, 52

— T —

Tame 124, 129, 132, 133
Tameside 4, 9, 198
Tattenhall 148, 161, 173
Tatton 175, 203, 219
Tawny Owl 174, 234
tellin 58, 60, 61, 65, 77–80, 82
temperature 16, 17, 52, 60, 65, 91, 181, 206, 244
Tephromela atra 192
Thurstaston 57, 76, 77
Toad 18, 47, 149, 166, 167
Trafford 4, 9, 144, 198
Trapeliopsis flexuosa 188
Tree Bumblebee 51, 52
Tree Pipit 237, 244, 245, 250
Tree Sparrow 6, 32–34, 242, 245, 247
Treecreeper 242
Trent & Mersey Canal 134
trichomonosis 242, 250
trout 81, 123, 128, 129, 140
Tufted Duck 228
Turnstone 81, 84, 85
Turtle Dove 237, 238, 244, 245, 248
Twite 242, 243, 248

— U —

Urban Mersey Basin 9, 10
urban wildlife 10, 11, 14, 38–55, 184, 186, 194, 212–214, 229, 230, 242
urchin 63, 74
Usnea spp. 185, 187

— V —

Variable Damselfly 174, 206
Verrucaria spp. 190, 193, 194
violet 20, 110, 137
volunteer 17, 32, 41, 121, 128, 145, 158, 159, 224

— W —

Wallasey 83, 89, 91, 138
Warrington 4, 7, 9, 25, 27, 42, 52, 54, 100, 118, 127, 158, 181, 182, 198, 224, 226, 247, 250
water abstraction 1, 107, 141
Water Crowfoot spp. 140, 174
Water Fern 13, 114, 116, 130, 131
Water Framework Directive 13, 125, 140, 144, 145
water quality 16, 80, 82, 120, 127, 128, 133, 135, 140, 141, 144, 145, 175, 194, 207, 216, 237, 247
Water Vole 15, 108, 122, 124, 130, 132, 137, 139, 144, 171, 174, 216, 220
watershed 124
Water-soldier 164
Weasel 213, 214
Weaver 8, 10, 125, 130, 133–135, 200, 202, 216, 229, 230, 244
Weaver Navigation Canal 134
West Kirby 57, 77, 94, 139
wetland 11, 99, 100, 106–110, 114, 116, 132, 149, 152, 154, 158, 163, 165, 174, 177, 178
whale 211, 212
wheat 27, 30
Wheatear 240
whelk 64, 73, 92
Whinchat 239, 240, 245, 248, 249
Whirley 162
White-clawed Crayfish 126, 130, 131, 135, 174
White-faced Darter 14, 116–118, 174, 205, 208
White-legged Damselfly 203, 204

Whitethroat 34, 139, 240, 241, 245
Whixall Moss 100, 117
Widnes 42–44, 54, 181, 182, 224
willow 8, 104, 174, 181, 184, 187–189
Willow Tit 238, 239, 250
Willow Warbler 241, 245
Wilmslow 49, 107, 109, 129, 214
Wincham 133–135, 161, 216
winkle 67, 83
Winsford 134, 170, 186, 202
Wood Mouse 48, 213
Wood Warbler 241, 244, 245, 248, 250, 251
Woodcock 233, 250
woodland 6–10, 13, 15, 26, 48, 51, 99, 107, 129, 132, 138, 174, 183–185, 187, 191, 194, 212, 213, 215, 217, 230, 234, 238–243, 247, 250
Woodpigeon 32, 33, 53, 237
Woolston (Eyes) 125, 127, 129, 225, 226, 229, 230
worm 59–62, 65, 77–80, 82, 83, 90–92, 145
wrack 72, 73, 86, 93, 94
wreck 63, 65, 67, 68
Wren 239, 244
Wybunbury Moss NNR 11, 103, 106, 109, 207
Wych 183–185, 215, 230

— X —

Xanthoparmelia spp. 192
Xanthoria spp. 181, 184, 185, 186, 190, 193

— Y —

Yellow Wagtail 6, 32, 33, 36, 236, 245, 246
Yellowhammer 53, 243, 245, 247
Yellow-necked Mouse 15, 215, 216, 220